Studies on Indian Medical History

INDIAN MEDICAL TRADITION

Edited by
DOMINIK WUJASTYK
&
KENNETH G. ZYSK

Vol. V

Studies on Indian Medical History

Edited by

G. Jan Meulenbeld
Dominik Wujastyk

MOTILAL BANARSIDASS PUBLISHERS
PRIVATE LIMITED • DELHI

First Edition : UK, 1987
Reprint Edition: Delhi, 2001

ISBN: 81-208-1768-0

Also available at:
MOTILAL BANARSIDASS
236, 9th Main III Block, Jayanagar, Bangalore 560 011
41 U.A. Bungalow Road, Jawahar Nagar, Delhi 110 007
8 Mahalaxmi Chamber, Bhulabhai Desai Rd., Mumbai 400 026
120 Royapettah High Road, Mylapore, Chennai 600 004
Sanas Plaza, 1302 Baji Rao Road, Pune 411 002
8 Camac Street, Kolkata 700 017
Ashok Rajpath, Patna 800 004
Chowk, Varanasi 221 001

Printed in India
BY JAINENDRA PRAKASH JAIN AT SHRI JAINENDRA PRESS,
A-45 NARAINA, PHASE-I, NEW DELHI 110 028
AND PUBLISHED BY NARENDRA PRAKASH JAIN FOR
MOTILAL BANARSIDASS PUBLISHERS PRIVATE LIMITED,
BUNGALOW ROAD, DELHI 110 007

Respectfully dedicated to the memory of

Vayaskara N.S. Mooss

a great exponent of *āyurveda*

Foreword

When *Studies on Indian Medical History* was first published over a decade ago, the interest in āyurveda was just beginning to appear outside of India; since then it has increased dramatically. Today, āyurveda has become important in the list of alternative and complementary medical therapies. Medicines derived from traditional āyurvedic formulas appear almost daily on the shelves of shops specialising in natural and organic foods and medicines; and ever-increasing numbers of practitioners of alternative as well as allopathic medicine are adopting the medical ideologies fundamental among others to āyurveda. Studies and reports from the medical communities are showing that these alternative approaches to health care do indeed have positive effects in the promotion of patients' health and well-being. Compared to other traditional and alternative medical systems such as Chinese Acupuncture and Germanic Homeopathy which have been around for quite some time, āyurveda is a relatively recent player in the alternative medicine game, yet it has existed for well over two millennia in India. All too often, the information about āyurveda coming from those close to the alternative medical movement reflects a rather naïve understanding of the roots and fundamental bases of the āyurvedic medical system. This reprint of *Studies on Indian Medical History* will improve the knowledge about āyurveda by providing a deeper and better understanding of the basic history and principles of āyurveda for individuals who have interest in the subject from both the practical and the scholarly perspectives. We might cite as an example G. J. Meulenbeld's article "Reflections on the basic concepts of Indian pharmacology." Based on original Sanskrit sources, this paper presents a clear and comprehensive picture of the often confusing and misunderstood theoretical basis of āyurvedic pharmaceutics. Individuals who routinely use and recommend āyurvedic medicines will derive great benefit from a close study of this paper, so that they can know the rationale for, and therefore make the best use of, these medicines. Although emphasising the classical system of āyurveda, the volume also contains essays devoted to other periods of traditional Indian medicine, including the colonial and modern periods. The papers were originally presented at an international workshop on the study of Indian medicine held at the Wellcome Institute for the History of Medicine in September 1985. The past fifteen years has witnessed numerous workshops and conferences on Indian medicine, but in spite of that, the quality and relevance of this particular collection of papers has remained unique. In keeping with the philosophy of offering scholarly excellence in Indian medicine, it is a pleasure to include *Studies on Indian Medical History* in the series of the *Indian Medical Tradition.*

KENNETH G ZYSK

Preface

This volume of studies presents the papers given at the second workshop of the European Āyurvedic Society, a group which was formed in Groningen in 1983. The volume is thus a sequel to *Proceedings of the international workshop on priorities in the study of Indian medicine.*[1] The workshop was held over a period of three days in September 1985, in the congenial surroundings of the Wellcome Institute for the History of Medicine in London, and it provided a splendid opportunity for scholars in the field of Indian medical history to meet in one place, and to share the latest research in their respective areas.

The studies here collected present an unusually wide variety of approaches to the study of the healing arts in India. The historical sources used range from ancient Sanskrit manuscripts and Tibetan blockprints, through nineteenth century Indian newspapers and government reports, to conversations held in the the consulting rooms of contemporary *āyurvedic* doctors. While each approach is both valid and valuable in its own terms, their combination in the present book provides a view of Indian medical history which transcends the barriers between scholarly disciplines and gives the reader some sense of the vastness of the subject.

The book is divided into three complementary parts: 'The classical tradition', 'Colonial interactions', and 'Modern observations'. This reflects both a division in the source materials, and the different scholarly skills required to exploit them, those of the indologist, the historian, and the medical anthropologist and pharmacognosist.

In Part I of the book the approach is mainly philological. Sanskrit works are scrutinised in order to explore the philosophical underpinnings of classical theory and text; a major Tibetan text on epilepsy is edited and translated with its Sanskrit parallels; the medical role of magic squares is described; and the meanings of certain plant and mineral names are explored.[2]

[1]Edited by G. Jan Meulenbeld (Groningen: Institute of Indian Studies, 1984).

[2]At the 1985 workshop, Hans Bakker contributed a valuable paper on 'Methodological consid-

Part II of the book presents three substantial historical studies, drawing from both popular and official sources provided by the major colonial powers who have ruled India. An overview of the reception of European medicine in India since the Portuguese is followed by studies of how the British dealt with the introduction of smallpox vaccination in India, and the treatment of the Indian insane. A notable lacuna is the viewpoint of the Islamic rulers and subjects of India, whose ideas and observations on *āyurveda* and *yūnānī* medicine still remain a relatively unexplored subject.

Part III begins with the pharmacognostic evaluation of a popular *āyurvedic* medicine widely sold in the markets of Sri Lanka, and continues with anthropological studies of the practice of traditional and folk healing in post-independence India.

It is hoped that this book may be read with profit by those interested in the state of current research in one of the specialist areas represented, and also by students of Indian medical history in general for whom it provides a survey of possible approaches to the subject. There will be few who can read all the chapters with equal expertise, but none will fail to benefit from the breadth of material presented.

The editors wish to express their thanks to the contributors, who took great care over the quality of their essays, and corrected several proofs. In harmony with the aims of the original workshop, several of the contributors corresponded with each other and with the editors, suggesting corrections, further references, and other improvements to various of the papers. This made for a refreshing sense of joint effort and scholarly cooperation which is evident throughout the book.

It is also our pleasant duty to offer our thanks to the Wellcome Trust, whose grants made possible both the workshop and the publication of this volume, and to the staff of the Wellcome Institute who were extremely helpful at all stages of the workshop and the production of this book. Steve Emberton, Frieda Houser and Marika Antoniw deserve special mention for their help.

This book is dedicated to the memory of Vayaskara N. S. Mooss, who did so much for the study Kerala's heritage of classical medicine. We also wish to remember here the contributions made to the history of Indian medicine by Professors A. L. Basham and D. V. Subba Reddy, both of whom passed away recently. This volume demonstrates the growth of interest in the field which they cultivated.

---

erations concerning critical editions of anonymous Sanskrit texts', an important topic for students of the early textual tradition. This paper was already promised for publication elsewhere, and therefore could not be included in the present book.

Contents

Part I

The classical tradition

Chapter 1

Reflections on the basic concepts of Indian pharmacology

G. Jan Meulenbeld

THE STUDY OF TRADITIONAL SYSTEMS OF KNOWLEDGE requires a fair description of each of these systems, i.e., a description that does not start from the demarcationist principle that Western science alone can be regarded as a system of knowledge based on rationality and directed at the structure of reality. Applied to *āyurveda*, this means that we need a description of this particular medical system that does not presuppose the universal validity of the methodological norms of Western medicine, thus degrading any system of medicine that differs from it. Fairness requires a thorough study of the metaphysical basis of *āyurveda*, its methodological and heuristic principles, as well as its adaptability and its potential for producing new knowledge. Research on this line will not only yield results which are theoretically interesting and useful for the comparative study of medical systems but will also serve practical aims since, to take one example, the degree of adaptibility of a medical system is of vital importance for its survival in a changing society. The required type of description does not yet exist with regard to *āyurveda*. The numerous books and articles on this subject by Indian authors are usually biased and contaminated by interpretations reflecting the struggle for power of the practitioners and their efforts to prove that their system is as valid as, or more valuable than, that of Western medicine. Attempts by non-Indian authors to provide us with a more adequate picture are not known to me.

[0]Abbreviations used in the footnotes: Ci.: Cikitsāsthāna; Śā.: Śārīrasthāna; Sū.: Sūtrasthāna; U.: Uttaratantra; Vi.: Vimānasthāna.

This is one of the reasons why I turned to the basic concepts of Indian pharmacology as an object of study. These concepts have the advantage of being restricted in number, interconnected, and linked to the theory of Indian medicine as a whole and to its philosophical basis.

According to the Indian classical tradition, medical science is not a product of human thought but part of an eternal truth revealed by the gods to humanity. It is therefore said to have no beginning in history and to be complete from the start. Does this mean that *āyurveda* is not a science, not even a traditional system of knowledge characterised by the aim to acquire knowledge of reality and to improve this knowledge by the application of methodological principles? My answer is that the divine character of *āyurveda* has been imposed upon it during a particular stage of its development and has not always been one of its characteristics.

The Indian medical system, as laid down in the classical *saṃhitās* of Caraka and Suśruta which recognise it as a divine revelation, is not an early type of medicine but the result of a long development. The *saṃhitās* contain numerous references to an earlier period that was characterised by a great diversity of opinions. Evidently, a generally accepted medical system did not yet exist in those early days, which implies that medical science was not yet regarded as divinely inspired. Unfortunately, medical treatises from that period have not survived. This is because one of the theories rose to ascendancy and succeeded in its claims to represent the eternal truth. One can only guess at the reasons for this development. One of these may have been an increased pressure of orthodox religion and its representatives on the medical theoreticians, who were regarded as heterodox and inclined to materialism. Clues pointing to the heterodoxy of old medical traditions are still found in the extant versions of the classical *saṃhitās*. The older, very diverse theories of the preceding ages in which theorising flourished are disclaimed and refuted in the *Carakasaṃhitā* by a sort of pope, speaking ex cathedra, Ātreya Punarvasu, whose name connects him with the Vedic tradition. Divodāsa, king of Kāśī, does the same in the *Suśrutasaṃhitā* and may be regarded as a representative of a later age, since he is said to be an incarnation of Dhanvantari, who is unknown in the Vedic tradition. When compared with Greek medical literature, the *saṃhitās* of Caraka and Suśruta have a position that resembles to a certain degree that of the works of Galen, who lived in approximately the same age. In contrast with Greek medicine, earlier works which represent a diversity of theoretical points of view, as the Hippocratic corpus does, have not been preserved in India.

The divine character of classical *āyurveda*, when taken strictly, would mean that it is a paradigm or disciplinary matrix, in Kuhn's sense, that can never be replaced by another paradigm.[1] Consequently, development would only be possible within the constraints imposed by this paradigm. Is *āyurveda* in its classical form, and regarded as being based on divine revelation, a closed system in the sense in which Horton describes it?[2] This would mean that it cannot be called a science since the right attitude for the progressive acquisition of knowledge, i.e., the awareness of the existence of alternatives, is absent. The sacredness of the Indian medical tradition, once accepted, became, it is true, an obstacle to fundamental innovations with regard to theory, but it was never completely closed as a system of knowledge. This means that the doctrine of its divine origin does not belong to its hard core, does not form part of its body in the sense given to this term by Elkana,[3] but should be regarded as one of the images of knowlege, an image influenced by developments in Indian society.

The study of Sanskrit medical literature gives ample proof that developments did take place, particularly with regard to practice. The history of the revival of *āyurveda* since the beginning of the nineteenth century and the type of *āyurveda* that has developed in recent times shows that considerable changes and re-interpretations are possible.

Doctrines embodied in the classical *saṃhitās* were even – admittedly in rare cases – put aside as incorrect. A remarkable example of straightforward criticism is found in the *Śārṅgadharasaṃhitā* (i. 1. 54) which contains the statement that a drug, although mentioned as a member of a group (*gaṇa*) regarded as useful in a particular disease, should never be prescribed in that disease if it has proved to be ineffective.

The tradition that *āyurveda* was transmitted to mankind by the gods evidently does not imply in the least that the theories expounded in the classical *saṃhitās* have already been systematised and made into a coherent whole. This I have tried to demonstrate in my paper. The traces of earlier theories are still present in these *saṃhitās* and conflicting points of view are recorded. In addition, Caraka and Suśruta disagree on a considerable number of issues. That is why the *āyurvedic* system of medicine cannot be described as completely closed. Disagrements among the authorities, contradictions and anomalies are admitted, and efforts are made in later ages, especially by the commentators, to smooth them out. The ways of reasoning resorted to and the concepts used in order to construct a unified theory

---

[1] Thomas S. Kuhn, *The structure of scientific revolutions*, 2 ed., (Chicago: Univ. of Chicago Press, 1970).

[2] Robin Horton, 'African traditional thought and western science', *Africa*, xxxiv (1967), 50–71 and 155–187; idem., 'Lévy-Bruhl, Durkheim and the scientific revolution', in *Modes of thought: Essays on thinking in Western and non-Western societies*, edited by Ruth Finnegan and Robin Horton, (London: Faber, 1973).

[3] Yehuda Elkana, 'A programmatic attempt at an anthropology of knowledge', in *Sciences and cultures*, edited by Everett Mendelsohn and Yehuda Elkana, (Dordrecht: Reidel, 1981).

are very rewarding as a field of study for those interested in the development of a traditional system of knowledge.

The way in which the philosophical systems, especially Vaiśeṣika and Sāṃkhya, succeeded in influencing medical theories is also interesting. I give below some examples showing that the way in which medical concepts are made to agree with philosophical ideas points to the secondary character of this connection. The nuclear medical concepts and theories have therefore in my view been developed in a milieu that differed from that of the philosophers.

This explains how parts of mutually incompatible philosophies are incorporated into the classical *saṃhitās* and that eclecticism is one of their characteristic features. This eclecticism is best illustrated by the well known verse of the *Suśrutasaṃhitā* (Śā. i. 11) stating that in medicine those with a broad view recognise the relevance of diverse points of view regarding the causes of what happens to human beings.

The pharmacological theory of Indian medicine is a remarkable achievement in its structure and its at least partly unique concepts, as well as for the scope it allows for empiricism. The rules which interconnect its basic concepts are very general ones with a large number of exceptions. These exceptions are extremely interesting as the products of actual observations on the actions of drugs.

The surest marker for empirical observations is undoubtedly the term *prabhāva*. I am convinced that wherever this term is employed, we are in touch with the practising ancient Indian physicians and their observational acumen. On the other hand, it must be added that it is also one of the basic characteristics of *āyurveda* that, despite this acumen and the recognition of numerous exceptions to the theoretical rules, the anomalies observed did not become an incentive for the improvement of the theory or the formulation of new or supplementary rules. The reason for this stagnation of creative thought in later times may have been the increasing domination of orthodox religion and the power of its representatives. This conclusion is in line with the views brought forward by Debiprasad Chattopadhyaya in his book *Science and society in ancient India* and is, in addition, supported by part of the material collected by Francis Zimmermann in his beautiful study entitled *La jungle et le fumet des viandes*.[4]

[4]Debiprasad Chattopadhyaya, *Science and society in ancient India* (Calcutta: Research India Publications, 1977); Francis Zimmermann, *La jungle et le fumet des viandes: un thème écologique dans la médecine hindoue* (Paris: Gallimard, Le Seuil, 1982).

The basic concepts

The basic concepts of Indian pharmacology are four: taste (*rasa*), post-digestive taste (*vipāka*), potency (*vīrya*), and specific action (*prabhāva*). By means of these four tools the ancient Indian physicians developed an intricate web of reasoning in order to account for the actions of drugs on living organisms. Study of the Sanskrit medical texts and their commentaries reveals that these concepts and their implications give rise to numerous questions which cannot readily be answered. Some of these questions constitute the subject of this paper.

Taste: *Rasa*

The tastes are six in number: sweet (*madhura*), acid (*amla*), salt (*lavaṇa*), pungent (*kaṭu*), bitter (*tikta*), and astringent (*kaṣāya*). Each taste is thought to be endowed with a series of properties (*guṇa*) and actions (*karman*).[5] According to the classical theory this does not mean that the tastes themselves, being properties (*guṇa*) of substances (*dravya*), possess other properties, since such a view would run counter to the tenet of the Vaiśeṣika philosophy that a property of a substance cannot be provided with another property.[6] The properties metaphorically (*upacārataḥ*) attributed to a taste are therefore properties of the substance possessing that taste, and can only be said to be associated with that taste.[7] In practice, however, Indian medicine takes the line that a taste and a particular group of other properties of a substance form a stable whole. The analysis of the properties and actions of the tastes presents many difficulties. Some of these can be solved by taking into consideration the elements (*mahābhūta*) which make up substances with a particular taste.[8] These elements are five in number: ether (*ākāśa*), wind (*vāyu*), fire (*agni*), water (*āpaḥ*), and earth (*pṛthivī*). Sweet substances are regarded as predominantly composed of water in the *Carakasaṃhitā*, of water and earth in the *Suśrutasaṃhitā* and in Vāgbhaṭa's works.

It is the element water in substances with a sweet taste that is responsible for that sweet taste being regarded as unctuous (*snigdha*) and cold (*śīta*) to the third, i.e., the highest, degree. It is the elements water and earth that are responsible for its being

[5] Caraka, *Carakasaṃhitā*, edited by Vaidya Jādavji Trikamji Āchārya, (Bombay, 1941) (henceforth Ca.), Sū. xxvi. 42–43; Suśruta, *Suśrutasaṃhitā*, edited by Vaidya Jādavji Trikamji Āchārya, (Bombay, 1938) (henceforth Su.), Sū. xlii. 10; Vāgbhaṭa, *Aṣṭāṅgahṛdayasaṃhitā*, edited by Hariśāstrī Parādkar, (Bombay, 1939) (henceforth A.h.), Sū. x. 2–22ab.

[6] See Ca.Sū. xxvi. 36, Su.Sū. xl. 17 and A.h.Sū. x. 1, together with their commentaries.

[7] A.h.Sū. ix. 4cd–5ab; the term employed is *sāhacarya* (association).

[8] Ca.Sū. xxvi. 40; Su.Sū. xlii. 3; A.h.Sū. x. 1.

heavy (*guru*) to the third degree.[9] Although the beneficial action of the sweet taste on the skin (*tvacya*) and hair of the head (*keśya*) may be derived from earth[10] because this element predominates in skin, hairs, nails, etc.,[11] the whole range of actions of sweet substances cannot possibly be elucidated by taking recourse to their being chiefly composed of earth and water. Generally, the doctrine of the *mahābhūtas* suffers from a lack of explanatory force with regard to the properties and actions of the tastes.[12] The commentators on the classical *saṃhitās* were well aware of this, as appears, for example, from remarks by Cakrapāṇidatta, who put forward the view that the inherent nature (*svabhāva*) of the elements is such that one cannot predict which properties will become manifest in a particular mixture of the elements because the choice of these properties is governed by the force of the invisible (*adṛṣṭaprabhāva*).[13] It is therefore not surprising to see that the ancient authorities were not agreed on the elemental (*mahābhautika*) composition of the tastes.[14] It is especially hard to understand the relationships postulated between substances of a particular taste and specific disorders. It remains to be investigated whether these relationships are a determining factor in the aetiology of diseases and a guiding element in therapeutic prescriptions.[15]

Taking all this into account it seems justifiable to suppose that the doctrines on the tastes form part of an old corpus of medical traditions, whereas the efforts to interpret these in the light of the theory of the five elements are of a later date.[16]

---

[9] Ca.Sū. xxvi. 54–55; A.h.Sū. x. 37–38.

[10] The *Carakasaṃhitā* mentions that the sweet taste is *tvacya* and *keśya* without admitting that earth is one of the elements predominating in it; according to the *Suśrutasaṃhitā*, the sweet taste is *tvacya* and *varṇya* (beneficial to a good colour of the skin).

[11] Ca.Śā. vii. 16.

[12] See also P. V. Sharma's reflections on the relationship between the tastes and the elements in his article 'Carakokta bheṣajavijñāna' in Hindī, *Journal of Ayurveda* iii (1), (1985), 46–47.

[13] *Ad* Ca.Sū. xxvi. 40. See also Śivadāsasena's comments on Cakrapāṇidatta, *Dravyaguṇasaṃgraha, with Śivadāsasena's commentary*, edited by Jīvānandavidyāsāgara (Calcutta, 1897) (henceforth Dravyaguṇa), i. 4.

[14] As already referred to, Caraka and Suśruta disagree on the element(s) dominating in the sweet taste. Moreover, Cakrapāṇidatta mentions (*ad* Ca.Sū. xxvi. 40) that Suśruta subscribed to the view that the salt taste derives from earth and fire, whereas it is said to be chiefly composed of water and fire in the *Carakasaṃhitā* (the printed text of Suśruta mentions, in agreement with Caraka, water and fire; a variant, rejected by the editor, reads earth and fire).

[15] In some cases these relationships do have consequences for therapy; the bitter taste, said to eliminate fever, actually does have a privileged place in the treatment of fever (see e.g., Cakradatta, *jvara*, 42).

[16] The author of the *Rasavaiśeṣikasūtra*, Nāgārjuna (later than Vāgbhaṭa but earlier than Candraṭa), is a representative of a medical school completely dominated by the theory of the five elements. See Nāgārjuna, *Rasavaiśeṣikasūtra, with Narasiṃha's commentary*, edited by N. E. Muthuswami, Kerala Government Ayurvedic Publication Series no. 2, (Trivandrum, 1976) (henceforth *Rasavaiśeṣikasūtra*).

Another problem connected with the theory of the tastes emerges when trying to imagine what happens to substances of a particular taste during the digestive process. Indian medical theory distinguishes two processes of digestion, called respectively *avasthāpāka* and *niṣṭhāpāka*. During *avasthāpāka* ingested substances pass through three stages in which they become successively sweet, acid, and pungent.[17] During *niṣṭhāpāka* the tastes are subject to a process governed by the rule that sweet, acid, and pungent substances do not change their taste, whereas the salt taste is transformed into a sweet one, and the bitter and astringent taste into a pungent one. These post-digestive tastes are called *vipāka*.[18]

One of the consequences of this theory is that the influence of the salt, bitter, and astringent taste on the organism will diminish during digestion and end with the completion of the process of *niṣṭhāpāka*. It is therefore not without interest to investigate the extent to which the ancient Indian physicians were aware of this problem and how they tried to solve it. A solution is necessary if one wants to defend the view that all the six tastes have general effects. A theoretical solution one can devise is to ascribe the general effects not to the tastes themselves but to the associated properties. This, however, would deprive the tastes of their specificity and moreover imply that all these associated properties are immune to digestion and able to operate independently.

The general properties (*sāmānyaguṇa*) of substances enumerated in medical texts are twenty in number and arranged in ten pairs of opposites.[19] These properties,

[17] See Ca.Ci. xv. 9–11, together with Cakrapāṇidatta's commentary.

[18] Ca.Sū. xxvi. 57cd–58; A.h.Sū. ix. 20–21. Suśruta (Su.Sū. xl. 10–12) recognises two types of *vipāka* only, sweet and pungent. The *saṃhitās* and their commentaries contain references to aberrant views: Cakrapāṇidatta *ad* Ca.Sū. xxvi. 63; Su.Sū. xl. 10–12; Hemādri *ad* A.h.Sū. ix. 21; Vāgbhaṭa, *Aṣṭāṅgasaṃgraha, with Indu's commentary*, edited by Ananta Dāmodara Āṭhavale (Pune, 1980) (henceforth A.s.), Sū. xvii. 26–28. The *vipāka* of the pungent, bitter and astringent tastes is respectively salt, sweet and acid according to the anonymous *Āyurvedasūtra, with the commentary of Yogānandanātha*, edited by R. Shama Sastry, University of Mysore Oriental Library Publications no. 61, (Mysore, 1922) i. 44–46.

[19] According to Caraka (Ca.Śā. vi. 10; Cakrapāṇidatta *ad* Ca.Sū. i. 49) and Vāgbhaṭa (A.h.Sū. i. 18, together with Aruṇadatta's and Hemādri's comments) these ten pairs are heavy (*guru*) and light (*laghu*), cold (*śīta*) and hot (*uṣṇa*), unctuous (*snigdha*) and dry (*rūkṣa*), sluggish (*manda*) and sharp (*tīkṣṇa*), immobile (*sthira*) and flowing (*sara*), soft (*mṛdu*) and harsh (*khara*), gross (*sthūla*) and subtle (*sūkṣma*), viscid (*sāndra*) and liquid (*drava*). Suśruta, although stating that the properties are twenty in number, actually enumerates twenty-four of them (Su.Sū. xlvi. 514–525ab); his list, also differing in some other respects from that found in Caraka and Vāgbhaṭa, consists of *guru* and *laghu*, *śīta* and *uṣṇa*, *snigdha* and *rūkṣa*, *mṛdu* (instead of *manda*) and *tīkṣṇa*, *manda* (instead of *sthira*) and *sara*, *viśada* and *karkaśa* (scabrous), *viśada* and *picchila*, *ślakṣṇa* and *śuṣka* (desiccated; it replaces *khara*), *āśukārin* (quickly acting; it replaces *sthūla*) and *sūkṣma*, *sāndra* and *drava*; he adds *sugandha* (fragrant) and *durgandha* (bad-smelling), *vyavāyin* (diffuse) and *vikāsin* (relaxation-promoting). For the theoretical position of the *guṇas* added by Suśruta and for some more properties, see Hemādri's comment *ad* A.h.Sū. i. 18.

thought to be endowed with specific actions,[20] are divided into two groups: twelve weak properties, affected by digestion, and eight strong ones, resistant to digestion on account of their potency (*vīrya*).

Our problem cannot be solved by assuming that the general effects of the tastes are actually brought about by the eight strong properties, since specific linkages between particular potencies and individual tastes are nowhere mentioned. Another type of solution would be reached invoking the *prabhāva* of the tastes, i.e., their specific action, which lies beyond all reasoning and is the effect of the *svabhāva*, the inherent nature, of a substance. The *prabhāva* of the tastes is indeed referred to in the *Carakasaṃhitā*.[21] Cakrapāṇidatta employs the term to explain the specific action of bitter drugs in counteracting fever.[22] Taking recourse to the concept of *prabhāva* is always a sure sign of embarrassment caused by the absence of a more adequate theoretical answer. A third solution was advanced by Śivadāsasena in his commentary on Cakrapāṇidatta's *Dravyaguṇasaṃgraha*.[23] This author examined the problem of how the six tastes can bring about their specific general effects despite the fact that the three stages of *avasthāpāka* are characterized by, successively, a sweet, an acid, and a pungent taste. His answer was that part of the original taste remains active during the entire process of digestion. Śivadāsasena's commentary does not contain a similar statement with regard to the transformation of the tastes during *niṣṭhāpāka*, but his view may be applied to that process as well since he mentions that tastes which are not subject to change during *niṣṭhāpāka* exert a much more powerful influence on the organism than those which are transformed. The weakness inherent in Śivadāsasena's exposition is that the general effects of the salt, bitter, and astringent tastes have to be attributed to remnants of these tastes and will always be weaker that those of the sweet, acid, and pungent tastes. It will be clear from the above that a large part of the actions of the six tastes can be accounted for only by assuming them to originate from *prabhāva*. This may appear to be an unsatisfactory conclusion that does no justice to Indian medical theories but, as we shall see, numerous actions of drugs can be explained in no other way.

The last question regarding tastes that I want to mention here is whether their effects are largely of a general nature or not. I am convinced that the statements found in the texts imply that all six tastes are able to influence the whole organism. This interpretation does not, however, go undisputed. P. V. Sharma has advanced

[20] See Hemādri *ad* A.h.Sū. i. 18 for a description of these actions. Compare Ca.Sū. xxii. 9–17.
[21] Ca.Sū. xxvi. 43; Vi. i. 12.
[22] *Ad* Ca.Sū. xxvi. 13.
[23] *Ad Dravyaguṇa* i. 9–10.

the view that the tastes have a local action[24] which makes its appearance immediately after their perception[25] and ends with the completion of *avasthāpāka*.[26] This view cannot possibly be made to agree with, for example, the *Carakasaṃhitā*, according to which the bitter taste is beneficial in cases of *kuṣṭha*, etc.

Post-digestive taste: *Vipāka*

Next to *rasa*, the concept of *vipāka*, i.e., the transformation of part of the tastes during the process of *niṣṭhāpāka*, calls for some comments. This concept, which is possibly peculiar to Indian medicine, was obviously developed in the wake of observations which established that the delayed action of drugs sometimes disagrees with their taste, being more in line with some other taste. Knowledge about the *vipāka* of a substance is therefore said to be acquired by means of inference (*anumāna*), the post-digestive taste itself being inaccessible to the senses (*nityaparokṣa*).[27] Apparently it was far from easy to infer the *vipāka* from its effects since widely divergent views were held by different authorities in pre-classical times.[28] General agreement had not yet been reached at the time of the redaction of the *Carakasaṃhitā* and the *Suśrutasaṃhitā*.

It is probably not accidental that the three *vipāka* tastes are the same as those which become predominant during *avasthāpāka*. The three tastes of *avasthāpāka* are accessible to the senses, and need not be inferred.[29] One of my conjectures is that the theory of *vipāka* is secondary and has been modelled upon that of *avasthāpāka*. The latter theory may be based on observations concerning the taste of eructations and of food vomited after partial digestion. This appears to be confirmed by a remark of Cakrapāṇidatta, who does not distinguish between *avasthāpāka* and *niṣṭhāpāka* when stating that the acid eructations occurring after eating *vrīhi* rice prove that its *vipāka* is of the acid type.[30]

The actions of the post-digestive tastes, which are without any doubt systemic,[31] are stronger than those of the tastes. The texts agree in stating that, when *rasa* and *vipāka* are of equal strength, it is *vipāka* that prevails.[32] The specification 'when of

[24] Suśruta distinguishes between local (*rasalakṣaṇa*) and general (*rasaguṇa*) actions of the tastes (Su.Sū. xlii. 9–10).

[25] Caraka says (Ca.Sū. xxvi. 66) that the tastes exert their influence as soon as they are perceived.

[26] *Dravyaguṇavijñāna* i. 219–220.

[27] Cakrapāṇidatta *ad* Ca.Sū. xxvi. 66.

[28] See note 14.

[29] Śivadāsasena *ad Dravyaguṇa* i. 1.

[30] *Ad* Ca.Sū. xxvi. 63.

[31] See, e.g., Ca.Sū. xxvi. 61–62.

[32] Ca.Sū. xxvi. 72cd–73ab = A.h.Sū. ix. 25 = A.s.Sū. xvii. 33.

equal strength' needs some elaboration. The classical *saṃhitās* do not contain any explicit statement on the strength of the sweet and pungent *vipāka* resulting from transformation of the salt, bitter, and astringent tastes, but a single verse found in the *Carakasaṃhitā* apparently implies that, for example, a very strong bitter taste changes into a pungent *vipāka* of the same strength.[33] As to the actions of the *vipāka* tastes, these are said to be similar to those of the sweet, acid, and pungent tastes,[34] the local effects of the latter excepted.[35]

Change of taste also means that the properties associated with the *vipāka* taste may disagree with those of the originally present taste. This problem has been noticed by Cakrapāṇidatta who remarks that the sweet *vipāka* of a salty substance does not prevent such a substance from provoking *pitta*, because the hot potency, associated with the salt taste, prevails over the sweet *vipāka*.[36] This means that the very hot potency, associated with the salt taste, is stronger than the very cold potency of the sweet post-digestive taste. Cakrapāṇi refrains from explaining why the potency of the taste is stronger than that of the post-digestive taste, which is apparently contrary to the rule that *vipāka* prevails over the *rasa* when both are of the same strength. As we shall see, the answer is that the hot or cold potency of the taste is usually supposed to be the stronger one.

The classical *saṃhitās* and the *nighaṇṭus* mention numerous exceptions to the rules with regard to the relationships between *rasa* and *vipāka*. Apart from that, many actions of drugs are hard to understand. A good example is *nimba*, of a bitter taste, and, according to the rule, of a pungent *vipāka*. The fact that *nimba*, in agreement with its taste and in spite of its *vipāka*, counteracts *pitta* is ascribed to the force of the taste itself and not, as would have been more plausible, to its cold potency. Another example is *mudga*, astringent and sweet as to taste and nevertheless of a light quality, although the astringent and sweet tastes are heavy; Cakrapāṇidatta explains this as a result of the *prakṛti* of *mudga*, without elucidating the meaning of that term in this context.[37]

Potency: *Vīrya*

The third basic concept of Indian pharmacology is potency (*vīrya*). First of all it has to be mentioned that the term *vīrya* is employed in both a wide and a restricted

[33] Ca.Sū. xxvi. 63.
[34] A.h.Sū. ix. 22ab.
[35] Aruṇadatta *ad* A.h.Sū. ix. 22ab.
[36] *Ad* Ca.Sū. xxvi. 63.
[37] *Ad* Ca.Sū. xxvi. 9. According to Ḍalhaṇa (*ad* Su.Ci. xxxiii. 32) *prakṛti* is sometimes a synonym of *prabhāva*.

sense. Caraka uses it in the wide sense when stating that all the actions of medicinal substances are brought about by *vīrya.*[38] When figuring in this sense, *vīrya* is called, according to Cakrapāṇidatta, *śaktiparyāya vīrya*, i.e., that *vīrya* which is synonymous with *śakti.*[39] The term *śakti* is rather frequent in the commentaries on the classical *saṃhitās*, though not in these treatises themselves, and it not only designates *vīrya* in its wide sense, but also *prabhāva*, the fourth concept to be dealt with. Potency in its restricted sense, called *pāribhāṣikavīrya*, i.e., *vīrya* as a technical term,[40] is the force ascribed to a special group of properties of medicinal substances. As already mentioned, usually eight out of the twenty properties are thought to be endowed with potency. These eight, arranged in four pairs of opposites, are hot (*uṣṇa*) and cold (*śīta*), heavy (*guru*) and light (*laghu*), unctuous (*snigdha*) and dry (*rūkṣa*), soft (*mṛdu*) and sharp (*tīkṣṇa*).[41] Knowledge about the *vīryas* can be acquired through the senses and by inference.[42] Agreement as to how many properties are to be called *vīrya* was never reached. The view that only hot and cold should be designated as such is also recorded in the classical *saṃhitās.*[43] The properties called *vīrya* owe their special position to their special force and their resistance to the digestive fire,[44] which makes their effects long lasting.[45] The special force of the *vīryas* enables them to prevail over *rasa* and *vipāka*. Consequently the potency predominates in a medicinal substance when its strength is equal to that of taste and post-digestive taste.[46] This statement has to be supplemented by the rule that, when the potency of a taste disagrees with that of its post-digestive taste, it is the *vīrya* of the taste that prevails.[47] For an adequate understanding of these rules it is necessary to be familiar with the fixed relationships between the tastes and the potencies, especially the hot and cold ones: the sweet, bitter, and astringent tastes are associated with a cold potency, the other three tastes with a hot potency.[48]

---

[38] Ca.Sū. xxvi. 65.

[39] *Ad* Ca.Sū. xxvi. 64–65.

[40] Cakrapāṇidatta *ad* Ca.Sū. xxvi. 64–65.

[41] Ca.Sū. xxvi. 64; A.h.Sū. ix. 12cd–13ab. The list found in the *Suśrutasaṃhitā* (Su.Sū. xl. 5; xli. 11) differs in replacing heavy and light by clear (*viśada*) and mucilaginous (*picchila*). According to P. V. Sharma (*Dravyaguṇavijñāna* i, 226) this difference is almost negligible, since the effects of *guru* and *laghu* on the one hand, and *viśada* and *piccila* on the other, are closely related.

[42] Su.Sū. xli. 11; Cakrapāṇidatta *ad* Ca.Sū. xxvi. 66.

[43] Ca.Sū. xxvi. 64d–65a; Su.Sū. xl. 5; A.h.Sū. ix. 17ab.

[44] Aruṇadatta and Hemādri *ad* A.h.Sū. ix. 14cd–16.

[45] See Ca.Sū. xxvi. 66.

[46] Ca.Sū. xxvi. 72cd–73ab; A.h.Sū. ix. 25.

[47] Cakrapāṇidatta *ad* Ca.Sū. xxvi. 63.

[48] Ca.Sū. xxvi. 45; Su.Sū. xlii. 7. The *saṃhitās* and *nighaṇṭus* record numerous exceptions to this rule.

Three grades of these potencies are distinguished: the pungent, acid, and salt tastes become hotter in this order, the bitter, astringent, and sweet tastes colder.[49] Similar relationships exist between the tastes and other *vīryas*. These correspondences reflect the *mahābhautika* composition of the tastes although this in itself fails to explain the grades of the *vīryas*. The highest degree of hotness, associated with the salt taste, implies that the quantity of the fiery element in it is larger than in the acid and pungent tastes, etc.

One of the questions regarding potency that is discussed by the ancient Indian physicians is the theoretical status of the concept itself, i.e., the category (*padārtha*) to which it belongs according to the Vaiśeṣika philosophy. Caraka, Suśruta, and Vāgbhaṭa regard *vīrya*, like *rasa* and *vipāka*, as belonging to the category 'property (*guṇa*),' but Nāgārjuna, the author of the *Rasavaiśeṣikasūtra*,[50] came to conclude that the category 'action (*karman*)' is more appropriate to it.[51]

One of the arguments adduced by him is that a *vīrya* can be active in the absence of *rasa* and *guṇa*, as e.g., in a mantra. Nāgārjuna's concept of *vīrya* is akin to that of *prabhāva* in the *saṃhitās* of Caraka and Vāgbhaṭa. Consequently this author distinguishes a large number of *vīryas*, completely different from those found in the lists of Caraka and Vāgbhaṭa, and comprising actions of drugs usually regarded as caused by *prabhāva*.

The theory of the eight potencies raises the question of why the remaining twelve *guṇas* are supposed to be weak and affected by the digestive fire. Moreover, their systemic effects cannot be accounted for if they are really weak, and become disintegrated during digestion. The general effects of all twenty *guṇas*, mentioned by Hemādri, do not enable us at all to distinguish the *vīryas* from the non-*vīrya* *guṇas*.[52] On the contrary, some of the ordinary properties, e.g., subtle (*sūkṣma*) and flowing (*sara*), are said to pervade the whole body, while other ones, e.g., immobile (*sthira*), are characterized by their prolonged action. Insoluble problems arise when the presence of a number of partly disagreeing potencies in a medicinal substance requires a decision as to which of these will exert the strongest influence. An example is milk, possessing a sweet taste and the cold, heavy and unctuous potencies. The cold potency would result in the provocation of *vāta*, but the sweet taste and the potencies heavy and unctuous are thought to alleviate this *doṣa*. The outcome, the alleviating action of milk on *vāta*, is attributed to the cumulative effect of the sweet taste and the potencies heavy and unctuous which, taken together, prevail

[49] Ca.Sū. xxvi. 53–56ab; A.h.Sū. x. 36cd–39ab.

[50] This work dates from the period between Vāgbhaṭa (sixth–seventh century) and Candraṭa (tenth century).

[51] *Rasavaiśeṣikasūtra* ii. 30–36.

[52] *Ad* A.h.Sū. i. 18.

over the cold potency.[53] This method of reasoning may imply that it is the number of properties with a related action which is decisive in such cases.

Specific action: *Prabhāva*

The fourth concept I want to discuss is *prabhāva*, i.e., specific action. It covers a wide range of phenomena but I shall confine myself to its use in pharmacological theory. The term *prabhāva* is, like *vīrya*, employed in both a wide and a restricted sense. When used in its wide sense it is called *cintyaśakti* 'conceivable power,' whereas in its restricted sense it is referred to as *acintyaśakti* 'non-conceivable power'.[54] *Cintyaśakti* is accessible to reasoning, *acintyaśakti* is beyond it. The *prabhāva* as *cintyaśakti* manifests itself in the actions of *rasa*, *vipāka* and *vīrya* when the three are in conformity with each other,[55] whereas *acintyaśakti* reveals itself when the actions of a substance cannot be deduced from its properties. A definition of *prabhāva* in its restricted sense is found in the *Carakasaṃhitā*:[56]

> When (different drugs) are similar with regard to their *rasa*, *vīrya* and *vipāka* and nevertheless show diversity of action, this should be seen as caused by *prabhāva*; *citraka* is considered to have a pungent *rasa* and *vipāka* and a hot potency, but *dantī*, which has the same properties, acts as a purgative on account of its *prabhāva* (whereas *citraka* does not).

The theoretical position of the concept of *prabhāva* is elucidated in Cakrapāṇidatta's comments on this definition. He regards *prabhāva* or *dravyaśakti* as a *sāmānyaviśeṣa* in the sense given to it in the Vaiśeṣika system.[57] Accordingly, the purgative action of *dantī* is an individual case (*vyakti*) belonging to this *sāmānyaviśeṣa* as a class (*jāti*), and it has to be regarded as linked to its nature as *dantī* (*dantīva*) since, in general, the *prabhāva* of a substance is its 'inherent nature (*svarūpa*).' This *svarūpa* or *svabhāva* of a substance is considered to be something beyond all reasoning. Cakrapāṇidatta refutes in this way the thesis of *śakti* being a separate category, a thesis that the Mīmāṃsā philosopher Prabhākara tried to establish.[58] Prabhākara considered *śakti* to differ from its cause, the substance (*dravya*), as opposed to Cakrapāṇidatta's view that it is the *svarūpa* of the substance itself. Prabhākara's way of reasoning in

---

[53] Aruṇadatta *ad* A.h.Sū. ix. 23cd–24.

[54] Cakrapāṇidatta *ad* Su.Sū. xl. 5 and 14; Ca.Vi. i. 4 and 14.

[55] Cakrapāṇidatta *ad* Ca.Vi. i. 12.

[56] Ca.Sū. xxvi. 67–68. More definitions are given by Hemādri *ad* A.h.Sū. ix. 26cd–27ab.

[57] See also Cakrapāṇidatta *ad* Su.Sū. xl. 14.

[58] See Erich Frauwallner, *Geschichte der indischen Philosophie* (Salzburg: O. Müller, 1953–), ii, 154–155.

defense of his thesis, unacceptable to the orthodox Vaiśeṣika philosophy, was also rejected by Cakrapāṇidatta. This appears from his manner of explaining why the purgative action of *dantī* is lost when this drug has been soaked in water. According to Prabhākara, this would prove that the *śakti* on which the purgative action of *dantī* is based is something separate from *dantī* as a substance. Cakrapāṇidatta, in conformity with the Vaiśeṣika system, refutes this view and argues that the phenomenon has to be explained by the presence of an impediment (*pratibandhaka*) which prevents the purgative action from manifesting itself.[59]

The concept of *prabhāva* is extremely interesting, since the term was used as a marker for phenomena that did not fit into the context of the theory. It is associated with the concept of *svabhāva* that refers to the substance as the substratum of any action seen as resulting from *prabhāva*.[60] The relationship between *svabhāva* and *prabhāva* is therefore said to be one between cause (*kāraṇa*) and effect (*kārya*).[61]

A noteworthy feature of the *Suśrutasaṃhitā* is the absence of the term *prabhāva*, although the concept itself was known to its author, as is apparent from the use of terms with a similar meaning, and from passages referring to the actions of drugs which are beyond any theoretical explanation.[62]

Which are the actions of drugs attributed to *prabhāva*, apart from those resulting from exceptions to the rules regarding *rasa*, *vipāka* and *vīrya*? The classical *saṃhitās* and their commentaries do not contain any systematic account with respect to this question. Consequently we are obliged to read through the texts in search of an answer. The *Carakasaṃhitā* mentions that emetic and purgative (*ūrdhvānulomika*) actions of drugs and the antitoxic effects of poisonous substances are based on their *prabhāva*.[63] The *Aṣṭāṅgasaṃgraha* adds the aphrodisiac (*vṛṣya*) action and the ability to allay excited *doṣas* (*śamana*).[64] A list of actions ascribed to *vīrya*, found in the *Suśrutasaṃhitā*, may throw light on the type of actions attributed to *prabhāva* in the *Carakasaṃhitā* because Suśruta's *vīrya* sometimes corresponds to Caraka's *prabhāva*.[65] According to P. V. Sharma this list is a composite one, being composed of actions partly caused by *prabhāva*, partly by *vīrya*.[66] In my view it is more likely that the

[59] Compare Cakrapāṇidatta *ad* Ca.Sū. i. 67.

[60] Indu *ad* A.s.Sū. xvii. 53–59.

[61] *Svabhāva* and *prabhāva* are regarded as synonyms by Ḍalhaṇa (*ad* Su.Ci. xxxiii. 33) and Aruṇadatta (*ad* A.h.Sū. ix. 26ab).

[62] Su.Sū. xl. 19: some actions of drugs are beyond reasoning (*amīmāṃsya; acintya*) and are caused by their *svabhāva*; Su.Sū. xl. 14: some drugs are active by means of their *ātman* (Cakrapāṇidatta regards *ātman* as a synonym of *prabhāva*).

[63] Ca.Sū. xxvi. 69.

[64] A.s.Sū. xvii. 58.

[65] Su.Sū. xl. 5.

[66] *Dravyaguṇavijñāna* i, 235.

whole series has to be interpreted as originating from *prabhāva*, in agreement with Cakrapāṇidatta's comment on the passage. This is confirmed by statements occurring in Āḍhamalla's commentary on the *Śārṅgadharasaṃhitā*;[67] Āḍhamalla regards a series of general actions of drugs, defined by Śārṅgadhara and also partly found in Suśruta's list, as brought about by *prabhāva*. Another list of particular actions of drugs, found in the *Carakasaṃhitā*, may in my opinion be based largely on *prabhāva*.[68] Since many of these actions are disease-specific, the ability of numerous drugs to counteract a particular disease, or group of diseases, i.e., their *vyādhipratyanīkatā*, may also be brought about by their *prabhāva*.[69]

Some considerations of the ancient Indian physicians, which led them to the conclusion that the *prabhāva* was involved in a particular case, are incidentally referred to in the commentarial literature.[70] Sometimes they were in doubt as to whether an action had to be seen as caused by *prabhāva* or by some other property.[71]

A point of view differing markedly from that of Caraka and Vāgbhaṭa, but related to that of Suśruta, is represented by Nāgārjuna in his *Rasavaiśeṣikasūtra*. As already mentioned, this author, who never employs the term *prabhāva*, distinguishes a large number of *vīryas* which are equivalent to actions said to find their origin in *prabhāva* in other texts.[72] Each of the *vīryas* mentioned by Nāgārjuna is said to be connected with one or more of the elements (*mahābhūta*) and to reside in particular tastes and properties. A system of fifteen *vīryas*, also associated with the elements, is attributed to an ancient authority called Nimi.[73]

Finally, I would like to discuss a few terms that have to do with *prabhāva*. Vāgbhaṭa employs two pharmacological terms, *sāmānyapratyayārabdha* and *vicitrapratyayārabdha*, which indicate whether the *rasa*, *vipāka*, and *vīrya* of a drug are in agreement with each other and therefore based on a common (*sāmānya*) mixture of elements (*pratyaya*), or otherwise, i.e., disagreeing and consequently based on different (*vicitra*) mixtures of elements.[74] The actions said to be *vicitrapratyayārabdha* bear some

[67] Āḍhamalla *ad Śārṅgadharasaṃhitā* i. 4.

[68] Ca.Sū. vi. Compare P. V. Sharma's list of actions attributed to the eight *vīryas* (*Dravyaguṇavijñāna* i, 228–230).

[69] See e.g., Ḍalhaṇa *ad* Su.U. xxvi.4–5ab.

[70] See e.g., Āḍhamalla *ad* Śārṅgadhara i. 4. 1: the fact that *miśi* is *dīpana* without being *pācana* cannot satisfactorily be explained by the preponderance of the element fire in its *dravya*.

[71] See e.g., Cakrapāṇidatta *ad* Ca.Sū. xxvii. 19–20 and Vi. i. 14.

[72] *Rasavaiśeṣikasūtra* iv. 1–30. The first series of *vīryas* enumerated by Nāgārjuna is closely related to the list of Su.Sū. xl. 5.

[73] Narasiṃha's commentary *ad Rasavaiśeṣikasūtra* iv. 30.

[74] A.h.Sū. ix. 27cd–28.

resemblance to those brought about by *prabhāva*, without being identical. The difference between the two terms has been elucidated by Śrīdāsapaṇḍita who says that the term *prabhāva* is applied when, one of two substances with the same *rasa*, *vipāka*, and *vīrya* presents a specific action that disagrees with its *rasa*, etc., whereas the term *vicitrapratyayārabdha* designates those actions which are brought about by a *vipāka* or *vīrya* which are not in conformity with the *rasa*.[75] Another term, of infrequent occurrence when used with respect to actions of drugs, is *vikṛtisamaveta*.[76] It is employed when some of the actions to be expected on account of *rasa*, etc., are absent for some unaccountable reason.

In this paper I have tried to sketch some of the problems raised by the basic concepts of Indian pharmacological theory. One of my conclusions is that this theory is not as coherent as might appear from descriptions found in a large part of the secondary literature. A more detailed study might reveal the various strands out of which a network of interconnected concepts has been braided and disclose both gaps and awkward knots.

[75] *Ad* A.h.Sū. ix. 27cd–28.

[76] See Cakrapāṇidatta *ad* Ca.Vi. i. 10: an example is *taṇḍulīyaka*, of a sweet taste, but not *snigdha* and *vṛṣya* as to be expected in a sweet substance.

Chapter 2

On the identification of a Vedic plant

Rahul Peter Das

DEALING WITH PLANT NAMES in *āyurvedic* texts is quite often a frustrating experience. Not only have we to consider a mass of synonyms for the same plant (the different synonyms often again having various synonyms of their own), as well as the same name denoting different plants, but also the possibility of a plant's having been replaced by a surrogate, with or without the literature or tradition expressly remarking on this. Added to this is the problem of the geographical distribution of plants. Since the burgeoning of synonyms and changing identification is diachronic, the more recent the texts consulted become the greater is the chance of adding to the confusion. All this may turn the efforts of the scholar attempting to identify the ingredients of a recipe mentioned in an *āyurvedic* text into a veritable nightmare; but it is only after some identification – be it ever so approximate and imprecise – has taken place, usually through a philologist, that pharmacologists and botanists can start their researches.[1]

It is obvious that if we manage to follow a plant name back in time and identify it accurately with regard to its oldest occurrence, we stand a far better chance of obtaining a really good base on which to build up further research, as all later mentions can always be referred back to this earliest occurrence and compared with it (e.g., with regard to properties, appearance, nomenclature, etc.). The ideal case would of course be if we could trace a plant right up to the Vedic *Saṃhitās*. There

[1] See also in this connection R. P. Labadie, 'Research considerations on traditional Indian medicine from a view point of drug research in pharmacognosy', in *Proceedings of the International Workshop on Priorities in the Study of Indian Medicine held at the State University of Groningen 23–27 October 1983*, edited by G. Jan Meulenbeld, (Groningen: Rijksuniversiteit te Groningen, 1984), 209–222.

are, in fact, quite a number of plant names known from later *āyurvedic* literature to be found in Vedic texts. Unfortunately the descriptions of appearance and properties of the plants designated by such names – if such descriptions are to be found at all – are on the whole hardly a great help in precise identification, added to which there are the difficulties of the language and general characteristics of Vedic literature. Thus the confusion is often increased instead of decreased. Nothing can exemplify such confusion more than the discussion on the identity of *sóma*. See in this connection now the paper 'Worum handelt es sich beim Soma?' of Rainer Stuhrmann[2] as well as R. E. Emmerick's 'Ein Männlein steht im Walde',[3] both with further bibliographic information. Another plant name mentioned in Vedic literature, *kúṣṭha* (already in the *Saṃhitā* of the *Atharvaveda*), is also still somewhat of a mystery. True, we have the Greek *kóstos* and Latin *costum*, loan-words taken from Indo-Aryan,[4] but as these loans are of a much later age, they are only of limited help.

This does not of course mean that all attempts at identification are doomed to failure from the very beginning. I would like to show here, by means of an example, that we *can* obtain results – at times quite startling – in our attempts at tracing plant names back in time as far as possible.

---

[2] *Indo-Iranian Journal*, xxviii (1985), 85–93. Stuhrmann comes to the conclusion that we actually still know nothing much about the plant (or plants) called *sóma*, especially regarding its description. There seems to be no evidence to support the now well-known theory that *sóma* was the name of the fly-agaric, but also, on the other hand, no descriptive evidence to disprove it. Stuhrmann, however, draws attention to certain properties and effects of the *sóma* which in his opinion seem to point to a plant containing alkaloid substances. In this connection it may be well to remember that tea and coffee were in previous times also used as intoxicants: it is only their constant use, leading to acclimatisation on the part of us users, which makes us tend to overlook their effects on those not in the habit of imbibing of them. There is thus always a possibility that what the Vedic poets describe is a plant which we today would not credit with having the effects described.

[3] In *Papers in honour of Professor Mary Boyce*, edited by Jacques Duchesne-Guillemin and Pierre Lecoq, (Leiden: Brill, 1985), i, 179–184.

[4] See Manfred Mayrhofer, *Kurzgefaßtes etymologisches Wörterbuch des Altindischen* (Heidelberg: Winter, 1956–1980), i, 246, (see also 566).

The case of *pāṭā́*

Two well-known plant names in *āyurvedic* literature are *pāṭhā* and *pāṭalā̆*.[5] The names are not Vedic.[6] But there is another word *pāṭā́*, the name of a plant as yet unidentified, which occurs only in Vedic texts. It has often been attempted to link *pāṭhā* with *pāṭā́*: in Middle Indo-Aryan, both could give *pāṭā*, so that *pāṭā́* might be a Middle Indo-Aryan loan in Vedic, or else *pāṭhā* a hypersanskritism for a correct *pāṭā* taken to be incorrect. On the other hand, *pāṭā́* and *pāṭalā̆* could be linked too, as both could be derived from **pāṭa*[7] possibly with just a minor shade of differentiation in meaning,[8] and could possibly refer to the same plant. Such postulated links show the importance of trying to identify *pāṭā́* even though it is not used in Vedic literature in what we would today call a medicinal manner. Moreover, W. W. Malandra has argued that in the *Atharvaveda-Saṃhitā (Śaunakīya)* (henceforth AV) *pāṭā́* is a synonym or surrogate of *sóma* (in AV ii. 27), which shows the importance of tackling the problem of *pāṭā́* from this angle too.[9] Note also in this connection that in *āyurveda* it is especially the roots of the plant *pāṭhā* which are considered to be 'most esteemed',[10] and that according to *Kauśikasūtra* xxxviii. 18 it is the roots of the *pāṭā́* which are supposed to have been consumed by Indra in AV ii. 27 to give him the strength to destroy his enemies.[11] However, the *Kauśikasūtra* is of a much later age than the *Saṃhitā* of the *Atharvaveda*, and the two may refer to different plants; but even if we could show that the *Kauśikasūtra* continues an old tradition, this still would not necessarily mean that *pāṭā́* and *pāṭhā* denote the same plant. Nevertheless, the matter remains intriguing.

[5] On various postulated identifications of these with known plants see G. J. Meulenbeld, *The Mādhavanidāna and its chief commentary. Chapters 1–10. Introduction, translation and notes* (Leiden: Brill, 1974), 573f.. They never seem to denote the same plant, although it is possible that sources Meulenbeld has not utilised might turn up such an identification.

[6] '*Pāṭalā*' mentioned in *Atharvapariśiṣṭa* xxxvi. 9. 3 (*The Pariśiṣṭas of the Atharveda*, edited by George Melville Bolling and Julius von Negelein, (Leipzig: Harrassowitz, 1909)) in all probability does not refer to a plant: *namaḥ kaṭavikaṭakaṇṭemāṭe pāṭale vikale asauryāsau asauryāsau . . .*

[7] See also Jacob Wackernagel, *Altindische Grammatik*, ii, 2, *Die Nominalsuffixe* von Albert Debrunner, (Göttingen: Vandenhoeck und Ruprecht, 1954), § 693.

[8] Ibid., § 693a.

[9] 'Atharvaveda 2.27: evidence for a *soma*-amulet', *Journal of the American Oriental Society*, xcix (1979), 220–224.

[10] K. R. Kirtikar and B. D. Basu, *Indian Medicinal Plants*, reprint (Dehra Dun: Bishen Singh Mahendra Pal Singh, 1980), i, 96.

[11] *The Kāuçika-Sūtra of the Atharva-Veda. With extracts from the commentaries of Dārila and Keçava*, edited by Maurice Bloomfield, (New Haven: American Oriental Society, 1890) = the *Journal of the American Oriental Society*, xiv (1890), without the 'Proceedings'.

AV ii. 27 reads as follows:[12]

1. *né[c] chátruḥ prā́śaṃ jayāti sáhamānābhibhū́r asi*
   prā́śaṃ prátiprāśo jahy arasā́n kṛṇv oṣadhe
2. *suparṇás tvā́nvavindat sūkarás tvākhanan nasā́*
   prā́śaṃ ...
3. *índro ha cakre tvā bāhā́v ásurebhya[ḥ]*[13] *stárītave*
   prā́śaṃ ...
4. *pāṭā́m índro vyā̀śnād ásurebhya[ḥ] starītave*
   prā́śaṃ ...
5. *táyāhám śátrūnt sākṣa índraḥ sālāvṛkā́m̐ iva*
   prā́śaṃ ...
6. *rúdra jálāṣabheṣaja nī́laśikhaṇḍa kármakṛt*
   prā́śaṃ ...
7. *tásya prā́śaṃ tvā́ṃ jahi yó na indrābhidā́sati*
   ádhi no brūhi śáktibhiḥ prāśí mā́m úttaraṃ kṛdhi

Translation

1. May the enemy by no means (*néd*[14]) win the case![15] Vanquishing, overpowering art thou! Smite the case of the legal adversary (or: Smite those counter-stating a statement[16]), make [them][17] sapless,

[12]Edition used: *Atharva Veda Sanhita*, edited by R. Roth and W. D. Whitney, 2nd improved edition by Max Lindenau, (Berlin: Dümmler, 1924). As in our editions of the *Ṛgveda-Saṃhitā*, so in this edition too the readings of the manuscripts, inasmuch as they differed from those adopted in the edition, are not given, which makes it difficult to call it critical. See too the edition mentioned in note 64 which generally also lists variants, though in the case of this hymn (*°vṛkám* for *vṛkā́m̐* in verse 5, *prā́śaṃ* for *prāśí* in verse 7) they are of little import. On the translation see also the remarks of Malandra, 'Atharvaveda 2.27'.

[13]Cf. Jakob Wackernagel, *Altindische Grammatik* i, *Lautlehre*, reprint (Göttingen: Vandenhoeck und Ruprecht, 1957), 287b.

[14]Though *néd* usually means 'so that not', it does not, especially in the oldest stage of the language, always have this meaning. The correctnesss of our above translation is borne out, moreover, by the missing accent of the verb.

[15]Note that 'case' in English means 'subject of question or inquiry' as well as 'legal statement or contention'; *prā́ś* too seems to have the same set of meanings (its literal meaning is 'question'). On this word see also Mayrhofer, *Kurzgefaßtes etymologisches Wörterbuch* ii, 376 and iii, 764.

[16]I.e., those presenting a counter-case or making a counter-statement. On the cognate accusative or accusative of implied object see Bertold Delbrück, *Altindische Syntax*, reprint (Darmstadt: Wissenschaftliche Buchgesellschaft, 1976), 168–170. As regards the alternative translations given above, verses 1a and 7ab would support the former, whereas 5a would support the latter. Cf. also the version of the Paippalāda recension given below.

[17]I.e., either the arguments of the legal adversary, or else the legal adversaries making a counter-

herb.

2. The *suparṇá* found thee out, the boar dug thee [out] with its snout. Smite ...
3. Now Indra made (= put)[18] thee on [his] arm, to prostrate the Asuras. Smite ...
4. Indra ate the *pāṭā́* up,[19] to prostrate the Asuras. Smite ...
5. Through it I defeat[20] the enemies, as Indra the hyenas. Smite ...
6. Rudra, whose medicine is cooling (?), whose hair-tuft is dark, doer of [magical][21] deeds! Smite ...
7. Smite thou the case of him, Indra, who bears us ill-will.[22] Prove us right[23] through [thy] powers, make me the superior in (or: with regard to) the case.

The parallel passage ii. 16 in the *Paippalāda-Saṃhitā* of the *Atharvaveda* (henceforth AVP) runs as follows (with the emendations of the editor;[24] 'Or' refers to the readings of the Orissan recension,[25] which was also consulted for purposes of checking, while 'Or*' shows that these readings seem actually to be supported by the readings of the Kashmiri manuscript):

1. *yā śatrūn sañjayāt* (Or: *prāśañjayā*) *sahamānābhibhūr asi*
   sāmūn pratiprāśo jayārasān (Or: *jahy arasān) kṛṇv oṣadhe*
2. *suparṇas tvānvavindat sūkaras tvākhanan nasā*
   indras tvā cakre bāhāv (Or*: *bāhvor) asurebhyaḥ starītave*
3. *pāṭām indro vyāśnād dhantavā asurebhyaḥ*
   tayāhaṃ (Or: *tvayāhaṃ*) *śatrūn sākṣya indraḥ* (Or*: *sākṣīyendraḥ*) *sālāvṛkām̐*
   (Or: *śā°*) *iva*

---

statement.

[18]Cf. Karl Hoffmann, *Aufsätze zur Indoiranistik*, edited by Johanna Narten, (Wiesbaden: Reichert, 1976), 579f.

[19]*ví* 'through and through', cf. Delbrück, *Altindische Syntax*, 466f.

[20]*sākṣe* is probably to be explained by analogy with *stuṣe/stuṣé, hiṣe, kṛṣe*, etc. *sākṣe* cannot be an infinitive (which could have been used as a finite imperative), as it has no accent. See also Johanna Narten, *Die sigmatischen Aoriste im Veda* (Wiesbaden: Harrassowitz, 1964), 265[835]

[21]See Hoffmann, *Aufsätze*, 24ff.

[22]*abhi* √ *dās*, German 'anfeinden'; cf. Narten, *Die sigmatischen Aoriste*, 140.

[23]*ádhi* ... √ *brū*, German 'recht geben'; cf. Delbrück, *Altindische Syntax*, 441.

[24]Edition used: 'The Kashmirian Atharva Veda, book two', edited, with critical notes, by LeRoy Carr Barret, *Journal of the American Oriental Society*, xxx (1909–1910), 187–258.

[25]*Paippalāda Saṃhitā of the Atharvaveda. Volume two*, edited by Durgamohan Bhattacharyya, (Calcutta: Sanskrit College, 1970)

4. *rudra jalāṣabheṣaja nīlaśikhaṇḍa karmakṛt*
   prāśaṃ (Or*: *praśnaṃ*) *durasyato jahi yo (a)smām̐ abhidāsati*
5. = AV ii. 27. 7 (Or*: *praśnaṃ* for *prāśaṃ*) (and °*dāsate* for °*dāsati* in the Kashmiri tradition?)

Translation

1. Who mayest vanquish[26] the foes (Or: Who art a case-vanquisher [of] the foes): vanquishing, overpowering art thou. [Thou that art] it, defeat (Or: smite) those legal adversaries, make [them] sapless, herb.
2. The *suparṇa* found thee out, the boar dug thee [out] with its snout. Indra made (= put) thee on [his] arm (Or: two arms), to prostrate the Asuras.
3. Indra ate the *pāṭā* up, to smite the Asuras. Through it (Or: thee) I shall (Or: may I) defeat the enemies, as Indra the hyenas.
4. Rudra, whose medicine is cooling (?), whose hair-tuft is dark, doer of [magical] deeds! Smite the case[27] of the one wishing to cause harm, who bears us ill-will.
5. = AV ii. 27. 7.

The name *pāṭā́* here, Malandra argues, probably refers to an amulet of *sóma*, and, moreover, the hymn 'can be offered as another piece of "circumstantial evidence" to support the view that *soma* should be regarded as a mushroom'.[28] The latter is stated in spite of the fact that the author expressly remarks on his scepticism with regard to the well-known theory of R. Gordon Wasson.[29] Though Malandra's argument that the mention of the *suparṇá* and Indra in the same hymn show that *pāṭā́* may have been *sóma* or used as a surrogate for *sóma* at the time of composition of the hymn deserves careful consideration, his arguments to prove that this plant may be a fungus are not convincing.

Boars, truffles and *sóma*

Malandra is of the opinion that the mention of a digging boar in AV ii. 27 points to '*sóma*' here being a truffle. Apart from the fact that we cannot *a priori* assume that one must have already required a surrogate for the Ṛgvedic *sóma* at the time of composition of this hymn, since it still remains to be definitively proved that the

[26] A wish, entreaty or requistion.
[27] Cf. note 15.
[28] Malandra, 'Atharvaveda 2.27', 223.
[29] *Soma: divine mushroom of immortality* (New York: Harcourt Brace Jovanovich, [1967]).

Atharvaveda-Saṃhitā is indeed in all its parts younger than the *Ṛgveda-Saṃhitā*,[30] this theory is clearly problematic, even if we disregard the fact that it also could imply that the Vedic Aryans were aware that truffles are, like mushrooms, botanically fungi. Actually, truffles have neither the colour nor the constituency attributed to the plant *sóma*, nor, as far as is known, does their juice have any of the effects related of *sóma*; truffles are prized for their flesh. As a rule they grow underground and are not perceivable to the eye. A handful of species may push their upper parts above the ground (e.g., *Cistaceae* sp. or *Choiromyces maeandriformis* – both non-Indian). Such truffles usually grow under shrubs, which, as we shall see below, precludes their being meant in AV ii. 27. 2.

The growth of truffles under the ground is the reason why in Mediterranean countries dogs (and in Europe – but only here, and as a rule in France only – pigs too) have from ancient times been used to sniff them out. Truffles were prized by Greeks and Romans, and it is known that the latter used dogs to sniff them out in Syria. Further to the east however this practice is and seems always to have been unknown. As a matter of fact, truffles are well known only in Europe and the regions bordering the mediterranean; several species of tuberous fungi do grow in India, and some of them are edible, like *Tuber cibarium* in Kashmir and Kangra, *Melanogaster durissimus* in the Kangra forests and some black and white truffles in West Bengal, but dogs or pigs are not used to find them.[31]

But there is another objection to projecting the well-known image of French truffle-seeking hogs onto India (actually, this method dates in France only to the fifteenth century, and is used especially for seeking the prized Périgord truffle). In none of the Buddhist texts Malandra quotes (albeit sceptically) is there any mention of truffle or mushroom-seeking or even mushroom-eating hogs.[32] In fact, the well-known *sūkaramaddava* which he discusses is explained as referring to mushrooms in one, and only one, late Indian text. But there the text explicitly states, in Malandra's own words: 'a mushroom sprung up in a place trampled by boars'. This is of course, as Malandra himself realises, not capable of serving as proof for his argument that in AV ii. 27. 2 we may have a description of a boar digging up a mushroom or

[30] See, e.g., Maurice Bloomfield, *The Atharvaveda* (Strassburg: Trübner, 1899), 41–50. See also Friedrich Knauer, 'Vedische Fragen', in *Festgruß an Rudolf von Roth zum Doktor-Jubiläum 24. August 1893* (Stuttgart: Kohlhammer, 1893), 61–67, as well as Alfred Hillebrandt, *Kleine Schriften*, edited by Rahul Peter Das, (Stuttgart: Steiner, 1987), 534f.

[31] On the occurrence of these fungi see *The Wealth of India. A dictionary of Indian raw materials and industrial products*, iv, (New Delhi: Council of Scientific and Industrial Research, 1956), 87, and George Watt, *A dictionary of the economic products of India*, vi(4), (London and Calcutta: Allen/Govt. of India, Dept. of Revenue and Agriculture, 1893), 203. On edible mushrooms see also R. P. Purakayastha and A. Chandra, *Indian edible mushrooms* (Calcutta: KLM, 1976).

[32] See Malandra, 'Atharvaveda 2.27', 222f.

something akin, or even searching for some such thing. That 'a certain tradition associated a food containing the word for "boar, hog" with mushrooms' is thus irrelevant.[33] Malandra has not drawn enough attention to the rather curious statement of the commentator that *sūkaramaddava* explained thus is not the name for mushroom or a species of mushroom, but is used to denote mushrooms sprung up in a certain place. This seems a rather laboured explanation, and one does get the impression that the commentator mentions it only because he cannot otherwise explain the word *sūkara* and at the same time let the Buddha not eat pig's meat that is bad.[34] The commentator, in contradistinction to some Western interpreters, has also not overlooked the fact that a mushroom poisonous to a human could possibly be so to a hog too, which could explain his 'place trampled by boars': the mushrooms are not eaten by the animals. And in any case, the mushrooms meant there are clearly above ground, as the name *ahicchattaka* 'snake's umbrella' shows (cf. the Bengali *byāṅer chātā* 'frog's or toad's umbrella', which is used for mushrooms growing above-ground). But such a mushroom, unless growing in dense undergrowth (concerning which see below), can be easily found by men and does not need searching for by hogs the way truffles do. Thus we cannot rely on any later evidence – at least not of the sort presented by Malandra – for an explanation of the AV-hymn.[35]

Eagles and high places

But why is the *suparṇá* (most probably a bird of the eagle-species, maybe the golden eagle)[36] mentioned with the boar? That the *suparṇá* discovered the plant in ques-

[33] Ibid., 223

[34] For the literature on the problem of the *sūkaramaddava* see Malandra, l.c. In this connection a mediaeval restraint cited by Vibhuti Bhushan Mishra, *Religious Beliefs and Practices of North India During the Early Mediaeval Period* (Leiden and Köln: Brill, 1973), 109, stating that mushrooms are not to be eaten, could be of importance. Note too that in the same list meat of unknown nature and meat which is not fresh also appear (similar restraints on meat are found in *āyurvedic* texts too). These could originally have been rules meant to prevent poisoning. Though the rule on mushrooms is non-Vedic, the fear of poisoning is of course old, a fact which we must always bear in mind when postulating the use of fungi – we ourselves incline to resist tasting any fungus until we are quite sure that it is not poisonous.

[35] With regard to mushrooms and the like, we still lack a thorough study of them in Indian literature, even though they play an important role in the *sóma* controversy. Some of the words referring to mushrooms are: *kṣúmpa, bhūmikapaṭu, deśakapaṭu, kapaṭu,* (on these four see also Hoffmann, *Aufsätze*, 566f.), *(ahic)chattraka, kavaka, ucchilīndhra, śilīndhra, aticchattra(ka), chattrāka, chattrikā̆, dilīra, mallipattra,* etc. On the problem of *sóma* and mushrooms see also H. W. Bailey, 'Vedic *kṣumpa-* and connected data' and F. B. J. Kuiper 'Was the *pūtī́ka* a mushroom?' in *Amṛtadhārā: Professor R. N. Dandekar felicitation volume,* edited by S. D. Joshi, (Delhi: Ajanta, 1984), 17–19 and 219–227 respectively.

[36] See also K. N. Dave, *Birds in Sanskrit literature* (Delhi, Varanasi, etc.: Motilal Banarsidass, 1985), 72ff. and 199ff., though Dave seems on the whole far too sure of his identifications and has moreover

tion must mean that it saw it somewhere where men cannot usually see it – if we leave out for the present all other but naturalistic implications. If we accept the contention of Malandra that the plant meant might be *sóma* or a surrogate, then the mention of the *suparṇá* seems to imply that the plant was found in some place where men usually do not or cannot go (since *sóma* often seems to have been obtained from such places) – in all probability some high, craggy mountain peak difficult of access. That the bird found the plant apparently also precludes its being an underground growth, since a mushroom living dependent on organic matter and growing in mycorrhizal relationship with trees (which truffles do) would obviously be difficult to spot from the air, even if some part of it were to protrude above the earth, because it would in all probability be hidden by foliage and/or undergrowth, as in the case of the truffle species mentioned above. This would incidentally also hold true for the fly-agaric with which Wasson, in his book *Soma*, would like to identify *sóma*. In fact the pictures in his book show that this mushroom thrives in the midst of greenery (cf. 'In the fall of the year, hard by a birch or a pine, one is apt to find the fly-agaric' [37]); it is best found by observation at ground-level. Of course we may still say that the fact that the *suparṇá* is a bird with mythical connections could imply that it could see even a mushroom hidden by foliage etc. Such speculation may be within the realm of possibility, but is it a probability? Wherever the *suparṇá* appears in the *Ṛgveda-Saṃhitā* (see the usual indexes), it is not its eyesight, but its power of flying to high and also distant places that is praised.

Now, since the *suparṇá* has already discovered the plant in question, the boar cannot be credited with finding it, which thus makes the picture of fungus-*seeking* hogs seem out of place here. But the boar is known as a digger; with its snout and tusks it can dig up even plants that have roots. And since in the above verse it has indeed dug up the plant, this must have needed digging up. We have seen above that the *suparṇá* could in all probability have found only a plant growing above the ground; since the boar has dug up this plant, it must have somehow been anchored in the earth, i.e., it must in all probability have had roots.

Roots are something one usually does not associate with mushrooms. But as a matter of fact, the filamentous outgrowths of the mycelium of mushrooms often look like roots. It is interesting to note that in mycorrhizal relationships of mushrooms with higher plants, the roots of the host plant do not develop hairs, the function of these being taken up by the filaments of the mushrooms. These filaments are often widely and densely spread in the soil. Plate IV of Wasson's work (facing page

---

more or less neglected other studies on the subject.

[37] Wasson, *Soma*, 35.

40) seems to show such filaments.[38] But it is a fact that mushrooms can be quite easily plucked; they need not be dug out (which perhaps explains why they are rarely thought of as having root-like structures), except for subterranean fungi such as truffles, and these apparently cannot be meant here. On the other hand, what would require digging up would be a plant with a well-developed root-system – for instance a succulent plant, since most succulents have very deep root-systems, which are also quite strong and resist being pulled up lightly. These plants (not to be confused with cacti, which are American in origin), very often leafless, can grow in arid mountainous climes too. Now most scholars researching on *sóma* have been of the opinion that the plant in question must have been a succulent, and it is also well known that *sóma* (or at least some of the plants which may all have been denoted by this name) grew on mountains. If Malandra's *sóma*-hypothesis be accepted, and if we link this with the mention of the *suparṇá* in AV ii. 27, then the digging up by a boar of such a plant by its roots is quite understandable and does not require the postulation of fungi of any sort.

There are however some peculiarities of certain kinds of truffles which we have hitherto neglected. French truffles, for instance, produce a patch of 'burnt earth' (which however only the expert truffle-seeker can – sometimes – identify). Now it could be conceded that it is possible to assume that the detection of a subterranean growth could, if it hindered other plants from growing in its vicinity, be facilitated by observation from the air, since the bald patch it created would show its existence. At the spot thus marked the growth could be dug out. This however does not mean that such a growth must needs have to have been a truffle. To prove the truffle theory, it would have to be shown that truffles or other underground fungi existing in India do hinder the growth of other plants in their vicinity, and, most important, that their juice has the powers attributed to *sóma*. The latter point in particular would be difficult to establish. But the truffle has entered Malandra's discussion only because of the *sūkaramaddava*, which, as we have seen above, cannot be used as an argument, as Malandra himself has hinted. Were we to neglect the truffle theory, however, we could still say that the growth mentioned in AV ii. 27 may be an undefined tuber or other underground growth, which, because it checked the

[38]In this context it may be debated whether the fact that the Vedic poets do not seem to mention certain parts of the plant *sóma* can, as an *argumentum ex silentio*, be permitted to have any value at all; that toes are not mentioned in the *Ṛgveda-Saṃhitā*, even though legs and feet are, does not mean that people at that time had none. Moreover, the most conspicuous part of a mushroom, the cap, is not mentioned either, in spite of Wasson's interpretations (*Soma*, 45f.), which John Brough has shown to be on the whole based on quotes taken out of context and thus totally misunderstood ('Soma and *Amanita muscaria*', *Bulletin of the School of Oriental and African Studies*, xxxiv (1971), 331–362, especially 356). Thus one could turn Wasson's *argumentum ex silentio* against him, should one choose to do so.

growth of other plants, the *suparṇá* was able to discover, allowing the boar to dig it up. But that also raises the question of whether the *suparṇá* is indeed mentioned because of its connection with *sóma*, or because it, as a bird, can be credited with being able to survey the earth from above, though we must remember that we are dealing with a *magical* piece of poetry and probably (though this is not quite certain) with an *amulet*, and that therefore not any bird can be credited with having found the place of growth, but only a bird known to have supernatural connections, if not powers. But if it is only the bird-nature of the *suparṇá* that is important here, then we need not suppose that the postulated amulet is a *sóma* amulet. This would indeed be more in keeping with the picture of the boar, since a boar is nowhere else associated with *sóma*. But without the *sóma* connection, we have no compelling need to postulate any fungus in AV ii. 27, though there still remains the possibility that we could have some other underground growth here. Even if we continue to maintain, however, that *pāṭā́* and *sóma* are related, our discussion above does still make it unlikely that a fungus could be meant.

Mythical and magical alternatives

Finally, there is one aspect of the whole problem which must not be overlooked. We have hitherto sought for a more or less naturalistic explanation. But in point of fact, it rather seems as if the boar were mentioned here for magical reasons and served a purpose commensurate with these reasons. The plant which is to provide victory must be thought of as possessing certain supernatural powers. Saying that the *suparṇá* found it and that the boar dug it up implies that it has been obtained by means other than those of mere mortals, that is, saying this of the plant actually being used and in actual fact obtained through mortal agency bestows upon it such properties, or else what we have here is a myth on the origin of the plant (similar descriptions of supernatural origins of other plants are not rare in Vedic literature, especially in the *Atharvaveda-Saṃhitā*). The well-known mythical and magical significance of the *suparṇá* implies, however, that not any animal that can dig can now be credited with rooting out the plant, but only one with mythical and magical connections and/or powers. Now the boar is indeed an animal with supernatural significance, both good and bad. An example for the former is the boar incarnation of Viṣṇu, for the latter the boar Emū̃ṣa, which may perhaps be identified with Vṛtra.[39] The conception of Viṣṇu as a boar is however known only from a later age.

[39]On the boar nature of Vṛtra see K. L. Janert, *Sinn und Bedeutung des Wortes 'dhāsi' und seiner Belegstellen im Rigveda and Awesta* (Wiesbaden: Harrassowitz, 1956), 74ff. The text on pages 74[22] and 77, line 10ff., in particular makes it highly probable that Vṛtra was pictured as a boar already in

Must we then assume that the boar here signifies forces inimical to the gods? That hardly seems likely, as the *suparṇá* is connected with divine, not with demoniacal mights.

The key to the problem seems to lie in the picture of Rudra portrayed, for instance, in *Ṛgveda-Saṃhitā* i. 114. 5:[40]

divó varāhám aruṣáṃ kapardínaṃ
tveṣáṃ rūpáṃ námasā ní hvayāmahe
háste bíbhrad bheṣajā̆ vā̆ryāṇi
śárma várma chardír asmábhyaṃ yaṃsat

Translation

We call down from heaven through our obeisance the reddish boar, the one characterised by braided hair, the strong/turbulent form [of

---

Indo-Iranian times, which would rule out the possibility of the boar myth in the *Ṛgveda-Saṃhitā* (henceforth ṚV) being Austroasiatic; cf. on this point F. B. J. Kuiper, *An Austro-Asiatic Myth in the Rigveda* (Amsterdam: Noord-Hollandsche Uitgevers Maatschapij, 1950), especially 11ff. (= 173ff.). The probable boar nature of Vṛtra as an Indo-Iranian feature would fit in well with the fact that the boar myth seems to be associated chiefly with the Kaṇvas (see Kuiper, *An Austro-Asiatic Myth*, 11 or 173), who probably came from the border region of Iran and the Indian subcontinent (see Hoffmann, *Aufsätze*, 16). Kuiper has failed to remark upon this very plausible theory. It could thus quite well be that the boar myth is Iranian in origin, but since much of old Iranian religion and mythology has been irretrievably lost due to the Zoroastrian revolution, we will probably never be in a position to verify this. It is however very interesting in this context that the songs of the Kaṇvas in the ṚV show many dialectical peculiarities not usual in the sacral *Hochsprache* of the ṚV (Hoffmann, ibid.); their name too is dialectical Indo-Aryan (Hoffmann, *Aufsätze*, 15–28). This makes it necessary to examine the name *Emū̆ṣá* for a possible dialectical Indo-Aryan or even Iranian origin, which Kuiper, in his zeal to prove the Austroasiatic origins of the boar myth, has failed to do. Of course it seems highly probably that the *original* boar myth was quite distinct from that of the serpent Vṛtra, but the two seem to have influenced each other and to some extent amalgamated. In this connection RV x. 99. 6 is of great interest, for in it Trita kills a boar, probably Viśvarūpa (cf. Hanns-Peter Schmidt, *Bṛhaspati und Indra. Untersuchungen zur vedischen Mythologie und Kulturgeschichte* (Wiesbaden: Harrassowitz, 1968), 134). Viśvarūpa and Vṛtra seem to be, if not identical, then at least similar (ibid., 131–135), and Trita and Bṛhaspati too have much in common (ibid.). Bṛhaspati, however, is only a deity developed out of Indra in his priestly capacity (ibid., 239). What is particularly intriguing here is that Trita, growing through Indra's might *(ójas)*, kills the boar *vipā̆ … áyoagrayā* 'through trembling [brought about by inspiration and concentration] whose tip is iron'. Could a similar picture lie at the root of Indra's shooting Emū̆ṣa? The problem deserves deeper investigation.

Note too that the flow of *sóma* is compared with a boar's gait in ṚV ix. 97. 7. In ṚV x. 67. 7, Bṛhaspati is helped to break open the Vala by the Aṅgirases, who are called bulls (*vṛ́ṣan*), boars (*varā̆ha*) and glowing with sweat (*gharmásveda*) (on the latter cf. Schmidt, *Bṛhaspati und Indra*, 226).

[40]Edition used: *The Hymns of the Rig-Veda in the Samhita and Pada Texts*, reprinted from the editio princeps by F. Max Müller, third edition, (Varanasi: Chowkhamba, 1965). Cf. also note 12.

> Rudra].[41] Carrying in his hand precious healing[42] herbs, may he hold [out] for us protection, armour, secure residence.[43]

Elsewhere in the ṚV too, Rudra is intimately connected with powerful herbs (ṚV ii. 33. 2, 4).[44] What is more, in the hymn in question (AV ii. 27), Rudra is actually invoked in verse 6 and asked to accomplish what the plant is to be used for. Rudra not only has great magical powers, but is also the causer of innumerable diseases, which suggests that he is also the one most likely to have the power to cure diseases. Thus, though *pāṭā́* here is not used medicinally in a medical sense, the connection with Rudra does seem to show that it was, in those days, at least potentially a medicinal plant, which shows once again the importance and justification of our present study.

All in all, the above seems to account better for the presence of the boar than the picture of (French) truffle seeking hogs. But even though the boar may have come into the hymn because of these mythological connections, we still cannot neglect the fact that the boar here does have a function which tallies closely with its natural behaviour. We are thus in the end left with two possible explanations for both *suparṇá* and boar appearing in the hymn, to wit, we are here either dealing with a plant (maybe succulent) growing in the mountains or some other inaccessible place (with the possibility that it just might be *sóma* – if not the original plant, then at least a surrogate), or else with an underground growth of unidentified nature (most probably, however, not a fungus). It should also be noted that the second theory would do away with the necessity of supposing that the plant in question grows in an inaccessible place, most probably on a mountain, a necessity which the other enjoins upon us. Can we however credit the ancient Indo-Aryans with having the same knowledge of aerial reconnaissance as we in our age of aeroplanes have? The answer would seem to be, on the basis of hymns such as ṚV x. 119. 6–8 and 11 or ṚV x. 136. 4f., that they had at least some knowledge, and this is in truth hardly surprising, as an observer on a hill or on a tall tree easily notices that he sees some things much more clearly than on the ground.

---

[41] I.e., Rudra in this special one of his many forms.

[42] Perhaps 'magical' would be better because of the intimate connection of magic and medicine in olden times. In this connection see my review of G. U. Thite's *Medicine: Its Magico-Religious Aspects according to the Vedic and Later Literature*, in *Indo-Iranian Journal*, xxvii (1984), 232–244.

[43] On the boar-nature of Rudra see also Walther Wüst, *Rudrá– m. n. pr.* (München: Kitzinger, 1955), 31f.

[44] See also Hermann Oldenberg, *Die Religion des Veda* (Darmstadt: Wissenschaftliche Buchgesellschaft, [5]1970), 219f. and Kenneth G. Zysk, *Religious Healing in the Veda* (Philadelphia: American Philosophical Society, 1985), 93ff.

Further references in the Kashmiri *Atharvaveda*

At this point we are stuck with our two alternatives. Luckily, however, AVP contains references to the plant *pāṭā* in vii. 12. Let us examine these; if we find something tallying with one of our alternatives, then we can be relatively sure that we are on the right track, and also that the plant name in the different hymns does indeed refer to the same plant.

AVP vii. 12 runs as follows:[45]

1. *ekarājñīm ekavratām ekasthām ekalāmikām*
   pāṭāṃ sapatnacātanīṃ jaitrāyācchāvadāmasi
2. *ekarājñy ekavrata ekastha ekalāmike*
   na tvā sapatnī sasāha . . .[46]
3. *uttarāham uttarābhya uttared adharābhyaḥ*
   adhas sapatnī sā makti adhared adharābhyaḥ
4. *na saindhavasya puṣpasya sūryaḥ snāpayati tvacā*
   pāṭe snāpayatu tvayā sapatnyā varca ādadhe[47]
5. *na vai pativahāsi subhagaṅkaraṇīd asi*
   pāṭe bhagam ā no dhehy atho mā mahiṣīṃ kṛṇu
6. *yat pāṭe adho vṛkṣe*[48] *vātaplavā mahīyase*
   jayantī pratyātiṣṭhantī sañjayā nāma vā asi
7. *uttānaparṇāṃ subhagāṃ sahamānāṃ sahasvatīm*
   acchā vṛhadvadā[49] *vada pāṭāṃ sapatnacātanīm*[50]
8. *pāṭām indro vyāśnād dhantavā asurebhyaḥ*
   tayā sapatnīṃ sākṣīya mahendro dānavān iva[51]
9. *pāṭā bibharty aṅkuśaṃ hiranyavantaṃ aṅkinam*
   tena sapatnyā varca ālumpasi samedhamat
10. *imāṃ khanāmy oṣadhīṃ vīrudhāṃ balavattamām*
    athā sapatnīṃ bādhate kṛṇute kevalaṃ patim

---

[45]Quoted, unless otherwise stated, with the emendations of the editor. Edition used: 'The Kashmirian Atharva Veda, book seven', edited by LeRoy Carr Barret, in *Journal of the American Oriental Society*, xl (1920), 145–169.

[46]Corrupt: *sasaha śairecanavāhyā* in the manuscript.

[47]Barret unnecessarily emends to *ādade.*

[48]Barret emends to *vṛṅkṣe.* On this see note 66.

[49]Barret unnecessarily emends to *°dāṃ.*

[50]Barret unnecessarily emends to *sapatnī°*

[51]ab of this verse = AVP ii. 16. 3 ab; cd of both verses have much in common.

Translation

1. For victory we address/invoke the (literally: towards the) *pāṭā*, the one ruling alone/sole queen,[52] the one whose vow is one [only],[53] the one that stands alone/[immovably] in [only] one place, the one that stays/enjoys itself[54] alone, the one driving away rivals.
2. [Thou who art] the one ruling alone/sole queen, the one whose vow is one [only], the one that stands alone/[immovably] in [only] one place, the one that stays/enjoys itself alone! The rival wife has not vanquished thee ...
3. Superior am I to [all] superiors, superior indeed to [all] inferiors. She, the rival wife, sinks[55] downwards, inferior indeed to [all] inferiors.[56]
4. The sun does not bathe (or: As the sun bathes) [any part] of the *saindhava* [and] the flower/the *saindhava*-flower[57] together with[58] their/its skin,[59] [but] it shall (or: [so] shall it), *pāṭā*, bathe [me] through/with thee [when I rub thee on myself/bathe with thee?]. The lustre of the rival wife I place on myself.
5. Thou art, forsooth, no carrier [away] of the husband; a maker of good apportioning indeed art thou. Secure for us, *pāṭā*, possession, and further make me chief queen.
6. Inasmuch as thou art, as a swimmer on/ in the wind, joyous/ mighty[60] in the lower region (= at the foot), under [thy] tree, thou art forsooth by name (*nāma*) 'Conquering [the wind]' (=*jayantī*), 'Steadfast' (=*pratyātiṣṭhantī*), 'Overcoming' (= *sañjayā*) / thou art forsooth conquering, steadfast, overcoming indeed (*nāma*).

---

[52]This probably means that the plant does not let other plants grow in its vicinity or that it grows where other plants do not usually grow, i.e., it has no rivals. On *ekarājñī* see also Hartmut Scharfe, 'The Vedic word for "King" ', *Journal of the American Oriental Society*, cv (1985), 543–548, especially 546f.

[53]This probably means that it has a vow which binds it only to its tree (= husband) and not to any other plants (= co-wives).

[54]*lāmikā* is probably derived from √ *lam* = √ *ram*.

[55]√ *majj*, 2nd class.

[56]This seems to point to a bathing ceremony.

[57]*saindhava* could refer to salt, but could equally refer to something else coming either from Sindh, the Sindhu (= Indus?) or from the sea. 'Flower' could refer to flowers in general. Or else we have here 'flower of the *saindhava*' or 'flower which is *saindhava*'. In any case, what is meant remains unclear. But compare, nevertheless, *sindhupuṣpa* 'conch shell', attested, however, only lexically in later classical Sanskrit.

[58]Or maybe: 'through' (= 'because of'?).

[59]Or maybe: 'The sun does not bath (or: As the sun bathes) on the skin (= the skin) of the *saindhava* ...'.

[60]This probably means that even a great gale cannot uproot the plant.

7. Address/Invoke (literally: speak towards), [O woman], as one who speaks mightily, the *pāṭā*, the one whose leaves are outstretched, the one whose apportioning is good, the vanquishing [one] the one characterised through might, the one driving away rivals.
8. Indra ate the *pāṭā* up, to smite the Asuras. Through it may I defeat the rival wife, as the Great Indra the Dānavas.[61]
9. The *pāṭā* bears a golden hook[62] with barbs (?). With it thou tearest out [O woman] the rival wife's lustre, [which is] characterised by radiance.[63]
10. This herb, [this] extremely powerful plant, I dig [up]. Now it oppresses the rival wife, the husband it makes exclusive [to me].

Several parts of this hymn have parallels in the AV: AVP vii. 12. 3 in AV iii. 18. 4, AVP vii. 12. 7 in AV iii. 18. 2, and AVP vii. 12. 10 in AV iii. 18. 1. These verses are similar, though not completely identical. The name of the plant is nowhere mentioned in AV iii. 18. However, the similarities between the two hymns must have been known to the indigenous scholastic tradition. Interestingly enough, in the commentary on AV iii. 18 we find the commentator explaining the plant in question as *pāṭhā*,[64] even though he quotes AV ii. 27. 4ab too (in his commentary on verse 2), in which we have *pāṭā́*. This is further proof of the fact that later scholars held *pāṭā́* and *pāṭhā* to be identical. AV iii. 18. 1, 2, 4 are also more or less the same as ṚV x. 145. 1, 2, 3; in the commentary on this hymn, the plant is identified by name by the commentator as *pāṭhā* again.[65]

Of course we cannot be sure, in spite of the intriguing parallels, that AV iii. 18, ṚV x. 145 and AVP vii. 12 all refer to the same plant, as the common verses of these hymns may have been taken from some other source and fitted into the respective contexts. And the equation *pāṭā́* = *pāṭhā* is of course still to be proved. Be all that as it may, we do have quite a good description of the plant mentioned in AVP vii. 12.

This description of AVP vii. 12 can be summed up as follows: the plant grows under a tree (maybe in some inaccessible place; see the discussion on AV ii. 27, p. 25

[61] Cf. AVP (Or) ii. 16. 3.

[62] Here we probably have one hook standing for many, or only one of the hooks is being used to 'tear out the lustre'.

[63] Cf. Paul Thieme, *Kleine Schriften*, [edited by Georg Buddruss], (Wiesbaden: Steiner, 1971), 160ff.

[64] *Atharvaveda (Śaunaka) with the Pada-pāṭha and Sāyaṇācārya's commentary*, edited by Vishva Bandhu, and Bhīmdev, Vidyānidhi and Munīshvar Dev, part I (kāṇḍas I–V), (Hoshiarpur: Vishveshvaranand Vedic Research Institute, 1960).

[65] *Rig-Veda-Sanhita, the sacred hymns of the Brahmans; together with the commentary of Sayanacharya*, edited by F. Max Müller, volume vi, (London: Allen, 1874).

above).[66] It stands alone, allowing no other plants (this must mean smaller plants) to grow near it. Gales cannot uproot it; it 'swims' on the wind, which would point to its probably having a well-developed root-system. It has curved, golden hooks, i.e., either thorns or similar structures or else curved sprigs (which must be hard, as they can be used for tearing out; cf. verse 9), and outstretched leaves. All this of course definitely precludes its being a fungus. It is obviously a thorny or (hard) sprigged (= prickly?), barbed (?), leafy plant, though the characterisation of the leaves as being outstretched could well point to its being a succulent plant, since several (not all, of course) such plants have fleshy, firm leaves which stick out rigidly. All this would make it very probable that the plant mentioned in AVP vii. 12 is indeed identical with the plant mentioned in AV ii. 27 (AVP ii. 16). A botanist should be able to draw up a list of plants which have the above characteristics and grow in the north and northwest of the Indian subcontinent (Afghanistan included).[67]

Some synonyms

Moreover, we could possibly have a list of synonyms of *pāṭā* in AVP vii. 12. 6, namely *jayantī*, *pratyātiṣṭhantī* and *sañjayā*, though *nāma* could be interpreted differently (see the above translation). Only the first word is known as a plant name in later times, but for *sañjayā* cf. the later names *vijayā* and *jayā* too: *jayā*, *vijayā* and *jayantī* are all synonyms, which is quite interesting in this connection (more below).

For convenience' sake, I shall here give a list of plants which have been identified as *jayantī*, *jayā* and *vijayā*. I shall not give detailed references, as this would make this

[66]If, however, we allow Barret's emendation (see note 48) to stand, then we would have to translate verse 6 as: 'Since thou bendest down/at the bottom part [of your stem], thou art, as a swimmer on/in the wind, forsooth by name ... /forsooth conquering ...'. This is, of course, a very appealing picture. The difficulty is, however, that we cannot yet be fully sure that √*vṛj*, conjugated medially, can indeed have the meaning 'bend oneself'; moreover, the reading of the manuscript too gives sense. Whether we read *vṛkṣe* or *vṛṅkṣe*, we have in both cases the image of yielding to ultimately further one's own ends. However, *vṛṅkṣe* would do away with the mention of a tree ('husband'), which fits so well into this hymn, and this would also mean that the plant in question may in fact grow alone, i.e., not even near a tree. But this would cause some difficulties with regard to *ekavrate* (see note 53), as well as to the reasons for specifically this plant being used in the above rite, for there are also other plants (especially in arid regions) which grow in solitude. All this has made me refrain from following Barret's emendation, though I must concede that it nevertheless remains a possiblity to be considered.

[67]The name *pāṭā* also occurs in the *Śāntikalpa* of the *Atharvaveda*, xix. 6. I have however not been able to obtain a copy of the edition of this text. But according to George Melville Bolling ('The Çāntikalpa of the Atharva-Veda', *Transactions and Proceedings of the American Philological Association*, xxxv (1904), 77ff., esp. 119), this passage does not contain any description or identification of the plant in question: 'With AV 2.27.1 [let him bind on] an amulet made from the root of the pāṭā plant (clypea hernandifolia) at the Aparājitā.'

paper too long. Exact references have been given in my note on *abhayā* in verse 254 of Surapāla's *Vṛkṣāyurveda*, which I have edited, translated into German and commented upon.[68]

1. *jayantī* is equated with
   - a. *vijayā*,
   - b. *jayā*,
   - c. *agnimantha* (probably a species of *Premna* or *Clerodendron*; on this name see Meulenbeld, *Mādhavanidāna*, 523, and Bt.,[69] 4f.),
   - d. *Sesbania aegyptiaca* Pers.,
   - e. S. *aculeata* Pers.,
   - f. a variety of barley,
   - g. *abhayā* (see below).
2. *vijayā* is equated with
   - a. *Cannabis sativa* Linn. = *siddhi* = *jayā*,
   - b. *abhayā*, which has the synonyms
     - i. *harītakī* (*Terminalia chebula* Retz. or *T. citrina* Roxb. ex Flem.; cf. Meulenbeld, 610f.),
     - ii. *cirbhiṭā* (see Meulenbeld, 553f. on *cirbhiṭa*; add *Momordica charantia* Linn.),
     - iii. *guḍūcī* (a *Tinospora* species; cf. Meulenbeld, 550),
     - iv. *vandhyā*; it is, however, not clear whether the passage on which this identification is based is listing as a synonym *vandhyākarkoṭī* (on this name see Bt., 81) or both *vandhyā* and *karkoṭī* (for details see my *Vṛkṣāyurveda* edition, l.c.). If *vandhyā* is indeed to be taken as a separate word, then it should also be pointed out that *vandhyā* could also be a synonym of *bālā*, and this latter has been identified with many plants (see Meulenbeld, 582) – among them also *pāṭhā*, though it is usually said to be *Pavonia odorata* Willd.,
     - v. *karkoṭī* (see Meulenbeld, 539),
     - vi. *mṛgādanī* (see Bt., 46), which is identified as
       - A. *Citrullus colocynthis* Schrad. (*indravāruṇī* = *aindrī*),
       - B. *Sida rhomboidea* Roxb. (*mahābalā*) (see also Bt., 428),
       - C. *Vernonia cinerea* Less. (*sahadevī*) (see also Bt., 428),

---

[68] To appear in 1987 in the series *Alt- und Neu-Indishce Studien* (Stuttgart: Steiner).

[69] Bt. = Balwant Singh and K. C. Chunekar, *Glossary of Vegetable Drugs in Bṛhattrayī* (Varanasi: Chowkhamba, 1972).

vii. *jayā*,

viii. *siddhi* (see above)

ix. *mṛṇāla*, on which see Meulenbeld, 482f.; also identified as *uśīra*, (see Meulenbeld, 529f.), most probably *Vetiveria zizanioides* Nash., but also as a species of *Valeriana* and as *Coleus vettiveroides* K. C. Jacob,

x. *palāśīlatā* (probably *Butea superba* Roxb.; see also Meulenbeld, 526),

xi. *kāñji* (*sauvīra*? i.e., a species of *Zizyphus* – cf. Meulenbeld, 609, or *laghujīvantī*?; *jīvantī* has many synonyms and identifications, see on these my note on *payasyā* in verse 273 of Surapāla's *Vṛkṣāyurveda*),

xii. the two *kāñcana* plants, maybe *raktakāñcana* (probably *Bauhinia variegata* Linn. or *B. purpurea* Linn.) and *śvetakāñcana* (*B. racemosa* Lamk.); other synonyms are (see also Bt., 90)

A. *nāgakesara* (see Meulenbeld, 566),

B. *udumbara* (prob. *Ficus racemosa* Wall.; see also Meulenbeld, 528f.),

C. *campaka* (*Michelia champaca* Linn.),

D. *dhustūra* = *dhattūra* (see Meulenbeld, 564 and Bt., 214),

E. *kovidāra* (a species of *Bauhinia*),

F. *vidala* (see Meulenbeld, 600),

xiii. a white variety of *nirguṇḍī*; *nirguṇḍī* is variously identified as *Vitex negundo* Linn., *V. trifolia* Linn. (*nīlanirguṇḍī*), *Symphorema polyandrum* Wight., *Justicia gendarussa* Linn.f. (*nīlanirguṇḍī*), *Nyctanthes arbor-tristis* Linn. = *(nīla)śephālikā*,

xiv. *mañjiṣṭhā* (probably *Rubia cordifolia* Linn.; see also Meulenbeld, 585),

xv. *jayantī*,

c. *harītakī* (see above),

d. *vacā*, identified usually as *Acorus calamus* Linn., but also as *Terminalia chebula* Retz. (*śvetavacā*, *śuklavacā*), *Zingiber zerumbet* Retz. and *Alpinia galanga* Willd. (*sugandhavacā*) (see also Bt., 354f.),

e. *śephālikā (see nirguṇḍī*, above),

f. *jayantī*,

g. *mañjiṣṭhā* (see above),

h. *śamī*, (prob. *Acacia sundra* DC. or *A. suma* Kurz ex Brandis or *Prosopis spicigera* Linn.; see also Meulenbeld, 538),

i. *nīladūrvā*, a variety of *Cynodon dactylon* (Linn.) Pers.

3. *jayā* is equated with

a. *jayantī*,

b. *agnimantha* (see above),

c. *siddhi* (see above) = *ṛddhi* = *vṛdhhi*,
d. *vijayā*,
e. *tarkārī*, identified as
    i. *Clerodendrum phlomidis* Linn. f.,
    ii. *Premna integrifolia* Linn.,
    iii. *Sesbania aegyptiaca* Pers.,
    iv. *Cassia tora* Linn.,
    v. *jayantī*,
f. *Sesbania sesban* (Linn.) Merr.,
g. *harītakī* (see above),
h. *nīladūrvā* (see above),
i. *japā* (*Hibiscus rosa-sinensis* Linn.).

Whether any of the above plants could be the *pāṭā́* we are dealing with remains for the specialist in botany (and pharmacology) to decide. We must not forget to compare the plants variously identified as *pāṭhā* and *pāṭalā̆* (see above) with the description of AVP vii. 12 either.

Red tubers?

I must also mention here that Professor W. W. Malandra was kind enough to let me have a copy of his unpublished paper 'OInd. *pāṭā́*:– an archaic word for "apple" ', which he presented at the Annual Meeting of the American Oriental Society 1981 in Boston.[70] In this paper he derives *pāṭā́* (the feminine of **pāṭa*) and *pāṭala* 'light red' from Indo-European **polto* from a base **pel* 'light grey, brown and yellow' and, we could add, 'light red,' given the – to speakers of European languages with a different system of colour values – vagueness associated with the above colour terms.[71] Malandra's hypothesis obviously necessitates the assumption that several different colours, sharing only the characteristic of paleness, were subsumed under one term. But, whatever the other merits of demerits of his hypothesis, there is no argument against this, for the problems the speaker of a modern European language faces when confronted with the phenomenon of colour perception in other cultures (including older Western cultures as well) are well known, it often being the case that not different hues, but different intensities or degrees of brightness were

[70]For copies contact Professor W. W. Malandra, Dept. of South Asian Studies, University of Minnesota, 192 Klaeber Court, 320 16th Avenue S. E., Minneapolis, Minnesota 55455, USA.

[71]Cf. also *piṅga*, *piṅgala* and, at the other end of the spectrum, *śyāma* and *śyāmala*.

or are given priority by the viewer, which of course led or leads to colour terms following a different pattern.[72]

Malandra explains *pāṭā́* and Old Iranian (Avestan) **pātā* as meaning 'apple' (because of their reddish colour); the Indian word would, according to this hypothesis, be attested only as 'earth apple' (cf. French *pomme de terre*, dialectical German *Erdapfel*, Dutch *aardappel*), i.e., 'tuber' (cf. the Iranian *ālū̆* used for plums, prunes and other round fruits growing on trees, secondarily also for yams and tubers, but in India only for tubers and the like). Whatever the merits or demerits of this derivation may be, it forces us to consider that

1. *pāṭā́* could possibly have referred to a plant as well as tubers (or possibly other fruits) of this plant (cf. *potato* in English), and
2. the plant and/or its tubers or fruits (if indeed it has such) could have a (light) red colour (it has golden hooks in any case, as we have seen above, and in Sanskrit the colour terms red and golden are, or were, frequently not differentiated).

The implications of Malandra's hypothesis for the postulated links between *pāṭā́* and *pāṭalā̆* and *pāṭhā* also need examining; I am not in a position to do so here.[73]

As regards the postulate that *pāṭā́* was a surrogate of *sóma* (or even the original *sóma*), the reddish colour obviously becomes important, especially if it could be shown that the juice of the plant *pāṭā́* too is reddish (or tawny or yellowish; see the remarks on colours, p. 36 above). But what is also quite interesting in this connection is the fact that *vijayā*, *jayā* and *jayantī* are all identified as an intoxicant (*Cannabis sativa* Linn.) too, though it would probably be rather far-fetched to postulate that

[72]Problems relating to such different modes and models of perception have been discussed in *The Realms of Colour. Die welt der Farben. Le Monde des couleurs*, edited by Adolf Portmann and Rudolf Ritsema, (Leiden: Brill, 1974). For a bibliography on and copious references to colours in Old and Middle Indo-Aryan, see Mathias Helmdach's unpublished MA thesis 'Farbbezeichnungen und Farbverständnis im alten Indien. (Dargestellt an Hand ausgewählter Werke der altindischen Literatur)' (München MA thesis, 1980). (I obtained a copy through the kind offices of Professor Dr Dieter Schlingloff, München.) See also Arthur Anthony Macdonell and Arthur Berridale Keith, *Vedic index of names and subjects*, reprint (Delhi: Motilal Banarsidass, 1982), ii, 1246f. and P. V. Sharma, *Indian medicine in the classical age* (Varanasi: Chowkhamba, 1972), 118–120. Cf. also Klaus L. Janert and P. Rajagopal Subramanian, 'Colours in early Tamil, a study based on Cilappatikaram', *International Journal of Dravidian Linguistics*, ii (1973), 141–150. Note too that *kṛṣṇa* and *śyāma* are differentiated in the *Carakasaṃhitā* (see *The Charakasaṃhitā by Agniveśa* ..., third edition, edited by Jādavaji Trikamji Āchārya, (Bombay: Nirṇaya Sāgar, 1941), Indriyasthāna i. 8; Śārīrasthāna viii. 12 and 15.

[73]On the etymologies of *pāṭalā̆* and *pāṭhā* see Mayrhofer, *Kurzgefaßtes etymologisches Wörterbuch*, ii, 245ff. and iii, 755.

this plant was *sóma* or its surrogate.[74]

I hope that these remarks will enable other specialists to make some headway in identifying the plant in question. As I remarked at the beginning of this paper, the precise identification of a plant mentioned in an ancient Vedic text would be a great help in the analysis and trying out of recipes and formulae of later texts.[75]

[74]In respect of *sóma* see also the remarks on *hūm* on pages 303f. and especially on page 303[1] in Jivanji Jamshedji Modi's *The Religious Ceremonies and Customs of the Parsees* (Bombay: British India Press, 1922). The *Ephedra* species used today as *hūm* (such plants grow in Iran, Afghanistan, Baluchistan, western Tibet and Kashmir) are described as having 'sprigs' and being 'golden-coloured' (p. 304). Moreover, several species of *Ephedra* yield ephedrine, a drug which is an alkaloid. (I wish to thank Dr G. Gropp, Hamburg, for having drawn my attention to the above publication). See also, however, Aurel Stein, 'On the Ephedra, the Hūm plant, and the Soma', *Bulletin of the School of Oriental Studies*, vi (1930–32), 501–514. On the *Ephedra* problem see also especially Mahdihassan,'A Persian painting illustrating Ephedra, leading to its identity as Soma', *Journal of Central Asia*, viii (1985), 171–177, which, in spite of its rather peculiar character, is of importance.

[75]I would like to thank Professors Dr S. A. Srinivasan and Dr R. E. Emmerick (Hamburg) for criticising drafts of this paper. My special thanks are due to Professor Dr M. Witzel of Harvard, who subjected a draft to a thorough critique and pointed out many facts that I had previously overlooked. All errors of omission and commission are, of course, my own. I do hope, however, that I have been able to show that philology, though often considered to be a subject for pedants and bores thriving in seclusion, is in fact of far more use than serving as a pastime for inhabitants of ivory towers. However, useful results can be obtained only by sound methods. Thus, though it mostly agrees with the above findings, I cannot cite H. G. Ranade's 'A note on "Pāṭā in Atharvaveda 2,27" ', *Studies in history of medicine*, v (1981), 225–227, as additional proof, as its unsound method of argumentation makes it appear superficial and tendentious.

Chapter 3

Carakasaṃhitā, Śārīrasthāna I and Vaiśeṣika philosophy

Antonella Comba

THE PHILOSOPHICAL BACKGROUND of the *Carakasaṃhitā* presents us with many interesting elements which require further research. The views propounded by this treatise are not uniform, but are inspired in an eclectic way by different schools of thought, e.g., Nyāya, Vaiśeṣika and Sāṃkhya.[1]

Previous accounts

One of the first accounts of the philosophical content of the *Carakasaṃhitā* was given by Julius Jolly, who referred only to Sāṃkhya doctrines.[2] At the beginning of this century, some historians of Indian philosophy were struck mainly by the Nyāya-Vaiśeṣika influences, perhaps following the reference of R. Bodas:[3] H. Jacobi noted

[0]Abbreviations used in the footnotes: Śā.: Śārīrasthāna; Sū.: Sūtrasthāna.

[1]On the first two schools of thought, see the bibliography given in K. H. Potter, *Encyclopedia of Indian Philosophies*, volume i, *Bibliography*, 2nd revised edition, (Delhi: Motilal Banarsidass, 1983), 677–688. On Sāṃkhya, see ibid., 691–702. The eclecticism of the *Carakasaṃhitā* is openly stated by Cakrapāṇidatta *ad* Sū. viii. 3: *yataḥ sarvapāriṣadam idaṃ śāstraṃ, tenāyurvedāviruddhavaiśeṣikasāṃkhyādi-darśanabhedena viruddhārtho 'bhidhīyamāno na pūrvāparavirodham āvahatīty arthaḥ* | Edition: *The Carakasaṃhitā of Agniveśa, revised by Caraka and Dṛḍhabala, with the Āyurveda-Dīpikā commentary of Cakrapāṇidatta*, edited by Vaidya Jādavaji Trikamji, 4th edition, (Delhi: Munshiram Manoharlal, 1981) (henceforth: *Caraka*).

[2]Julius Jolly, *Indian medicine*, (1st edition Strassburg, 1901) translated by C. G. Kashikar, 2nd revised edition, (New Delhi: Munshiram Manoharlal, 1977), 56–57.

[3]See the introduction of R. Bodas to Annaṃbhaṭṭa, *Tarkasaṃgraha*, (1st edition 1897), 2nd edition (Poona: Bhandarkar Institute Press, 1963), xxviii: 'The six categories as well as the proofs are mentioned in the medical work of *Caraka* . . . '.

that the *Carakasaṃhitā* was the oldest text based on Vaiśeṣika and Nyāya theories, but the fact that there are some differences between the *Carakasaṃhitā* and Nyāya texts suggested the existence of a parallel Nyāya school.[4] L. Suali made use of some passages of the *Carakasaṃhitā* to demonstrate the antiquity of the reciprocal influence between Nyāya and Vaiśeṣika.[5] H. Ui did not say anything on the question of the Vaiśeṣika references in the *Carakasaṃhitā*, as he just quoted Jolly and Jacobi,[6] while B. Faddegon, in discussing the date of the *Vaiśeṣikasūtras*, referred to Suali.[7] A. B. Keith, on the contrary, refused to make use of the *Carakasaṃhitā* doctrines in outlining a history of Nyāya-Vaiśeṣika because the work 'has suffered refashioning,' and because 'an unscientific exposition of this kind need reflect nothing more than the lack of knowledge of its author'.[8] Much more weight was given to the *Carakasaṃhitā* in the work of Vidyābhūṣaṇa on the history of logic, published posthumously in the same year as Keith's book: according to Vidyābhūṣaṇa, while the logical doctrines of Medhātithi Gautama were incorporated into Ātreya's *Carakasaṃhitā* by Caraka in a crude form, Akṣapāda elaborated them in the *Nyāyasūtras*.[9]

The turning point in the critical evaluation of the *Carakasaṃhitā* from a philosophical point of view was the work of S. N. Dasgupta: he referred to *āyurveda* as a specific school of thought, 'interesting even to a student of pure philosophy'.[10] Dasgupta summarized and provided a deeper knowledge of the data collected by the preceding scholars, and made important new observations.[11] We cannot analyse all his remarks here, but we may observe that, as regards the relation of the *Carakasaṃhitā* with the *darśanas*, he stressed the fact that the Sāṃkhya doctrines are expounded in the first chapter of the Śārīrasthāna, the Vaiśeṣika ones in the first chapter of the Sūtrasthāna, and the Nyāya ones in the eighth chapter of the

[4]H. Jacobi, 'Zur Frühgeschichte der indischen Philosophie', *Sitzungberichte der Kgl. Preussischen Akademie der Wissenschaften, Phil. hist. Kl.*, (1911), 732, footnote 2 and 736, footnote 1.

[5]L. Suali, *Introduzione allo studio della filosofia indiana* (Pavia: Mattei e C., 1913), 28.

[6]H. Ui, *The Vaiśeṣika philosophy according to the Daśapadārthaśāstra*, (1st edition 1917), 2nd edition, (Varanasi: Chowkhamba Sanskrit Series Office, 1962), 39.

[7]B. Faddegon, *The Vaiśeṣika-system, described with the help of the oldest texts*, (1st edition 1918), (Wiesbaden: Martin Sändig, 1969), 11.

[8]A. B. Keith, *Indian logic and atomism*, (1st edition Oxford, 1921) (New Delhi: Oriental Books Reprint Corporation, 1977), 13.

[9]S. C. Vidyābhūṣaṇa, *A history of Indian logic*, (1st edition Calcutta, 1921), (Delhi: Motilal Banarsidass, 1978), 26. Abstracts translated from *Caraka* Vimānasthāna viii are given at pp. 27–35.

[10]S. N. Dasgupta, *A history of Indian philosophy*, (1st edition Cambridge, 1922), (Delhi: Motilal Banarsidass, 1975), i, 273. The references to the *Caraka* are mostly in volume i, 213ff., 280–281, and in volume ii, 273ff. Dasgupta refutes Vidyābhūṣaṇa's thesis: see Dasgupta, i, 392ff.

[11]E.g., according to him the account of Sāṃkhya given in *Caraka* 'agrees with the system of Sāṃkhya propounded by Pañcaśikha ... in the *Mahābhārata* XII, 219' (Dasgupta, *History*, i, 216).

Vimānasthāna.[12] He did not at all exclude, for example, the possibility of finding some Vaiśeṣika elements in a passage other than the Sūtrasthāna's first chapter,[13] but in general he followed rather faithfully the aforesaid scheme and did not collect in a unifying vision all the elements of the *darśanas* scattered in the text.

The historiography following Dasgupta may, on the whole, be divided into three large groups:

1. Those who lay stress on the Sāṃkhya topics of the *Carakasaṃhitā*, or rely exclusively on Dasgupta's account to speak about *Carakasaṃhitā*, or object to the parallels drawn by Dasgupta between the *Carakasaṃhitā* and Pañcaśikha's doctrines as laid down in the *Mahābhārata*;[14]

2. Those who are mainly interested in the Nyāya theories expounded in the *Carakasaṃhitā*;[15]

---

[12]Dasgupta, *History*, i, 213ff.; ii, 369–372; and ii, 376–389, respectively.

[13]Ibid., ii, 310.

[14]See O. Strauss, *Indische Philosophie* (München: Ernst Reinhardt, 1925), 130, 140; E. H. Johnston, *Early Sāṃkhya*, (1st edition London, 1937), (Delhi: Motilal Banarsidass, 1974), especially p. 10; H. von Glasenapp, *Filosofia dell'India*, Italian translation of *Die Philosophie der Inder* (1st edition 1949), (Torino: Societá Editrice Internazionale, 1962), especially pp. 140 and 208; K. Krishnamoorthy, 'The conception of personality in the *Carakasaṃhitā* and the concept of *prajñāparādha*', *Poona Orientalist*, xv (1950), 65–89; R. F. G. Müller, *Manas und der Geist altindischer Medizin* (Leipzig: J. A. Barth, 1952); C. G. Kashikar and S. G. Vartak, *Āyurvedīya-padārthavijñāna*, (Bombay: The Board of research in Āyurveda, 1953); V. M. Bedekar, 'Studies in Sāṃkhya: Pañcaśikha and Caraka', *Annals of the Bhandarkar Oriental Research Institute*, xxxviii (1958), 140–147; K. B. Ramakrishna Rao, 'The Sāṃkhya philosophy in the *Carakasaṃhitā*', *Adyar Library Bulletin*, xxvi (1962), 193–205; R. C. Majumdar, 'Medicine', in *A concise history of science in India*, edited by D. M. Bose, S. N. Sen, and B. V. Subbarayappa, (New Delhi: Indian National Science Academy, 1971), 235ff.; G. J. Larson, *Classical Sāṃkhya*, (1st edition Delhi, 1969), 2nd edition, (Delhi: Motilal Banarsidass, 1979), especially pp. 103–104; M. Hulin, *Sāṃkhya Literature*, volume vi(3) of *A history of Indian literature*, edited by J. Gonda, (Wiesbaden: Harrassowitz, 1978), 135: M. G. Weiss, *Carakasaṃhitā* on the doctrines of karma', in *Karma and rebirth in the Indian classical tradition*, edited by W. D. O'Flaherty, (Berkeley: Univ. of California Press, 1980), 90–115, especially p. 91; M. Gangopadhyaya, *Indian atomism* (Calcutta: K. P. Bagchi & Co., 1980) especially p. 121.

[15]See S. Radhakrishnan, *Indian philosophy*, (1st edition 1923), seventh impression, (New York: MacMillan Company, London: George Allen & Unwin, 1962), ii, especially p. 37, footnote 1; H. N. Randle, *Indian logic in the early schools*, (1st edition Oxford, 1930), (New Delhi: Oriental Books Reprint Corp., 1976), especially pp. 11–12 and 178; W. Ruben, *Geschichte der indischen Philosophie* (Berlin: Deutschen Verlag der Wissenschaften, 1954), 212–223; M. Biardeau, *Théorie de la connaissance et philosophie de la parole dans le brahmanisme classique* (Paris–La Haye: Mouton, 1964), especially pp. 444–447; A. Wezler, 'Die "dreifache" Schlussfolgerung im *Nyāyasūtra* 1.1.5', *Indo-Iranian Journal*, xi (1969), 190–211; B. K. Matilal, *Logic, language and reality*, (Delhi: Motilal Banarsidass, 1985), especially pp. 2–4 and 10–12.

3. Those who have remarked on, among other things, the importance of the Vaiśeṣika doctrines in the *Carakasaṃhitā*.[16]

The division between these categories is obviously not so sharp, because many authors may be placed in more than one group,[17] but it gives a first arrangement to the matter. Outside these groups, there are some recent authors who touch incidentally upon the *Carakasaṃhitā* in tracing the history of the Nyāya-Vaiśeṣika, but without entering in detail upon the part played by that text in this school of thought.[18] Apart from them, there are other scholars who leave the *Carakasaṃhitā* completely out of their researches on the Vaiśeṣika categories,[19] or on the relation between the *Vaiśeṣikasūtras* and the history of science.[20] An attempt to investigate the philosophical background of the *Carakasaṃhitā* comprehensively has been made by S. Śrīvāstavya,[21] who has succeeded better than others in pointing out the eclecticism of this text, but sometimes he is more inclined to describe and paraphrase the relevant philosophical passages, than to analyse them critically.[22]

In the present work we shall try, in the light of some Vaiśeṣika texts, to give a first and very limited essay on the research which is needed to clarify the philosophical contents of the *Carakasaṃhitā*. Our starting point will be four quotations from Kaṇāda's *Vaiśeṣikasūtras*, which occur in the first chapter of the Śārīrasthāna.[23]

[16]See J. Filliozat, 'Le Vaiśeṣika', in L. Renou and J. Filliozat, *L'Inde classique*, (Paris–Hanoi: Imprimerie Nationale – École Française d'Extrême-Orient, 1953), ii, 71: G. Patti, *Der Samavāya im Nyāya-Vaiśeṣika-System*, (Roma: Pontificio Istituto Biblico, 1955), 15–16; D. S. Gaur and L. P. Gupta, 'The theory of *pañcamahābhūta* with special reference to Āyurveda', *Indian Journal of History of Science*, v (1970), 51–67; H. Narain, *Evolution of Nyāya-Vaiśeṣika categoriology. I: Early Nyāya–Vaiśeṣika categoriology* (Varanasi: Bharati Prakashan, 1976), especially pp. 106–110; A. Roşu, *Les conceptions psychologiques dans les textes médicaux indiens* (Paris: Institut de Civilisation Indienne, 1978).

[17]See, for example, the relations between the *Carakasaṃhitā* and the *darśanas* as dealt with by Ruben, *Geschichte*, 213ff., and by Roşu, *Conceptions psychologiques*, especially pp. 125ff.

[18]See B. K. Matilal, *Nyāya-Vaiśeṣika*, volume vi(2) of *A history of Indian literature*, edited by J. Gonda, (Wiesbaden: Harrassowitz, 1977), 55, 76–77; K. H. Potter, *Encyclopedia of Indian philosophies*, volume ii, *Indian metaphysics and epistemology: the tradition of Nyāya-Vaiśeṣika up to Gaṅgeśa* (Delhi: Motilal Banarsidass, 1977), 180 and 211.

[19]See the works of W. Halbfass, especially 'The Vaiśeṣika concept of *guṇa* and the problem of universals', *Wiener Zeitschrift für die Kunde Südasiens und Archiv für Indische Philosophie*, xxiv (1980), 225–238.

[20]See B. V. Subbarayappa, 'An estimate of the *Vaiśeṣika Sūtra* in the history of science', *Indian Journal of History of Science*, ii (1967), 24–34.

[21]S. Śrīvāstavya, *Carak Saṃhitā kī dārśanik pṛṣṭhabhūmi* (Allahabad: Pīyūṣ Prakāśan, 1983).

[22]See, e.g., ibid., 239ff.

[23]On this chapter and its content see Dasgupta, *History*, i, 213ff.; ii, 372: 'the whole chapter does not appear to fit in with the rest of the work, and it is not referred to in other parts of the book. It is not improbable that this chapter was somehow added to the book from some other treatise';

The *Carakasaṃhitā*, Śārīrasthāna, i. 18 quotes the *Vaiśeṣikasūtra* iii. 2, 1;[24] *Caraka* Śā. i. 59b quotes *Vaiśeṣikasūtra* iv. 1, 1;[25] *Caraka* Śā. i. 70–72 quotes *Vaiśeṣikasūtra* iii. 2, 4 (a sort of counter-quotation is given in Śārīrasthāna i. 152 and in Śārīrasthāna v. 12);[26] *Caraka* Śā. i. 138–139 quotes *Vaiśeṣikasūtra* v. 2, 16–17 (that this is also a

---

Johnston, *Early Sāṃkhya*, 10, who declares that the Sāṃkhya passage in the Śa. is by a single hand; Krishnamoorthy, 'The conception of personality', 87, who observes that in the first chapter of the Śā. 'we may see an attempt made at a happy reconciliation of the conclusion reached by the different schools of Indian philosophy, viz., Yoga, Sāṃkhya and Vedānta'; Müller, *Manas und der Geist*, 26ff., who does not completely agree with Dasgupta's thesis, because he has not sufficiently reckoned the Yoga influence; Kashikar and Vartak, *Āyurvedīya-padārthavijñāna*, 214, according to whom, 'an elucidation of the *Sāṃkhya* theory is clearly given in *Carakasaṃhitā*, *Śārīra*. chap. 1' and 'the coordination of theories of *Sāṃkhya* and *Vaiśeṣika* . . . is nowhere found in Āyurvedic books'; Bedekar, 'Studies in Sāṃkhya', 140ff., who demonstrates that, 'there is no basic similarity between the doctrines of Pañcaśikha and Caraka'; Ramakrishna Rao, 'The Sāṃkhya philosophy', 203, who remarks that here, 'the Self is not only a *sākṣin* and *bhoktṛ*, as in the classical [Sāṃkhya] system, but also pre-eminently the *kartṛ* of all actions . . .'; Ruben, *Geschichte*, 213; Roşu, *Conceptions psychologiques, passim*; Śrīvāstavya, *Carak Saṃhitā kī dārśanik pṛṣṭhabhūmi, passim.*

[24] *Caraka* Śā. i. 18: *lakṣaṇaṃ manaso jñānasyābhāvo bhāva eva ca* |
sati hy ātmendriyārthānāṃ sannikarṣe na vartate ||

Vaiśeṣikasūtra of Kaṇāda, with the commentary of Candrānanda, edited by Śrī Jambuvijayajī, (Baroda: Oriental Institute, 1961) (henceforth: *Vaiśeṣika* (Jambuvijaya)), iii. 2, 1: *ātmendriyārthasannikarṣe jñānasyābhāvo bhāvaś ca manaso liṅgam* || Here the *Caraka's* quotation is nearer to the critical edition of the *Sūtras* than to the *sūtrapāṭha* glossed by Śaṅkaramiśra: see *Vaiśeṣikadarśane maharṣipravarapraśastadevācārya-viracitaṃ praśastapādabhāṣyam* . . . *śaṅkaramiśravinirmitaḥ upaskāraś ca*, edited by Ḍhuṇḍhirāja Śāstri, (Kāśī: Caukhamba, 1923) (henceforth: *Vaiśeṣika* (Śāstri)), iii. 2, 1.

[25] *Caraka* Śā. i. 59c: *sad akāraṇavan nityam* . . . ||

Vaiśeṣika (Jambuvijaya) iv. 1, 1: *sad akāraṇavat tan nityam* || In this case the text of the *Caraka* is exactly the same as *Vaiśeṣika* (Śāstri) iv. 1, 1. Cakrapāṇidatta (*ad* Śā. i. 59) underlines that this passage expresses a view which belongs to 'another' *śāstra*, namely, different from the Sāṃkhya: *atraivānāder nityatve śāstrāntarasammatim apy āha – sad ity ādi* | This very *sūtra* is also quoted by Dalhaṇa *ad Suśrutasaṃhitā* Śā. i. 16 (edition: *Suśrutasaṃhitā of Suśruta, with the Nibandhasaṅgraha commentary of Śrī Ḍalhaṇācārya*, edited by Jādavji Trikamji and Nārāyaṇ Rām, 4th edition, (Varanasi, Delhi: Chaukhamba Orientalia, 1980)).

[26] *Caraka* Śā. i. 70–73: *prāṇāpānau nimeṣādyā jīvanaṃ manaso gatiḥ* |
indriyāntarasaṃcāraḥ preraṇaṃ dhāraṇaṃ ca yat || *70* ||
deśāntaragatiḥ svapne pañcatvagrahaṇaṃ tathā |
dṛṣṭasya dakṣiṇenākṣṇā savyenāvagamas tathā || *71* ||
icchā dveṣaḥ sukhaṃ duḥkhaṃ prayatnaś cetanā dhṛtiḥ |
buddhiḥ smṛtir ahaṅkāro liṅgani paramātmanaḥ || *72* ||
yasmāt samupalabhyante liṅgāny etāni jīvataḥ |
na mṛtasyātmaliṅgāni tasmād āhur maharṣayaḥ || *73* ||

Vaiśeṣika (Jambuvijaya) iii. 2, 4: *prāṇāpānanimeṣonmeṣajīvanamanogatīndriyāntaravikārāḥ sukhaduḥkhe icchādveṣau prayatnaś cety ātmaliṅgāni* ||

Here the *Carakasaṃhitā's* passage is slightly different from both editions: if, on the one hand, the compound *ātmaliṅgāni* is present in *Caraka* Śā. i. 73, on the other the expression *ātmano liṅgāni* may correspond to *liṅgāni paramātmanaḥ* in *Caraka* Śā. i. 72.

quotation is clear from the context).[27]

Mind (*manas*) and its relation to self (*ātman*)

The first quotation is on the character of the *manas* (usually translated as 'mind'), as an instrument of knowledge. The existence of the *manas* is inferred from the fact that even when there is contact between *ātman*, sense organs (*indriya*) and sense objects (*artha*), sometimes knowledge is produced and sometimes not. In this context, the *Carakasaṃhitā* attributes to the *manas* atomicity and oneness,[28] as do the *Vaiśeṣikasūtras*.[29]

A point which it may be useful to clear up is whether the *Carakasaṃhitā* really does sometimes agree and sometimes disagree with the Vaiśeṣika on the question of the *indriyatva* (sense-organ-ness) of the *manas*, as is stressed by Cakrapāṇidatta.[30] The *Vaiśeṣikasūtras* never clearly state that the *manas* is an *indriya*, on the contrary they describe it as something very different from the sense organs: the *manas* is a substance (*dravya*),[31] while the sense organs are made of substances but do not constitute separate substances;[32] the *manas* is eternal,[33] while the sense organs die with the body, because of their composite and elemental nature; the functions of the *manas* are totally different from the functions of sense organs, and this is what makes us infer the existence of the *manas*;[34] every time that the *sūtras* speak of the *manas* and the sense organs, they are listed separately.[35] Nevertheless, in the *Nyāyabhāṣya*

---

[27] *Caraka* Śā. i. 138–139: *ātmendriyamanorthānāṃ sannikarṣāt pravartate* |
sukhaduḥkham anārambhād ātmasthe manasi sthire || *138* ||
nivartate tad ubhayaṃ vaśitvaṃ copajāyate |
saśarīrasya yogajñās taṃ yogam ṛṣayo viduḥ || *139* ||

Vaiśeṣika (Jambuvijaya) v. 2, 16–17: *ātmendriyamanorthasannikarṣāt sukhaduḥkhe tadanārambhaḥ* || *16* || *ātmasthe manasi saśarīrasya sukhaduḥkhābhāvaḥ sa yogaḥ* || *17* ||

In this case *Caraka* follows *Vaiśeṣika* (Jambuvijaya) more closely than *Vaiśeṣika* (Śāstri).

[28] *Caraka* Śā. i. 19. On the impossibility of simultaneous perceptions, besides Cakrapāṇidatta's commentary to this passage, see *Caraka* Sū. viii. 5 and Cakrapāṇidatta; cf. also Cakrapāṇidatta *ad* Sū. xi. 38.

[29] *Vaiśeṣika* (Jambuvijaya) iii. 2, 3; viii. 1, 30.

[30] *Caraka* refers to six sense organs (five sense organs plus the *manas*) in Sū. xxvi. 43, whilst in Sū. viii. 4 says that the *manas* is *atīndriya*, beyond the senses. Cakrapāṇidatta connects the first statement to the Vaiśeṣika opinion (*ad Caraka* Sū. viii. 3).

[31] *Vaiśeṣika* (Jambuvijaya) i. 1, 4.

[32] Ibid., viii. 15.

[33] Ibid., iii. 2, 2.

[34] Ibid., iii. 2, 1.

[35] Ibid., iii. 1, 13; iii. 2, 1; v. 2, 16; ix. 15.

Vātsyāyana says:[36]

> [even though the (Nyāya) *Sūtra* does not mention the mind among the 'sense-organs'], the fact that the mind is a 'sense-organ' can be learnt from another philosophical system (the Vaiśeṣika); and it is a rule with all systems that those doctrines of other systems which are not directly negated are meant to be accepted as true.

As a matter of fact, Praśastapāda explicitly states that the *manas* is a sense organ;[37] but the silence on this point of *Vaiśeṣikasūtras*, *Nyāyasūtras* and *Daśapadārthaśāstra*[38] leads to the supposition that this statement comes from the texts of the Vaiśeṣika's 'dark period' now lost, but known to Vātsyāyana.[39]

Another noteworthy Vaiśeṣika characteristic attributed to the *manas* in the first chapter of *Carakasaṃhitā's* Śārīrasthāna is the *kriyāvattva*, i.e., the fact of being endowed with action or movement, while the *ātman* is the agent (*kartṛ*).[40] According to the *Carakasaṃhitā's* Śārīrasthāna the *manas* is unconscious but endowed with action, whereas the *ātman*, which is conscious, is different in that it is not possessed of motion; nonetheless the acts of the *manas* are attributed to the all-pervading *ātman*, because it is the ultimate source of these acts (and as such it may be regarded as the real *kartṛ*), and is connected to the *manas*.[41] The *ātman* is called the agent because it is conscious, while the mind is not so called because it is devoid of consciousness, although it is endowed with motion.[42] Cakrapāṇidatta explains that the motions of the *manas*, governed by the *ātman*, are said to be the actions of the *ātman* only metaphorically; when the *manas* is controlled by the conscious *ātman*, it performs actions, when it is not controlled, it doesn't. Therefore, just as he by whom an action is

[36] Vātsyāyana, *Nyāyabhāṣya ad Nyāyasūtra* i. 1, 4. Edition: *Nyāyadarśanam, with Vātsyāyana's Bhāṣya, Uddyotakara's Vārttika, Vācaspati Miśra's Tātparyaṭīkā & Viśvanātha's Vṛtti*, reprint, (Kyoto: Rinsen Book Co., 1982) (henceforth: Nyāyasūtra). The quotation is from the translation of Gaṅgānāth Jhā, (Poona: Oriental Book Agency, 1939), 25; in this very passage there is the *tantrayukti* quoted by Cakrapāṇidatta glossing *Caraka* Sū. viii. 4: *paramatasyāpratiṣedhāt svayam apy anumatam*.

[37] *The Praśastapādabhāṣya with commentary Nyāyakandalī of Śrīdhara*, edited by V. P. Dvivedin, 2nd edition, (Delhi: Sri Satguru Publications, 1984) (henceforth: *Praśastapādabhāṣya* and *Nyāyakandalī*), 186.

[38] See Ui, *Vaiśeṣika philosophy*, 142.

[39] On the Vaiśeṣika 'dark period,' see Matilal, *Nyāya-Vaiśeṣika*, 59ff.

[40] The *manas* is defined *kriyāvant* in *Caraka* Śā. i. 75–76; the *ātman* is called *kartṛ* in *Caraka* Śā. i. 39, 44, 49, 56 and 76. On the *kartṛtva* of the *ātman*, see E. Frauwallner, *History of Indian philosophy*, (1st edition Salzburg, 1953–1956), translated from German by V. M. Bedekar, reprint, (Delhi: Motilal Banarsidass, 1984), ii, 42ff.

[41] *Caraka* Śā. i. 75.

[42] Ibid., i. 76.

performed is said to be 'endowed with action,' the *manas* is called *kriyāvant*; but it is not called agent, because in reality it acts depending on another, i.e., the *ātman*.[43]

In the *Vaiśeṣikasūtras* the word *kriyāvant* occurs thrice: the first time in the definition of substance, the second time in the demonstration that the wind is a substance, and finally in the statement that space, time and *ākāśa*, being different from substance endowed with motion, are not mobile.[44] Substance is different from qualities (*guṇa*) and motions (*karman*) in that it can be possessed of motions (*kriyāvant*): in this context *kriyā* has exactly the same meaning of *karman*, namely, a sort of 'natural' movement, different for each substance.[45] The all-pervading substances have no motion: this is the reason why the *ātman* cannot be called *kriyāvant*.[46] Two *sūtras*, however, make reference to the *karmans* of the *ātman*:[47] with regard to the first, both Candrānanda and Śaṅkaramiśra interpret the word *ātman* as 'a part of the body';[48] the word *ātman* of the second one is glossed as *manas* by Candrānanda, while Śaṅkaramiśra holds on to the word *ātman*.[49] . As a matter of fact, the *Vaiśeṣikasūtras* do not explicitly call the *ātman* a *kartṛ*, an agent. But this view may be implied by the passages about *karman*, where the contact between the *ātman* and the hand is said to be the cause of the hand's movement.[50]

Praśastapāda classifies earth, water, fire, air and mind as substances endowed with movement, form, distance, proximity and speed.[51] The word 'movement' is glossed by Vyomaśiva with *calanarūpa*, 'shaking motion',[52] and by Śrīdhara as 'throwing up etc.' (*utkṣepaṇādi*), i.e., the five types of *karman*.[53]

In the view of Praśastapāda, *ākāśa*, time, space and *ātman* are all-pervading, have the largest dimension (*paramamahattva*) and are the common receptacle of all

---

[43] Cakrapāṇidatta *ad Caraka* Śā. i. 75–76.

[44] *Vaiśeṣika* (Jambuvijaya) i. 1, 14; ii. 1, 12; v. 2, 23, respectively.

[45] Cf. Candrānanda *ad Vaiśeṣika* (Jambuvijaya) i. 1, 14: *utkṣepaṇādikaṃ karma kriyā yathāsaṃbhavaṃ yasmin yatsamavāyena vartate tat kriyāvat anyatrākāśakāladigātmabhyaḥ* |

On the Vaiśeṣika theory of motion, see S. N. Sen, 'The impetus theory of the Vaiśeṣika', *Indian Journal of the History of Science*, i (1966), 34–45.

[46] *Vaiśeṣika* (Jambuvijaya) v. 2, 23 is supplemented by Candrānanda with the word *ātman*, implied by the word *ca*; the same is done by Śaṅkaramiśra (*ad Vaiśeṣika* (Śāstri) v. 2, 21).

[47] *Vaiśeṣika* (Jambuvijaya) v. 1, 6: *tathātmakarma hastasaṃyogāc ca* ||

Vaiśeṣika (Jambuvijaya) vi. 2, 19: *ātmakarmasu mokṣo vyākhyātaḥ* ||

On these *sūtras*, see B. Faddegon, *The Vaiśeṣika-system*, 113–114 and 166.

[48] Candrānanda *ad Vaiśeṣika* (Jambuvijaya) v. 1, 6: *ātmeti śarīraikadeśaḥ*;

Śaṅkaramiśra *ad Vaiśeṣika* (Śāstri) v. 1, 6: *ātmaśabdaḥ śarīrāvayavapara upacārāt* |

[49] See Candrānanda *ad Vaiśeṣika* (Jambuvijaya) vi. 2, 19; Śaṅkaramiśra *ad Vaiśeṣika* (Śāstri) vi. 2, 16.

[50] See *Vaiśeṣika* (Jambuvijaya) v. 1, 1ff.

[51] *Praśastapādabhāṣya*, 21.

[52] *Vyomavatī of Vyomaśivācārya*, edited by Gaurinath Sastri (Varanasi: Sampūrṇānandasaṃskṛtaviśvavidyālaya, 1983) (henceforth: *Vyomavatī*), 46.

[53] *Nyāyakandalī*, 21.

conjunct (*saṃyogin*) things,[54] but they are not endowed with any action because, although they are substances, they are shapeless, like universals, and action is concomitant with shape (*mūrta*).[55] In this way Praśastapāda supplements *sūtra* v. 2, 23 with the word *ātman*. The agency (*kartṛtva*) of the *ātman* is among the first features described by Praśastapāda in the passage devoted to the *ātman*:[56]

> Since the instruments as the axe and the like are to be used by a doer, a cogniser is inferred from the cognition of the sound etc. [This character] does not belong to the body, to the sense organs or to the *manas*, because they are unconscious ... Consciousness cannot belong to the *manas*, because if it could be independent from the other organs, there would be the wrong consequence of simultaneity of perception and remembrance, and because it is an instrument.

We cannot discuss here in detail the question of how the agency of the *ātman* is demonstrated, and its relations with the theory of causality.[57] But we may add two supplementary remarks, to understand better the position of the *Carakasaṃhitā*: it is true that from the point of view of *mokṣa* the liberated self is not a *kartṛ*,[58] and that sometimes the *kartṛtva* of the selves is pointed out by the Vaiśeṣika's own representatives as a misleading concept, not belonging to the true nature of the *ātman*;[59] but from the point of view of the state of bondage, the *ātman* is called *kartṛ* in Nyāya-Vaiśeṣika and in Jainism,[60] and *akartṛ* by the *Sāṃkhyas*.[61] This difference of opinions gave rise to many discussions between these schools of thought, and was for them a very important matter of debate. E.g., the *Yuktidīpikā*, a commentary on the *Sāṃkhyakārikās* dated about AD 550,[62] refutes the Pāśupata view that the *puruṣa*

[54] *Praśastapādabhāṣya*, 22.

[55] Ibid., 308.

[56] Ibid., 69. Cf. *Vyomavatī*, 139; *Nyāyakandalī*, 72–73.

[57] See, e.g., *Vyomavatī*, 137.

[58] Cf. *Caraka* Śā. i. 57.

[59] See *Nyāyakandalī*, 196: *asmadādibhir ātmā sarvadaivāhaṃ mameti kartṛtvasvāmitvarūpasaṃbhinnaḥ pratīyate ubhayaṃ caitaccarīrādyupādhikṛtaṃ rūpaṃ na svābhāvikam ata evāhaṃ mameti pratyayo mithyādṛṣtir iti gīyate sarvapravādeṣu viparītarūpagrāhakatvāt* |

Cf. *Nyāyakandalī*, 279: *svarūpatas tāvad ātmā na kartā na bhoktā kintūdāsīna eva*; on the same page Śrīdhara quotes *Sāṃkhyakārikā* 65 to confirm his view (edition: *The Sāṃkhyakārikā of Īśvarakṛṣṇa, with the commentary of Gauḍapāda*, edited and translated by T. G. Mainkar, (Poona: Oriental Book Agency, 1964)). Cf. also *Nyāyakandalī*, 281. Śrīdhara's criticism on the Sāṃkhya conception of *mokṣa* regards mainly the destiny of *prakṛti* after deliverance (see p. 4). The Sāṃkhya influences on Śrīdhara are yet to be investigated.

[60] See Radhakrishnan, *Indian philosophy*, i, 292; cf. Frauwallner, *History of Indian philosophy*, ii, 186.

[61] See *Sāṃkhyakārikā* 19–20.

[62] See Frauwallner, *History of Indian philosophy*, i, 226.

is *kartṛ*, and attributes the same doctrinal defect to the Vaiśeṣikas;[63] according to the *Dīpikā*, the *puruṣa* is conscious and all-pervading, but it cannot be endowed with action because only unconscious things like milk are *kriyāvant*. The *puruṣa* is agent only metaphorically (*bhaktyā*).[64]

For this reason, being the agency of the *ātman* expounded by the *Carakasaṃhitā* with a wealth of detail, and upheld against Buddhist opponents, it is better to recognize the Vaiśeṣika orientation of these passages, rather than interpret them purely as metaphors, with regard to the basic Sāṃkhya and Vedānta views.[65]

In the *Carakasaṃhitā*, doctrinal cornerstones of Vaiśeṣika are often presented side by side with the main doctrines of other systems: another example of this procedure may be found in the conception of the *buddhi* in the chapter at issue. In four passages the *buddhi* is seen from a Sāṃkhya point of view,[66] in two passages undoubtedly from a Vaiśeṣika point of view,[67] while two other passages are rather ambiguous, but more Vaiśeṣika than Sāṃkhya.[68]

The Sāṃkhya system regards the *buddhi* or *mahat* (usually translated as 'intellect') as the first evolute of the *prakṛti*;[69] its characteristic (*dharma*), or mark (*lakṣaṇa*) is ascertainment (*adhyavasāya*), which is contained in the intellect like the future germinating sprout in the seed.[70] We cannot discuss here the problem of the oneness or multiplicity of the *buddhi*, which seems to have had different solutions by the early and by the late followers of the school;[71] nor need we establish here up to what point the *buddhi* can be defined an 'organ' or not. But it is interesting to note that Śrīdhara clearly attributes to the Sāṃkhya the doctrine of *buddhi's* singleness,[72] and the view that the *buddhi*, called also *mahat* and *citta*, is an internal organ which comes into contact with the external objects through the sense organs.[73] According to Śrīdhara, Praśastapāda's statement that *buddhi*, *upalabdhi*, *jñāna*, and *pratyaya* are

---

[63] See *Yuktidīpikā ad Sāṃkhyakārikā* 15, in *Sāṃkhyakārikā with … Yuktidīpikā Vivṛti by unknown author*, edited by R. S. Tripathi, (Varanasi: Krishnadas Academy, 1982) (henceforth: *Yuktidīpikā*) and G. Chemparathy, 'The testimony of the *Yuktidīpikā* concerning the Īśvara doctrine of the Pāśupatas and the Vaiśeṣikas', *Wiener Zeitschrift für die Kunde Süd- und Ostasiens und Archiv für Indische Philosophie*, ix (1965), 119–146.

[64] *Yuktidīpikā ad Sāṃkhyakārikā* 19–20.

[65] Cf. Śrīvāstavya, *Carak Saṃhitā kī dārśanik pṛṣṭhabhūmi*, 270–271.

[66] *Caraka* Śā. i. 63, 66, 99, 109.

[67] Ibid., i. 32–34 and 72.

[68] Ibid., i. 132, 146.

[69] *Sāṁkhyakārikā*, 22.

[70] Ibid., 23 and commentary of Gauḍapāda thereon.

[71] See, e.g., J. Filliozat, 'Le Vaiśeṣika', 40.

[72] *Nyāyakandalī*, 172.

[73] Ibid., 171.

synonymous aims at refuting these Sāṃkhya opinions.[74] From the Vaiśeṣika point of view, the *buddhi* (usually translated as 'knowledge' or 'cognition') is a quality or property (*guṇa*) of the *ātman*,[75] and is one of the signs from which its existence can be inferred.[76] There is no 'organ of thought' called *buddhi* apart from cognition: there are only the 'agent' *ātman* and his property, the *buddhi*.[77] Every cognition, i.e., *buddhi*, has a particular individual object, and as objects are endless, the *buddhis* too must be endless.[78]

The *Carakasaṃhitā* maintains not only that the *buddhis* are many, but that they differ according to the organ by the contact of which they arise, like the sound produced by the contact between a finger and the thumb is different from that of *tantrīvīṇā* (a stringed instrument) and the fingernail.[79]

The *ātmaliṅgas*

Turning now to the *Carakasaṃhitā's* third quotation from the *Vaiśeṣikasūtras*, dealing with the *ātmaliṅgas*,[80] there are a few remarks which may be made. All the twelve marks of the *ātman* mentioned by the *Vaiśeṣikasūtras* are present in the list of the *Carakasaṃhitā*, except *unmeṣa*, included in the term *ādya*.[81] The second source quoted by the *Carakasaṃhitā* in this passage is the *Yājñavalkyasmṛti*;[82] but although the order of the *ātmaliṅgas* given by the *Vaiśeṣikasūtras* has been exactly preserved in the *Carakasaṃhitā*, with the exception of the couple *icchā-dveṣa*, which has been put before the couple *sukha-duḥkha*,[83] the order of the *Yājñavalkyasmṛti's liṅgas* has been completely changed: not even a sequence of two words has been kept in the same order.

---

[74]Ibid., 172.

[75]See *Vaiśeṣika* (Jambuvijaya) i. 1, 5: here the word *buddhi* is in the plural (*buddhayaḥ*).

[76]See below.

[77]*Nyāyakandalī*, 172.

[78]*Praśastapādabhāṣya* and *Nyāyakandalī*, 172.

[79]*Caraka* Śā. i. 32–34.

[80]On the *ātmaliṅgas*, see J. C. Chatterji, *Hindu realism*, (reprint of the 1912 edition), (Delhi: Swastika Publications, 1975), 61–87; Ui, *Vaiśeṣika philosophy*, 74–75; Faddegon, *The Vaiśeṣika-system*, 247–259; Keith, *Indian logic*, 238ff.; Dasgupta, *History*, i, 285 and 362–363; Frauwallner, *History of Indian philosophy*, ii, 38ff.; Biardeau, *Théorie de la connaissance*, 109ff.; Roşu, *Conceptions psychologiques*, 130–131; Śrīvāstavya, *Carak Saṃhitā kī dārśanik pṛṣṭhabhūmi*, 261–263. For a buddhistic refutation of the *ātmaliṅgas*, see G. Tucci, 'Le çento strofe' (*Śataśāstra*): testo buddhistico mahāyāna tradotto dal cinese', *Studi e materiali di storia delle religioni*, i(1/2–3) (1925), 90ff.

[81]See *Vaiśeṣika* (Jambuvijaya) iii. 2, 4 and *Caraka* Śā. i. 70–72.

[82]*Yājñavalkya's Gesetzbuch*, edited by A. F. Stenzler, (1st edition 1849), (Osnabrück: Biblio Verlag, 1970) iii. 174–175 (henceforth: *Yājñavalkya* (Stenzler)). We propose to deal more extensively with the relationship between the *Caraka* and the *Yājñavalkyasmṛti* elsewhere.

[83]See *Caraka* Śā. i. 72: *icchā dveṣaḥ sukhaṃ prayatnaś* ...
Vaiśeṣika (Jambuvijaya) ii. 2, 4: *sukhaduḥkhe icchādveṣau prayatnaś* ...

One of the possible reasons for this procedure is that the list of the *Vaiśeṣikasūtras* has been taken as a basis in the first place; then it has been divided in two parts, on one side the biological-perceptive-sensorial phenomena and on the other the properties of the *ātman* with the various subdivisions of knowledge; the *Yājñavalkyasmṛti's* *liṅgas* have been added to each of these two half-lists. The compound *indriyāntaravikāra* of the *Vaiśeṣikasūtras* has been replaced by *indriyāntarasaṃcāra* taken from the *Yājñavalkyasmṛti*;[84] the *liṅga* of the connection between the two eyes is not listed in any of the sources;[85] some *liṅgas* of the *Smṛti* are omitted (*medhā* and *svarga*), some others have undergone slight changes (*bhāvānāṃ preraṇaṃ* has become simply *preraṇaṃ*, *svapna* has become *deśāntaragatiḥ svapne*, and *ādānaṃ pāñcabhautikam* has been changed to *pañcatvagrahaṇaṃ*).[86] It is interesting to note that, while the list of the *Vaiśeṣikasūtras* is well fixed, has no variants in the different editions and is explained by the commentators in a very similar way,[87] the *Smṛti's* list has many variants according to the editions, and often the comments interpret the *liṅgas* differently.[88] One of the most singular interpretations is that given by Aparārka to the variant *manaso'gatiḥ*, which also appears in the text glossed by Viśvarūpa. According to Aparārka, the fact that the *manas*, which is very subtle, dwells in a body having many apertures without slipping out, is due to the *adṛṣṭa* inhering the *ātman*, and therefore it is a sign of the *ātman*;[89] Visvarūpa, on the contrary, refers the absence of *manas's* motion to the state of deep sleep.[90] Another interesting variant is *svapne sargaś ca bhāvānāṃ* in the edition commented on by Viśvarūpa, where the other three editions consulted have *svargaḥ svapnaś ca*, and join the

The order of the *liṅgas* in *Caraka* is different even from that of *Nyāyasūtra* i. 1, 10: *icchādveṣaprayatna-sukhaduḥkhajñānany* ... ||

[84]Cf. *Caraka* Śā. i. 70, *Vaiśeṣika* (Jambuvijaya) iii. 2, 4 and *Yājñavalkya* (Stenzler) iii. 174.

[85]Cf. *Caraka* Śā. i. 71, *Vaiśeṣika* (Jambuvijaya) iii. 2, 4 and *Yājñavalkya* (Stenzler) iii. 174–175.

[86]Cf. *Caraka* Śā. i. 70–72 and *Yājñavalkya* (Stenzler) iii, 174–175.

[87]Cf. *Vaiśeṣika* (Jambuvijaya) iii. 2, 4, and Candrānanda thereon; *Vaiśeṣika* (Śāstri) iii. 2, 4 and Śaṅkaramiśra thereon; *Praśastapādabhāṣya* and *Nyāyakandalī*, 69ff.; *Vyomavatī*, 134ff.

[88]Cf. *Yājñavalkya* (Stenzler) iii. 174–175; *The Yājñavalkyasmṛti, with the commentary Bālakrīḍā of Viśvarūpācārya*, edited by T. G. Śāstri (Trivandrum: Superintendant Government Press, 1924), volume ii (henceforth *Yājñavalkya* (Śāstri)), iii. 165–166 and Viśvarūpa thereon; *Yājñavalkyasmṛti of Yogīśvara Yājñavalkya, with the Mitākṣarā commentary of Vijñāneśvara*, edited by U. C. Pāndey, (Varanasi: Chowkhamba Sanskrit Series Office, 1967) (henceforth: *Yājñavalkya* (Pāndey)), iii. 174–175 and Vijñāneśvara thereon; *Aparārkāparābhidhāparādityaviracitaṭīkāsametā yājñavalkyasmṛtiḥ* (Poona: Ānandāśrama, 1904), volume ii (henceforth: *Yājñavalkya* (Poona)) iii. 174–175 and Aparārka thereon.

[89]Aparārka *ad Yājñavalkya* (Poona) iii. 175.

[90]Viśvarūpa *ad Yājñavalkya* (Śāstri) iii. 166.

word *bhāvānāṃ* with the following *preraṇaṃ*:[91] this could explain why in the *Carakasaṃhitā* we do not find *svarga* as a sign of the *ātman*, and why the word *preraṇa* is not accompanied by *bhāvānāṃ*, so that Cakrapāṇidatta interprets it as referred only to the *manas*.[92] In general, Cakrapāṇidatta does not dwell very much on the *liṅgas* coming from the *Vaiśeṣikasūtras*, whereas he glosses those coming from the *Yājñavalkyasmṛti*, but often in a way different from Viśvarūpa, Vijñāneśvara and Aparārka: a good example of this procedure is the comment *maraṇajñāna* referred to *pañcatvagrahaṇa* in the Cakrapāṇidatta text.[93] Evidently Cakrapāṇidatta has considered *pañcatvagrahaṇa* as an anticipation of the remarks on death which immediately follow the list of the *liṅgas*.[94] The rest of Cakrapāṇidatta's commentary follows the Nyāya-Vaiśeṣika argumentation on the subject: he demonstrates, closely following Praśastapāda, that the *ātman* cannot be identified with the elements, nor with the mind, nor with the sense organs.[95]

The arguments relating to the elements and the mind are also advanced among others by Praśastapāda,[96] while the proof concerning the difference between the *ātman* and the sense organs is absent in Praśastapāda, but it summarizes a very complex argumentation in Uddyotakara's *Nyāyavārttika*.[97] Stating that *ahaṃkāra* is here only a kind of *buddhi*, Cakrapāṇidatta acknowledges openly the Vaiśeṣika use of this word; apparently it would be incompatible with the Ṣāṃkhya concept of *ahaṃkāra*, but Cakrapāṇidatta avoids laying any stress on this question and he does not comment in detail on this *ātman's* proof, even if many *Vaiśeṣikasūtras* and passages from other texts are devoted to it.[98]

Two other concepts appearing in the first chapter of the *Carakasaṃhitā's* Śārīrasthāna which may be of Vaiśeṣika provenience are *upadhā* and *mokṣa*.

---

[91] Cf. *Yājñavalkya* (Śāstri) iii. 166; *Yājñavalkya* (Stenzler) iii. 175; *Yājñavalkya* (Pāndey) iii. 175 and Vijñāneśvara thereon; *Yājñavalkya* (Poona) iii. 175 and Aparārka thereon.

[92] *Caraka* Śā. i. 70–71 and Cakrapāṇidatta thereon.

[93] Cf. ibid., Viśvarūpa *ad Yājñavalkya* (Śāstri) iii. 166: *ādānaṃ grahaṇaṃ trividhakarmānusāreṇa* | *pāñcabhautikaṃ pṛthivyādipañcabhūtaviṣayam* |

Vijñāneśvara *ad Yājñavalkya* (Pāndey) iii. 175: *pañcabhūtānām upādānam* ...

Aparārka *ad Yājñavalkya* (Poona) iii. 175: *dehatvena pañcānāṃ bhūtānāṃ parigrahaḥ svīkartary ātmani liṅgam* ||

[94] See *Caraka* Śā. i. 73–74.

[95] See Cakrapāṇidatta *ad Caraka* Śā. i. 70–74 and *Praśastapādabhāṣya*, 69–70.

[96] Ibid.

[97] See *Nyāyavārttika ad Nyāyasūtra* i. 1, 10.

[98] See *Vaiśeṣika* (Jambuvijaya) iii. 2, 9–14; *Praśastapādabhāṣya*, 70; *Nyāyakandalī*, 84–86; *Vyomavatī*, 135 and 152.

Upadhā

The concept of *upadhā* is introduced in the *Carakasaṃhitā* by a question of Agniveśa about the treatment of past, present and future diseases.[99] First Ātreya Punarvasu answers to the question in medical terms; but then he affirms that the most radical treatment is the elimination of *upadhā*.[100] The end of *upadhā* is conducive to the removal of pain, for *upadhā* produces pain and also the receptacle of pain, the body.[101] Cakrapāṇidatta glosses *upadhā* as *tṛṣṇā* 'thirst, desire', and in fact this word occurs in the following *ślokas* as synonymous with *upadhā*.[102] The current meaning of this term is 'imposition, forgery, fraud, deceit'.[103]

We find *upadhā* in the *Vaiśeṣikasūtras*, in the second *āhnika* on *dharma*, where it has a central position. These are the *sūtras* referring to it:[104]

> *cāturāśramyam upadhā anupadhāś ca* ||
> *bhāvadoṣa upadhā 'doṣo 'nupadhā* ||

According to Candrānanda, for those belonging to the four stages of life (*āśrama*), an action which is with *upadhā* is conducive to *adharma*, and vice versa. *Upadhā* is deceitfulness etc. of the intention.[105] Śaṅkaramiśra says that *upadhās* are defects which negatively affect confidence (i.e., *śraddhā*, here a synonym of *bhāva*), and vice versa; they are means for *dharma* and *adharma*; by the word *upadhā* all that is *adharma* is meant. Commenting on the following *sūtra*, Śaṅkaramiśra further explains *upadhā* as the defects of *bhāva* (*icchā, rāga*), e.g., negligence, lack of trust, lust, self-conceit, envy.[106]

---

[99] *Caraka* Śā. i. 11–12.

[100] Ibid., i. 86–94.

[101] Ibid., i. 95.

[102] Cakrapāṇidatta *ad Caraka* Śā. i 95; *Caraka* Śā. i. 96 and 134–135.

[103] See, e.g., M. Monier-Williams, *A Sanskrit–English Dictionary*, reprint, (Delhi: Motilal Banarsidass, 1976), 199. But cf. F. Edgerton, *Buddhist hybrid Sanskrit grammar and dictionary*, volume ii, *Dictionary*, reprint, (Delhi: Motilal Banarsidass, 1977), 135: *upadhi* is 'attachment, bond uniting one to existence ... *upadhi* includes also *kilesa* ... *kāma* and *kamma*'.

[104] *Vaiśeṣika* (Śāstri) vi. 2, 3–4. The reading of this edition is more correct than *Vaiśeṣika* (Jambuvijaya) vi. 2, 3–5:

> *cāturāśramyam upadhāc cānupadhāc ca* || *3* ||
> *bhāvadoṣa upadhā* || *4* ||
> *adoṣo'nupadhā* || *5* ||

[105] Candrānanda *ad Vaiśeṣika* (Jambuvijaya) vi. 2, 3: *yad idaṃ caturṇām āśramiṇāṃ karma tadupadhayā prayujyamānam adharmāyānupadhayā tu dharmāya bhavati | kā upadhā? bhāvasya abhisandher dambhādidoṣa upadhety arthaḥ* ||

[106] Śaṅkaramiśra *ad Vaiśeṣika* (Śāstrī) vi. 2, 3–4.

As a result of this comparison, the concept of *upadhā* appears to have a similar value in the *Carakasaṃhitā* and in the *Vaiśeṣikasūtras*. But what is the opinion of Praśastapāda? He speaks of *upadhā* in the chapter dedicated to *icchā*, which is a *guṇa* of the *ātman* and designates desire in a general way. Praśastapāda lists many sub-divisions of *icchā*, among which one is *upadhā*, the desire to cheat others (*paravañcanecchā*); there is also *bhāva*, innermost desire (*antarnigūḍhecchā*).[107] So the effort of systematic exposition may possibly have led Praśastapāda far from other interpreters of Kaṇāda's doctrine, and in this context the *Carakasaṃhitā* seems to adhere more to the letter of the *Vaiśeṣikasūtras*.

Mokṣa

The word *mokṣa* occurs twice in the *Vaiśeṣikasūtras*,[108] and the passages concerned have been commented on in different ways, because their formulation is extremely obscure.[109] Praśastapāda spends a few more words in describing the state of final emancipation:[110]

> ... having brought about happiness due to the vision of highest truth, this *dharma* also disappears. And thus, there being a complete cessation, the soul becomes 'seedless'; and when the present body etc., falls off, the soul takes no other bodies etc., and this cessation of equipment with bodies etc., being like the extinguishing of fire on all its fuel being burnt up, constitutes what is called *mokṣa*, 'final deliverance.'

An important tenet of the Vaiśeṣika conception of *mokṣa* is therefore the absence in the *ātman* of all the *guṇas*, including bliss, as against the Vedāntic view.[111] But

---

[107] *Praśastapādabhāṣya*, 261. Cf. *Nyāyakandalī*, 262: *paravañcanecchā parapratāraṇecchā upadhā* |

[108] *Vaiśeṣika* (Jambuvijaya) v. 2, 20: *tadabhāve saṃyogābhāvo 'prādurbhāvaḥ sa mokṣaḥ* ||

Vaiśeṣika (Jambuvijaya) vi. 2, 19: *ātmakarmasu mokṣo vyākhyātaḥ* ||

The word *niḥśreyasa* occurs in *Vaiśeṣika* (Jambuvijaya) i. 1, 2. On the *mokṣa* doctrine in Vaiśeṣika and Nyāya, see Chatterji, *Hindu realism*, 133ff.; Ui, *Vaiśeṣika philosophy*, 74, 164ff.; Faddegon, *The Vaiśeṣika-system*, 351–353; Keith, *Indian logic*, 250, *et passim*; Dasgupta, *History*, i, 283, 366; Radhakrishnan, *Indian philosophy*, ii, 224–225; Frauwallner, *History of Indian philosophy*, ii, 101–108; Potter, *Indian metaphysics and epistemology*, 28–34; on deliverance in Navya-Nyāya, see S. Sen, 'The Nyāya-Vaiśeṣika theory of salvation', in *The cultural heritage of India*, (Calcutta: Śrī Ramakrishna Centenary Committee, 1937), i, 449–458.

[109] Cf. Candrānanda *ad Vaiśeṣika* (Jambuvijaya) v. 2, 20 and vi. 2, 19; Śaṅkaramiśra *ad Vaiśeṣika* (Śāstri) v. 2, 18 and vi. 2, 16.

[110] *Praśastapādabhāṣya*, 282, in the translation (slightly changed) of G. Jhā, reprint, (Varanasi: Chaukhamba Orientalia, 1982), 601.

[111] Cf. the refutation of the Vedāntic views by Śrīdhara, *Nyāyakandalī*, 3–4 and 286–287.

what is the destiny of the *manas* belonging to the liberated man? It is not possible to include the *manas* in the word *ādi* of the compound *śarīrādinivṛtti* occurring in the aforesaid passage of Praśastapāda, or at least the *manas's nivṛtti* is to be different from the *śarīra's nivṛtti*, because the *manas*, being atomic, is also eternal, and as such cannot decompose. Śrīdhara refers explicitly to the *manas* in the state of liberation only while refuting an opponent, who maintains that bliss is experienced in the state of deliverance. According to Śrīdhara, it is not possible to point out a cause for this bliss, because of the extinction of the body and the organs; nor can the cause be the contact of the *ātman* with the inner organ (i.e., *manas*), because,[112]

> the *manas* aids in this manner when it is influenced by *dharma* and *adharma*, and when the mind is such as has all seeds of good and evil rooted out of it, it can never function towards any purpose of the *ātman*.

This statement of Śrīdhara is based upon *Vaiśeṣikasūtra* v. 2, 14 ('the initial motion ... of the *manas* is caused by the *adṛṣṭa*');[113] nevertheless, it does not solve the basic problem of the relations between *ātman* and *manas* in the emancipated condition: they are two eternal substances, the first all-pervading, the second of atomic size, and they are to be connected in some way, like *ākāśa* and atoms. As a matter of fact, Śrīdhara refutes an opponent's view that conjunction between *ākāśa* and atoms is eternal, saying that the conjunction, being produced by the atom's motion, is not permanent, because it is only partial, like the conjunction of a man who goes up and down a banyan tree from the roots to the top and vice versa.[114] But the case of the *ātman* and *manas* is evidently different, since in *mokṣa* no new conjunction between them can be effected, as the *adṛṣṭa* no longer moves the *manas*.[115]

We shall not analyse here in detail all the aspects of the conception of *mokṣa* in the *Carakasaṃhitā*; certainly it does not always agree with the Vaiśeṣika views, since on this, as on other subjects, the text tends to be eclectic.[116] But in the first chapter of the Śārīrasthāna there are some *ślokas* which remind us of the Vaiśeṣika doctrine of liberation. The first is likely to be a paraphrase of *Vaiśeṣikasūtra* v. 2, 20: *tadabhāve* has become *rajastamo 'bhāvāt balavatkarmasaṃkṣayāt*; *saṃyogābhāvo* has been changed into *viyogaḥ sarvasaṃyogair*; *aprādurbhāvaḥ* is modified to *apunarbhava*.[117] The word

[112]Cf. *Nyāyakandalī*, 286 (Jhā's translation, 610).

[113]... *manasaś cādyaṃ karmety adṛṣṭakāritāni* ||

[114]See *Nyāyakandalī*, 149–150.

[115]Cf. Candrānanda *ad Vaiśeṣika* (Jambuvijaya) vi. 2, 19: *ātmeti manaḥ manaḥkarmasu tadabhāve saṃyogābhāvo 'prādurbhāvaś ca sa mokṣa iti mokṣo vyākhyātaḥ* ||

[116]See, e.g., *Caraka* Śā. i. 155.

[117]Cf. *Vaiśeṣika* (Jambuvijaya) v. 2, 20 and *Caraka* Śā. i. 142.

tad in the compound *tadabhāve* is glossed by Candrānanda with *adṛṣṭa*,[118] and by Śaṅkaramiśra with *saṃyoga*:[119] neither of them refers it to *rajas* and *tamas*. The compound *saṃyogābhāvo* is explained by Candrānanda as 'the absence of the conjunction between *ātman* and *manas* which is called life';[120] according to Śaṅkaramiśra, when there is no production of a future body we have the absence of conjunction.[121] On the other hand, Cakrapāṇidatta interprets *sarvasaṃyogair* in an eclectic way: he refers the disjunction effected in liberation to all the things which are in relation with the *ātman*: the body, the cognition, the *ahaṃkāra*, etc.[122]

The second *śloka* contains the statement that in the condition of final renunciation, all sensations and all cognitions cease,[123] just as the Vaiśeṣika system maintains. This passage, together with the preceding one, seems to point out that the *Carakasaṃhitā* admits the separation of the *ātman* and the *manas* in the final emancipation and that the passage on the inseparability of *ātman* and *manas* is to be referred only to the state of bondage.[124].

[118]Cf. Candrānanda *ad Vaiśeṣika* (Jambuvijaya) v. 2, 20.

[119]Śaṅkaramiśra *ad Vaiśeṣika* (Śāstri) v. 2, 18.

[120]Candrānanda *ad Vaiśeṣika* (Jambuvijaya) v. 2, 20: *jīvanākhyasyātmamanaḥsaṃyogasyābhāvo-* . . .

[121]Śaṅkaramiśra *ad Vaiśeṣika* (Śāstri) v. 2, 18.

[122]See Cakrapāṇidatta *ad Caraka* Śā. i. 142.

[123]*Caraka* Śā. i. 154.

[124]Ibid., iii. 18.

Chapter 4

Epilepsy according to the *Rgyud-bźi*

R. E. Emmerick

Introductory remarks

THE CHAPTER OF THE RGYUD-BŹI that concerns epilepsy (Tibetan *(b)rjed-byed* 'causing forgetfulness') was recently presented for the first time in an English translation. The translation is to be found in Terry Clifford's book called *Tibetan Buddhist Medicine and Psychiatry: the Diamond Healing.*[1] A note on p. 250 makes clear that,

> The translation was done by Ven. Namdrol Gyamtso and Lodro Thaye and is based primarily on the oral instructions and explication of the Tibetan lama–doctor Dodrag Amchi of KSL Monastery, Bodhnath, Nepal. The Scottish yogi Gyurmed-Dorje helped make the preliminary translation. Ven. Geshe Jamspal of the Buddhist Institute of New Jersey made a final reading with corrections.

The fact that I nevertheless offer here my own rendering of the chapter is due not so much to any wish to challenge the accuracy of the translation published by Terry Clifford as to the need to provide a rendering according to the principles I have adopted elsewhere in order to enable a systematic comparison with the Tibetan version of the corresponding chapter of Vāgbhaṭa's *Aṣṭāṅgahṛdayasaṃhitā* to be made.

Even so, attentive readers will notice some differences between the two renderings. Thus, the verse:

> *rluṅ gyur rkaṅ-lag hdar reṅs yaṅ-yaṅ ldaṅ*

---

[0]Abbreviations used: Ci.: Cikitsāsthāna, Ni.: Nidānasthāna, Utt.: Uttaratantra.
[1]York Beach, Maine: S. Weiser, 1984.

which I render:

> (In the case of epilepsy that) has arisen due to wind, the arms and legs tremble, and when they have become stiff it rises again and again (after he has digested food).

is in the Clifford version:

> Arising from the life wind there is quaking of hands and feet; and agitated getting up and down again and again.

To this is appended the note: 'Acts startled, jumpy; knees are stiff and rigid.' The verb *ldaṅ* appears to have been assigned in the Clifford version the meaning 'getting up and down' in this verse, yet in the next verse *źu dus ldaṅ* is rendered '[the sickness is] worse at mealtimes', where I have 'it rises (especially) at the time of digestion'. The verb *ldaṅ* clearly cannot refer in either verse to the patient's getting up and down but is used in its normal technical meaning of the increase in intensity of a disease. It is for instance used in the triad *gsog/ldaṅ/źi* applied to the accumulation, increased activity, and subsidence (Sanskrit *caya/kopa/praśama*) of the humours.[2] My own addition '(after he has digested food)' is based on the well-known commentary *Vaiḍūrya sṅon-po*,[3] which here has: *yaṅ-yaṅ kha-zas źu rjes ldaṅ* (72.1) 'it rises again and again after he has digested food'.

It is, however, not my intention to provide on this occasion a detailed commentary on this chapter of the *Rgyud-bźi* nor to undertake a close examination of the version provided by Clifford, which undoubtedly reflects adequately the gist of the chapter. It would of course be instructive to investigate the chapter in detail, but much remains to be done in this field. On this occasion I wish to draw attention to certain features of the chapter which agree with or differ from the Tibetan version of the corresponding chapter of Vāgbhaṭa's *Aṣṭāṅgahṛdayasaṃhitā*. Unfortunately, the latter has not hitherto been edited or translated and I have accordingly provided for comparison a first tentative edition and translation.

It will at once be clear that in the case of this chapter the *Rgyud-bźi* is not as heavily dependent upon Vāgbhaṭa as it sometimes is: see for instance my article on the 'Sources of the *Rgyud-bźi*'.[4] There are here no identical verses, and there are even some significant differences of doctrine. Most noticeable is the fact that

[2] Cf. R. E. Emmerick, 'A chapter from the *Rgyud-bźi*', *Asia Major*, n.s. xix (2)2 (1975), 157.

[3] Sde-srid saṅs-rgyas rgya-mćho, *Vaiḍūrya sṅon-po*, edited by T. Y. Tashigangpa, vols.1–4 (Leh, 1973).

[4] *Zeitschrift der Deutschen Morgenländischen Gesellschaft*, supplement III.2, (Wiesbaden, 1977), 1135–1142.

		Verses
I. *dbye-ba*	1. *rluṅ*	2
	2. *mkhris*	2
	3. *bad-kan*	2
	4. *dug*	2
	5. *gdon*	2
II. *rtags*	0. *byuṅ-ćhul*	3–7
	1. *rluṅ*	8
	2. *mkhris*	9
	3. *bad-kan*	10
	4. *dug*	11
	5. *gdon*	12
III. *bcos-thabs*		13–30

Table 1: *The structure of the chapter.*

epilepsy is classified by the *Rgyud-bźi* into five kinds according to whether it is due to wind, bile, phlegm, poison, or demons whereas the standard Indian doctrine is that there are four kinds: those due to wind, bile, and phlegm separately, and that kind which is due to the concerted action of the humours.[5]

It is no easy task to translate the *Rgyud-bźi* and this chapter is no exception. In most cases the difficulty is caused by the conciseness of its wording. Often the missing links are supplied by the *Vaiḍūrya sṅon-po*, but that is not always the case.

The structure of the chapter is clear. It conforms to the programme announced in the first two verses. The scheme is as shown in Table 1 (p. 59). The only difficulty here is that the number of *rtags* is not specifically stated and it is not clear how the first item relates to the five kinds of epilepsy, to which a line each is devoted (8–12). My impression is that the author distinguishes between those symptoms which

[5]See here Vāgbhaṭa, *Aṣṭāṅgahṛdayasaṃhitā*, edited by Hariśāstrī Parāḍkar Vaidya, 6th ed., (Bombay, 1939) (henceforth: Ah.), Utt. vii. 5, which is the same as idem, *Aṣṭāṅgasaṅgraha*, edited by Vaidya Anaṃta Dāmodar Aṭhavale, (Poona, 1980) (henceforth: As.), Utt. x. p. 80a, which accords with Caraka, *Carakasaṃhitā*, edited by Vaidya Jādavji Trikamji Achārya, 3rd ed., (Bombay: Nirṇaya Sāgar Press) (henceforth: Caraka), Ci. x. 8 and Suśruta, *Suśrutasaṃhitā*, edited by Vaidya Jādavji Trikamji and Nārāyaṇ Rām Achārya, repr. 4th ed., (Varanasi–Delhi: Chaukambha Orientalia, 1980) (henceforth: Suśruta), Utt. lxi. 10 and Bhela, *Bhelasaṃhitā*, edited by Vaidya Viśārada V. S. Veṅkaṭasubrahmaṇya Śāstrī and Vaidya Viśārada C. Rājarājeśvaraśarma, (New Delhi: Central Council for Research in Indian Medicine and Homoeopathy, 1977) (henceforth: Bhela), Ni. viii. 1 and Ravigupta, *The Siddhasāra of Ravigupta, vol. 1: the Sanskrit text*, edited by R. E. Emmerick, (Weisbaden: F. Steiner Verlag, 1980) (henceforth: Ravigupta), Si. xx. 15.

indicate the impending onset of epilepsy and those which characterise its course. Certainly it is difficult to believe that the symptoms listed in verses 6–7 are just added as an afterthought as the Clifford version seems to suggest. The words *nad laṅs dus* at the end of verse 4 are there rendered 'at the time the sickness arises', yet the perfect tense form of *laṅs* seems inappropriate to convey this meaning. We may note that in the Vāgbhaṭa version the precise Sanskrit use of the future tense (*utpatsyamāne* in vii. 6) is closely rendered by *de ni skye-bar hgyur-bahi ćhul.* I propose accordingly to understand *nad laṅs dus* as coordinated with what precedes but introducing what follows.

All the symptoms listed in verses 3–7 correspond closely to the Vāgbhaṭa version as shown in Table 2.

Rgyud-bźi	Vāgbhaṭa
sñiṅ hdar	*sñiṅ hdar* 7.6
mgo hthom	*mgo hkhor* 7.6
rṅul hbyuṅ	*rṅul hbyuṅ* 7.7
sbo	*lto sbos* 7.7
stobs chuṅ	*ñams-stobs ẓad-pa* 7.7
rus-śiṅ na	*yan-lag na* 7.8
kha-chu sna-chu maṅ	*kha-chu snabs ni hj́ag-pa* 7.7
hgyel	*sa-la hgyel* 7.4
so hchah	*so hchah* 7.3
rkaṅ-lag g-yob-pa	*lag-pa rkaṅ-pa g-yob-pa* 7.3
lbu-bar skyug	*lbu-ba skyug-pa* 7.3
mun-par źugs sñam sem	*mun-par źugs-śiṅ sñiṅ sems* 7.3

Table 2: *Symptoms.*

The symptoms said to characterise the three kinds of epilepsy due to the three humours show some correspondence, as in Table 3.

rkaṅ-lag hdar 8	*hdar* 7.10
bźin-ser 9	*gdoṅ ... ser* 7.13
kha skam 9	*skom-dad che-ba* 7.13
kha-chu maṅ 10	*kha-chu maṅ* 7.14

Table 3: *Symptom correspondences.*

However, there is nothing corresponding to the difficult *reṅs yaṅ-yaṅ ldaṅ* in verse 8, to *źu dus ldaṅ* in 9, or to *ćhigs riṅ* in 10. *yaṅ-yaṅ* in 8 has a counterpart in 7.9 in *yaṅ daṅ yaṅ-du*, but the context is different. Similarly, *riṅ* occurs twice in 7.14, but there seems to be no connection with *ćhigs riṅ*.

The final section on treatment (*bcos-thabs*) begins with two verses (13–14) on the general preparatory treatment. There are four items, as shown in Table 4. Vāgbhaṭa does not mention in this connection the use of nasal rinses, but the four

Rgyud-bźi	Vāgbhaṭa
ni-ru-ha̱	*bkru-sman* 7.16 (bile)
sna-bśal	—
skyugs	*skyug-sman* 7.17 (phlegm)
khrus	*hjam-rći* 7.16 (wind)

Table 4: *General preparatory treatments.*

items listed are in fact four of the well-known group of five kinds of treatment called *pañca-karma.* They are implied by the words *tīkṣṇaiḥ ... karmabhir vamanādibhiḥ* in Utt. vii. 16. The matter is made clear by a passage that is found in the Tibetan and Khotanese versions of Ravigupta's *Siddhasāra* but not in the original Sanskrit. There it is specifically stated that nasal rinses are beneficial in the case of all kinds of epilepsy. Moreover, the discrepancy between *Rgyud-bźi khrus* and Vāgbhaṭa's *hjam-rći* is accounted for by the same passage of the *Siddhasāra* since there it is stated that both *bkru-sman drag-po* and *hjam-rći* are appropriate in the case of epilepsy due to wind. This is in any case necessary to account for the missing fifth item of the *pañca-karma.* On the whole complex see Ravigupta, Si. xx. 18–19.

The first three methods of treatment have been taken from Vāgbhaṭa. Only these will be considered here. Verses 15–16 correspond quite closely with the Tibetan version of Utt. vii. 33. Notice first the correspondences shown in Table 5. Why *mārjāra* 'cat' has been rendered 'monkey' I have no idea. As for *khyi* 'dog' and *rta* 'horse', it is clear from the Tibetan version of Vāgbhaṭa that *khyi-rta* was originally just a transcription of Sanskrit *kīṭa* 'insect'. No variant reading is involved. The Sanskrit tradition is consistent and supported by the commentators. In his commentary on Caraka, Ci. x. 51, where the same verse is found, Cakrapāṇidatta glosses *kīṭaḥ* by *vṛścikādiḥ* and in his own *Cikitsāsārasaṅgraha* (xxi. 6)

Rgyud-bži	Vāgbhaṭa	
	Tibetan	Sanskrit
hug-pa	*hug-pa*	*ulūka*
bya-rog	*bya-rog*	*kāka*
bya-rgod	*bya-rgod*	*gṛdhra*
zer-mo	*sre-mo*	*nakula*
sbrul	*sbrul*	*ahi*
khyi	*khyi*	—
spre	*sprehu*	*mārjāra*!
rta	*rta*	—

Table 5: *Animal correspondences.*

he has *kīṭaḥ paścimadeśajo vṛścikaḥ* 'the *kīṭa* is a scorpion in the western country'.[6] It is interesting to see that the *Rgyud-bži* is clearly the borrower here because the original transcription *khyi-rta* was reinterpreted and then used in the different order *khyi spre rta*.

The relationship between *zer-mo* and *sre-mo* is obscure and points perhaps to an error due to oral transmission. *zer-mo* is not found in Jäschke's dictionary and Clifford offers no explanation of it. *sre-mo* on the other hand is said by Jäschke to be a 'weasel'.[7] In fact it is used to translate Sanskrit *babhru* in Vagbhaṭa, Ah., Sū. vi. 47 and its synonym *nakula* here. As Dr G. J. Meulenbeld points out to me, the Tibetan translation has rendered Sanskrit *babhru* and *nakula* 'mongoose' by Tibetan *sre-mo* 'weasel' because weasels but not mongooses are found in Tibet. *zer-mo* is said by Dge-bśes chos-kyi grags-pa[8] to be the same as *gzugs-mo*. Both *sre-mo* (variant *sre-moṅ*) and *gzugs-mo* are illustrated and described on folio 248 of Hjam-dpal rdo-rje's work: *An illustrated Tibeto-Mongolian materia medica of Ayurveda*.[9] They are clearly two different animals. I have accordingly rendered *zer-mo* as 'antelope' to preserve a distinction. This is based on Sarat Chandra Das, who defines *gzugs-mo* as 'a species of antelope said to live on the higher regions of the Himalayan range between 9

[6] Cakrapāṇidatta, *Cikitsāsārasaṅgrahāparanāmā Cakradattaḥ*, edited by Āyurvedācārya Śrījayadeva Vidyālaṅkāra, (Varanasi: Chowkhamba Sanskrit Series Office, 1928).

[7] H. A. Jäschke, *A Tibetan–English dictionary* (London: Routledge & Kegan Paul, 1881, repr. 1958), s.v.

[8] *Brda-dag miṅ-ćhig gsal-ba* (Peking: mi-rigs dpe-skrun-khaṅ, 1957), s. v.

[9] Edited by Lokesh Chandra, (New Delhi: International Academy of Indian Culture, 1971).

to 18 thousand feet above the level of the sea'.[10] However, the *gzugs-mo* described by Hjam-dpal rdo-rje appears to be rather some kind of weasel. It is said to have the ear of an antelope, which may be the reason for Das' entry. Incidentally, the Chinese gloss on *sre-moṅ* in Hjam-dpal rdo-rje's work is *huang-shu-lang*, which is said to be the 'weasel'.[11] (There is also a bird called *zer-mo*. It is illustrated on folio 229 of Hjam-dpal rdo-rje's work.)

Verse 17 presents an exact counterpart to Ah., Utt. vii. 29cd and verse 18 looks like a curious blend of Utt. vii. 24cd–25ab with vii. 34d. Utt. vii. 24cd–25ab contains the prescription for the Brāhmī ghee, which is found in many of the Indian sources.[12] It is no doubt significant that the *Rgyud-bźi* version omits both the items that could be represented in the version of Vāgbhaṭa only by means of transcriptions.

---

[10]Sarat Chandra Das, *Tibetan-English dictionary with Sanskrit synonyms* (Calcutta: Bengal Secretariat Book Depot, 1902), 1106 s.v. *gzugs-mo*.

[11]*Mathews' Chinese–English dictionary*, revised American edition, (Cambridge, Mass.: Harvard Univ. Press, 1960), 2297.112

[12]Ah., Utt. vii. 24cd-25ab, which is the same as As., Utt. x. 39; Caraka, Ci. x. 25; Bhāvamiśra, *Bhāvaprakāśa*, edited by Śrī Brahmaśaṅkara Miśra, part ii, 3rd ed., (Varanasi: Chowkhamba Sanskrit Series Office, 1961), xxiii. 18; Cakrapāṇidatta, *Cikitsāsārasaṅgraha*, xxi. 19; Vaṅgasena, *Bang-Sen*, edited by Pt. Nandkumār Gosvāmī Vaidya, (Calcutta, 1889), apasmāra, 50; Vṛnda, *Vṛndamādhavāpara-nāmā siddhayogaḥ*, edited by V. G. Apte, (Poona, 1943). xxi. 15; *Yogaratnākara*, edited by Brahmaśaṅkara Śāstrī, (Varanasi, 1955), p. 500 (1) (with minor variants); and in a different formulation Ravigupta, Si. xx. 21.

Text of *Rgyud-bźi* iii. 79

Readings have been collated from the following sources:

A, B = Xylographs in the library of the Société Asiatique (Collection Henriette Meyer)

C = *Rgyud bzhi, a reproduction of a set of prints from the 1888 Lha-sa lcags-po-ri blocks* (Leh, 1978) (Smanrtsis Shesrig Spendzod, vol. 87)

L = *bdud-rći sñiṅ-po yan-lag brgyad-pa gsaṅ-ba man-ṅag-gi rgyud ces bya-ba bźugs-so,* bod-ljoṅs mi-dmaṅs dpe-skrun-khaṅ, (Lhasa, 1982)

Z = *Gyud bzhi, a reproduction of a set of prints from the 18th century zung-cu ze blocks from the collections of Prof. Raghu Vira,* edited by O-rgyan Namgyal, (Leh, 1975) (Smanrtsis Shesrig Spendzod, vol. 68)

de-nas yaṅ draṅ-sroṅ rig-pahi ye-śes-kyis hdi skad ces gsuṅs-so || *kye draṅ-sroṅ chen-po ñon-cig* ||

brjed-byed dbye-ba rtags daṅ bcos-thabs gsum ||
dbye-ba rluṅ mkhris bad-kan dug gdon lṅa ||
de rtags byuṅ-ćhul sñiṅ hdar mgo-bo hṭhom ||
rṅul hbyuṅ sbo-źiṅ stobs chuṅ rus-śiṅ na ||
kha-chu sna-chu maṅ-źiṅ nad laṅs dus ||
hgyel-źiṅ so hchah rkaṅ-lag g-yob-pa[1] *daṅ* ||
lbu-bar[2] *skyug-ciṅ mun-par źugs sñam sem* ||
rluṅ gyur rkaṅ-lag hdar reṅs yaṅ-yaṅ ldaṅ ||
mkhris-pa bźin ser kha skam źu dus ldaṅ ||
bad-kan ćhigs riṅ khyad-par kha-chu maṅ ||
dug gyur nad rtags mi-gsal śes-pa hkhrul ||
gdon gyur sṅar-bas spyod-pa gźan-du hgyur ||
bcos-thabs ni-ru-h̲a daṅ sna-bśal daṅ ||
skyugs khrus rno-bas bu-ga dag-par sbyaṅ ||
hug-pa bya-rog bya-rgod zer-mo sbrul ||
khyi spre rta-yi chu sgro brun dud bdug ||
ba ser mkhris-pahi khu-ba sna-sman btaṅ ||
śu-dag ru-rta mar rñiṅ sbraṅ sbyar byin ||
bog yun riṅ-na sor-mo ñi-śu bsreg ||
hjam-rći bur-chaṅ btaṅ-źiṅ rluṅ-gsaṅ bsro ||
srog-rća myos-byed gsaṅ-la me-thur bya ||
bye-brag gso-ba smyo-byed dag daṅ hdra ||
spyir-na smyo-byed brjed-byed gaṅ-la yaṅ ||
khrag-mkhris ćha-bahi phugs bcas bcos mi-len ||
de phyir ćha-ba dag-par sbyaṅ bya-ste ||

[1] *g-yob-pa* AC : *g-yab-pa* BZ
[2] *lbu-bar* BCZ : *sbu-bar* A

de hog zas sman drod-bcud me-thur bya[3] ||
smyo daṅ brjed-byed phal-cher gdon gyur-pas ||
bskaṅ bśags khrus gtor bden bdar źi-bas bsten ||
chu-gtor klu-chog gtor-mas brid-la bcos ||
tha-ma drag-pohi las-kyis mthah-ru bskyal ||

źes gsuṅs-so ||

bdud-rći sñiṅ-po yan-lag brgyad-pa gsaṅ-ba man-ṅag-gi rgyud-las brjed-byed-kyi nad gso-bahi lehu-ste bdun-cu-rća dgu-paho ||

Translation of *Rgyud-bźi* iii. 79

Then again the seer Vidyājñāna spoke thus:

'Hear, O great seers! (As for) epilepsy, (there are) three (items): classification, symptoms, and methods of treatment.

'(As for its) classification, (there are) five (items): wind, bile, phlegm, poison, and demons.

'(As for) its symptoms, (there are first of all those that are) indications of its occurrence: the heart trembles, the head is dull, sweat occurs, (the stomach) swells, there is little strength, the back of the neck aches, and there is much water in the mouth and nose. (Next there are those symptoms that characterise it) at the time when the disease has arisen: he falls down, grinds his teeth, moves his arms and legs violently, vomits froth, and thinks he has entered darkness.

'(In the case of epilepsy that) has arisen due to wind, the arms and legs tremble, and when they have become stiff it rises again and again (after he has digested food).

'(In the case of epilepsy that has arisen due to) bile, the complexion is yellow, the mouth is dry, and it rises especially at the time of digestion.

'(In the case of epilepsy that has arisen due to to phlegm, the joints are long, and there is especially much mouth water.

'(In the case of epilepsy that) has arisen due to poison, the signs (characteristic of epilepsy due to the humours) are not clear, (but the faculty of) knowing is disturbed.

'(In the case of epilepsy that) has arisen due to demons, the behaviour becomes different from before.

[3] *bya* BCZ : *gso* A

'(As for) the methods of treatment, one must thoroughly clean the orifices with sharp cathartics, nasal rinses, emetics, and washing.

'One must fumigate (the patient) with the smoke from the beak, feather, and dung of the owl, the crow, the vulture, the antelope, the snake, the dog, the monkey, and the horse.

'One must administer as nasal medicine the liquid from the bile of a yellow cow. One must give him sweet flag, costus, and old ghee mixed with honey.

'If he has fallen down (and remained unconscious) for a long time, one must burn his twenty fingers and toes.

'After administering as an enema sugarcane liquor, one must heat the *rluṅ-gsaṅ* points and one must apply moxibustion to the point (known as) *srog-rća myos-byed.*

'In detail, the treatment (of epilepsy) resembles the purifying of madness. In general, in the case of both madness and epilepsy, if the treatment is not effective because (the patient) has the utmost hot blood-bile, on account of that one must (first) thoroughly remove the heat and after that one must (give him) food, medicine, and heat(-producing) nourishment, and one must apply moxibustion. One who has madness and epilepsy that has arisen in some way due to a demon must (first) adhere calmly to expiatory rites, confession, ablution, oblations, and honouring the truth, and he must treat (the demons) seductively with water offerings, nāga offerings, and oblations, and finally he must in the end adopt severe action.'

Thus he spoke.

The seventy-ninth chapter on healing epilepsy from the Tantra of Instruction concerning the nectar-essence that consists in eight branches (and is) secret.

Text and translation of Vāgbhaṭa's *Aṣṭāṅgahṛdayasaṃhitā*, Uttaratantra vii

Readings have been collated from the Derge (D) and Peking (P) xylograph editions of the Tibetan text of Vāgbhaṭa's *Aṣṭāṅgahṛdayasaṃhitā.*[1]

de-nas rjed-byed[2] *gso-ba bśad-par byaho* || D 262a7; P 238b3

Next the treatment of epilepsy is to be expounded.

athāto 'pasmāra-pratiṣedhaṃ vyākhyāsyāmaḥ

Uttaratantra vii. 1

rjed-byed[3] *dran-pa ñams-pa-ste*
de ni sñiṅ-stobs blo hkhrul daṅ
sems-las mya-ṅan hjigs[4] *sogs-kyis*
gnod gyur sems-las byuṅ-ba yin

Epilepsy (*apasmāraḥ*) being impairment of the memory (*smṛty-apāyo*), it (*sa*) originates (*jāyate*) due to the mind (*citte*) having been injured (*abhihate*) through the mental strength (*dhī*) (and) the intellect (*sattva*) being disturbed (*-abhisaṃplavāt*) and through the activity of the mind (*cintā*), affliction (*śoka*), fear (*bhaya*) etc. (*-ādibhiḥ*),

smṛty-apāyo hy apasmāraḥ sa dhī-sattvābhisaṃplavāt
jāyate 'bhihate citte cintā-śoka-bhayādibhiḥ

Uttaratantra vii. 2

lus sems gtogs-pahi[5] *nad-kyis ni*
smyo-byed bźin-du khrugs[6] *gyur-pas*[7]
sñiṅ-stobs ñams-śiṅ[8] *sñiṅ daṅ ni*
hdu-śes rgyu-bahi rća-sbubs khyab

---

[1] For details of these editions see, e.g., Claus Vogel, *Vāgbhaṭa's Aṣṭāṅgahṛdayasaṃhitā : the first five chapters of its Tibetan version* (Wiesbaden: F. Steiner Verlag, 1965), 21ff.
[2] *brjed-byed* D
[3] *brjed-byed* D
[4] *hjig* P
[5] *rtogs-pahi* P
[6] *hkhrug* D
[7] *hgyur-bas* D
[8] *ñams-źiṅ* D

(and due to) the mental strength (*sattve*) having been impaired (*hate*) by the humours (*malaiḥ*) pertaining to the body (and) mind (*citta-deha-gatair*) having been disturbed (*prakupitaiś*) as in the case of insanity (*unmāda-vat*) (and due to) the heart (*hṛdi*) and the passages (*kheṣu*) along which the consciousness flows (*saṃjñā-vāhiṣu*) having been penetrated (*vyāpte*) (by them).

unmāda-vat prakupitaiś citta-deha-gatair malaiḥ
hate sattve hṛdi vyāpte saṃjñā-vāhiṣu kheṣu ca

Uttaratantra vii. 3

mun-par źugs-śiṅ sñiṅ sems rmoṅs[9]
hjigs-su ruṅ-bahi bya-ba byed
so hchah lbu-ba skyug-pa daṅ
lag-pa rkaṅ-pa g-yob-pa daṅ

Having entered (*viśan*) darkness (*tamo*), (his) heart (and) mind (*-matir*) stultified (*mūḍha*), he does (*kurute*) acts (*kriyāḥ*) that are apt to (induce) fear (*bībhatsāḥ*), he grinds (his) teeth (*dantān khādan*), vomits froth (*vaman phenaṃ*), strikes out (*vikṣipan*) with (his) arms (and) legs (*hastau pādau ca*);

tamo viśan mūḍha-matir bībhatsāḥ kurute kriyāḥ
dantān khādan vaman phenaṃ hastau pādau ca vikṣipan

Uttaratantra vii. 4

gzugs med-par yaṅ mthoṅ-ba daṅ
hkhrul-źiṅ[10] *sa-la hgyel-ba daṅ*
smin-ma mi-g-yo[11] *nad śugs daṅ*
bral-nas sad-par gyur-pa daṅ

moreover, he sees (*paśyann*) forms (*rūpāṇi*) that are not there (*asanti*), being disturbed (*praskhalan*) he falls (*patati*) to the ground (*kṣitau*), and when he is rid (*atīte*) of the force of the disease (*doṣa-vege*), he wakes up (*vibudhyate*) without moving (*vijihma*) his eye-brows (*akṣi-bhruvo*);

paśyann asanti rūpāṇi praskhalan patati kṣitau
vijihmākṣi-bhruvo doṣa-vege 'tīte vibudhyate

---

[9] *mun-par źugs sñam sems-śiṅ rmoṅs* D; *mun bźugs-śiṅ sñiṅ sems rmoṅs* P
[10] *hkhru-źiṅ* P
[11] *mig g-yo* P

Uttaratantra vii. 5

de ni dus gźan-dag-tu yaṅ
de-bźin-du ni spyod-pa yin
rluṅ-la sogs daṅ hdus-pa-yi
dbye-bas rjed-byed[12] *rnam-pa bźi*

at other times (*kālāntareṇa*) too (*punaś ca*) he (*sa*) behaves (*viceṣṭate*) thus (*evam eva*). Epilepsy (*apasmāraś*) is of four kinds (*catur-bhedo*) due to the analysis by wind etc. (*vātādyair*) and by (all the humours) having come together (*nicayena ca*).

kālāntareṇa sa punaś caivam eva viceṣṭate
apasmāraś catur-bhedo vātādyair nicayena ca

Uttaratantra vii. 6

de ni skye-bar hgyur-bahi[13] *ćhul*
sñiṅ hdar khoṅ stoṅ mgo hkhor-la
mun-par mthoṅ-źiṅ sems khoṅ chud
smin-ma mi-sdug mig[14] *hgyur daṅ* P 239a

As for the manner of its arising (*rūpam utpatsyamāne 'smin*), the heart trembles (*hṛt-kampaḥ*), the inside is empty (*śūnyatā*), the head reels (*bhramaḥ*), he sees (things) in darkness (*tamaso darśanam*), he ponders in (his) mind (*dhyānaṃ*), (his) eyebrows are ugly (*bhrū-vyudāso*), (his) eyes change (*akṣi-vaikṛtam*);

rūpam utpatsyamāne 'smin hṛt-kampaḥ śūnyatā bhramaḥ
tamaso darśanaṃ dhyānaṃ bhrū-vyudāso 'kṣi-vaikṛtam

Uttaratantra vii. 7

sgra mi-thos-śiṅ rṅul hbyuṅ-la
kha-chu snabs ni hjag-pa daṅ
mi-hju yi-ga hchus-śiṅ brgyal
lto sbos ñams-stobs zad-pa daṅ

---

[12] *brjed-byed* D
[13] *gyur-pahi* D
[14] *mi* P

he does not hear sounds (*aśabda-śravaṇaṃ*), sweat emerges (*svedo*), mouth water (*lālā*) (and) mucus (*siṅghāṇaka*) flow out (*-srutiḥ*), he does not digest (*avipāko*), his appetite is spoilt (*arucir*), he faints (*mūrcchā*), his belly swells (*kuksy-āṭopo*), his strength fails (*bala-kṣayaḥ*);

aśabda-śravaṇaṃ svedo lālā-siṅghāṇaka-srutiḥ
avipāko 'rucir mūrcchā kuksy-āṭopo bala-kṣayaḥ

Uttaratantra vii. 8

gñid med skom-źiṅ yan-lag na
rmi-lam glu len gar byed daṅ
til-mar chaṅ ni hthuṅs-pa[15] *daṅ*
de gñis[16] *gcin-du hbyuṅ-ba rmi*

he cannot sleep (*nidrā-nāśo*), he is thirsty (*tṛṭ*), his limbs ache (*aṅga-mardas*), he dreams (*svapne*) that he sings (*gānaṃ*) and dances (*sa-nartanam*), and that when he has drunk (*pānaṃ*) sesame oil (*tailasya*) (and) liquor (*madyasya*), they both (*tayor*) come out as urine (*mehanam*).

nidrā-nāśo 'ṅga-mardas tṛṭ svapne gānaṃ sa-nartanam
pānaṃ tailasya madyasya tayor eva ca mehanam

Uttaratantra vii. 9

de-la rluṅ gyur[17] *brla hgul-źiṅ*
yaṅ daṅ yaṅ-du hgyel-ba daṅ
yaṅ daṅ yaṅ-du dran-pa stor
hdu-śes rñed-nas mi-gsal ṅu

Among those (*tatra*) (kinds of epilepsy, if he has the one that) has arisen due to wind (*vātāt*), his thighs shake (*sphurat-sakthiḥ*), he falls down (*prapataṃś*) again and again (*muhur muhuḥ*), he loses his memory (*apasmarati*) again and again, and when he regains (*labhate*) consciousness (*saṃjñāṃ*), he weeps (*rudan*) indistinctly (*visvaraṃ*).

tatra vātāt sphurat-sakthiḥ prapataṃś ca muhur muhuḥ
apasmarati saṃjñāṃ ca labhate visvaraṃ rudan

---

[15] *hthuṅ-ba* D
[16] *ñid* D
[17] *hgyur* P

Uttaratantra vii. 10

mig hbur yaṅ-yaṅ dbugs hbyin-źiṅ
lbu-bar skyug-ciṅ hdar-ba daṅ
so hchah mgo ni rdebs-pa[18] *daṅ*
rluṅ-gis[19] *gre-ba rgyas-par byed*

His eyes protrude (*utpiṇḍitākṣaḥ*), he emits breath (*śvasiti*) again and again, vomits froth (*phenaṃ vamati*), trembles (*kampate*), grinds his teeth (*dantān daśaty*), and tosses his head (*āvidhyati śiro*); the wind enlarges his neck (*ādhmāta-kandharaḥ*).

utpiṇḍitākṣaḥ śvasiti phenaṃ vamati kampate
āvidhyati śiro dantān daśaty ādhmāta-kandharaḥ

Uttaratantra vii. 11

yan-lag kun-tu[20] *rdebs-pa*[21] *daṅ*
sor-mo mi-sñoms hgugs-pa daṅ
mig daṅ pags-pa sen-mo ni
gnag-ciṅ rćub-mor snaṅ-ba daṅ

He strikes out (*vikṣipaty*) everywhere (*parito*) with his limbs (*aṅgaṃ*), he bends his fingers (*vinatāṅguliḥ*) unevenly (*viṣamaṃ*), and his eyes (*akṣi*), skin (*tvaṅ*), and nails (*nakha*) appear black (*śyāva*) and rough (*rūkṣa*);

parito vikṣipaty aṅgaṃ viṣamaṃ vinatāṅguliḥ
rūkṣa-śyāvāruṇākṣi-tvaṅ-nakhāsyaḥ kṛṣṇam īkṣate

Uttaratantra vii. 12

gzugs ni mi-brtan rćub-pa daṅ
mi-sdug bźin-ras ṅan-pa yin
mkhris-pa-las gyur rjed-byed[22] *ni*
dran-pa yaṅ-yaṅ ñams-pa daṅ

---

[18] *brdeb-pa-pa* P
[19] *rluṅ-gi* P
[20] *kun-du* D
[21] *brdeb-pa* P
[22] *brjed-byed* D

his form (*rūpaṃ*) is not firm (*capalaṃ*), (and it is) rough (*paruṣaṃ*), and disagreeable (*virūpaṃ*), and his face is ugly (*vikṛtānanam*). As for (the kind of) epilepsy that has arisen due to bile (*pittena*), (the one who has that) has impaired memory (*apasmarati*) again and again (*muhuḥ*);

capalaṃ paruṣaṃ rūpaṃ virūpaṃ vikṛtānanam
apasmarati pittena muhuḥ saṃjñāṃ ca vindati

Uttaratantra vii. 13

mig gdoṅ[23] *pags-pa lbu-ba ser*
sa-la rdeg-par[24] *byed-pa daṅ*
hjigs ruṅ hbar-źiṅ khro-ba-yi
gzugs mthoṅ skom-dad che-ba yin

his eyes (*akṣi*), face (*vaktra*), skin (*tvag*), and froth (*phena*) are yellow (*pīta*), he strikes at (*āsphālayati*) the ground (*medinīm*), he sees (*-darśī*) the form (*rūpa*) of one who is likely (to inspire) fear (*bhairava*), who is ablaze (*ādīpta*) and is wrathful (*ruṣita*), and he has great thirst (*tṛṣānvitaḥ*).

pīta-phenākṣi-vaktra-tvag āsphālayati medinīm
bhairavādīpta-ruṣita-rūpa-darśī tṛṣānvitaḥ

Uttaratantra vii. 14

bad-kan-las gyur riṅ-nas hjin
yun[25] *riṅ ñid-nas sad-par byed*
g-yo hgul ñuṅ-źiṅ kha-chu maṅ
kha mig pags-pa sen-mo dkar

(In the case of one suffering from epilepsy that) has arisen due to phlegm (*kaphāc*), it takes hold (*grahaṇaṃ*) (of him) only after a long time (*cireṇaiva*) and it wakes him up (*vibodhanam*) only after a long time. He moves and shakes little (*ceṣṭālpā*), (but) he has much mouth water (*bhūyasī lālā*). His mouth (*āsya*), eyes (*netra*), skin, and nails (*nakha*) are white (*śukla*).

kaphāc cireṇa grahaṇaṃ cireṇaiva vibodhanam
ceṣṭālpā bhūyasī lālā śukla-netra-nakhāsya-tā

---

[23] *mdog* D
[24] *brdeg-par* P
[25] *yuṅ* D

Uttaratantra vii. 15

gzugs-rnams dkar-por mthoṅ-ba yin D 263a
mćhan-ñid kun daṅ ldan-pa spaṅ[26]
de-nas blo sems dran-pa daṅ
sñiṅ-gahi sbubs ni sad byed-pahi

He sees forms (*rūpa-darśitvaṃ*) as white (*śuklābha*). One must abandon (*varjayet*) one who has (the kind of epilepsy that is accompanied by) all the (above) characteristics (*sarva-liṅgaṃ*). Next (*prāk*) one must awaken (*prabodhanam*) the passages (*-khānāṃ*) of the intellect (*dhī*), the mind (*citta*), the memory, and the heart (*hṛt*):

śuklābha-rūpa-darśitvaṃ sarva-liṅgaṃ tu varjayet
athāvṛtānāṃ dhī-citta-hṛt-khānāṃ prāk prabodhanam

Uttaratantra vii. 16

slon-sman-la sogs las-rnams ni
rnon-po-yis[27] *ni sbyaṅ-bar bya*
rluṅ gyur[28] *hjam-rći maṅ-du bya*
mkhris gyur phal-cher bkru-sman gtaṅ[29]

one must cleanse them with sharp (*tīkṣṇaiḥ*) treatments (*karmabhir*) such as emetics (*vamanādibhiḥ*). (In the case of one who has epilepsy that) has arisen due to wind (*vātikaṃ*), one must apply many oily enemas (*basti-bhūyiṣṭhaiḥ*). (In the case of one who has epilepsy that) has arisen due to bile (*paittaṃ*), one must administer mainly (*prāyo*) cathartics (*virecanaiḥ*).

tīkṣṇaiḥ kuryād apasmāre karmabhir vamanādibhiḥ
vātikaṃ basti-bhūyiṣṭhaiḥ paittaṃ prāyo virecanaiḥ

Uttaratantra vii. 17

bad-kan phal-cher[30] *skyug-sman ni*
btaṅ-bas rjed-byed[31] *gso-bar bya*

---

[26] *spaṅs* P
[27] *rnon-po yin* P
[28] *hgyur* P
[29] *btaṅ* P
[30] *phan-che-ra* P
[31] *brjed-byed* D

rnam-pa kun-tu legs dag-ciṅ
legs-par spro ni bsriṅs-pa-la[32]

(In the case of one who has epilepsy that has arisen due to) phlegm (*ślaiṣmikaṃ*), one must usually (*-prāyair*) treat (*upācaret*) the epilepsy (*apasmāram*) by administering emetics (*vamana*). In the case of one who has been made thoroughly well clean (*sarvataḥ suviśuddhasya*) and well comforted (*samyag-āśvāsitasya ca*),

ślaiṣmikaṃ vamana-prāyair apasmāram upācaret
sarvataḥ suviśuddhasya samyag-āśvāsitasya ca

Uttaratantra vii. 18

rjed-byed-las[33] *ni thar byahi phyir*
źi-bar bya-bahi sbyor-ba[34] *ñon* P 239b
ba-lcihi[35] *khu-ba ho-ma daṅ*
źo daṅ gcin daṅ mar bskol-ba

hear (*śṛṇu*) the prescriptions (*yogān*) for making him calm (*saṃśamanān*) in order to free (*vimokṣārthaṃ*) him from epilepsy (*apasmāra*): one must give him to drink (*pibet*) decoctions (*śṛtaṃ*) of liquid (*svarasa*) from cow dung (*gomaya*), milk (*kṣīra*), thick sour milk (*dadhi*), urine (*-mūtraiḥ*), and ghee (*haviḥ*),

gomaya-svarasa-kṣīra-dadhi-mūtraiḥ śṛtaṃ haviḥ
apasmāra-vimokṣārthaṃ yogān saṃśamanān śṛṇu

Uttaratantra vii. 19

rjed-byed[36] *rims daṅ smyo-byed daṅ*
mig-ser sel-bar byed-pa blud
rća-ba bcu-pa[37] *hbras-bu gsum*
dug-mo-ñuṅ śun ser-po gñis

---

[32] *bsriṅ-ba-la* D
[33] *brjed-byed-las* D
[34] *sbyor-bar* D
[35] *ba-lci* D
[36] *brjed-byed* D
[37] *bcu daṅ* P

which remove (*antakaraṃ*) epilepsy (*apasmāra*), fever (*jvara*), insanity (*unmāda*), and jaundice (*kāmalā*). (Take) the group of ten roots (*dvi-pañca-mūla*), the three fruits (*triphalā*), the kurchi plant (*kuṭaja*), cinnamon bark (*tvacaḥ*), the two yellow plants (*dvi-niśā*),

apasmāra-jvaronmāda-kāmalāntakaraṃ pibet
dvi-pañca-mūla-triphalā-dvi-niśā-kuṭaja-tvacaḥ

Uttaratantra vii. 20

'a-pa-marga lo-ma bdun
ni-li-ni daṅ pu-će-śel
doṅ-ga[38] *puṣkar-mū-la*[39] *daṅ*
phal-guhi[40] *rća-ba byi-ćher sraṇ*

rough chaff tree (*apāmārgaṃ*), dita (*sapta-parṇam*), indigo plant (*nīlinīṃ*), kurroa (*kaṭu-rohiṇīm*), drumstick tree (*śamyāka*), puṣkara-mūla (*puṣkara-jaṭā*), the root of the red-wood fig (*phalgu-mūla*), camel thorn (*-durālabhāḥ*) – two ounces each;

sapta-parṇam apāmārgaṃ nīlinīṃ kaṭurohiṇīm
śamyāka-puṣkara-jaṭā-phalgu-mūla-durālabhāḥ

NB: At first sight it would appear that the Tibetan version has omitted *jaṭā*, but as Dr G. J. Meulenbeld pointed out to me, *jaṭā* has here been taken to mean 'root', a meaning it sometimes has in medical literature. This meaning is specifically listed in such *nighaṇṭus* as the *Vaidyaśabdasindhu* of Kaviraāj Umeśacandra Gupta Kaviratna (Calcutta, 1894), and Śāli-grāma's *Śāligrāmauṣadhaśabdasāgara*, edited by Khemarāja Śrī-kṛṣṇadāsa, (Bombay, 1896).

Uttaratantra vii. 21

gñis gñis chu bre bcu-drug naṅ
bskol-ba-la ni bźi-cha lus
ga-brahi rća-ba du-ba-ri
pa-ta dan-ta[41] *dur-byid daṅ*

---

[38] *doṅ-ka* P
[39] *puṣkar-mula* P
[40] *phal-gul* P
[41] *dan-da* D

boil (*paktvā*) them up in sixteen bre of water (*salila-droṇe*) until (only) a quarter remains (*pādāvaśeṣite*); (in it) boil the root of beetle-killer (*bhārgī*), pigeon pea (*āḍhakī*), velvetleaf (*pāṭhā*), wild croton (*nikumbha*), turpeth (*kumbha*),

NB: *āḍhakī* = *tuvarī Dhanvantarinighaṇṭu*, in *Rājanighaṇṭusahito dhanvantarīyanighaṇṭu*, edited by Vaidya Nārāyaṇa Śāstrī Purundare and V. G. Apṭe, 2nd ed., (Poona, 1925) (henceforth: Dh. N), 226
dantī = *nikumbhā* Dh. N 53

dvi-palāḥ salila-droṇe paktvā pādāvaśeṣite
bhārgī-pāṭhāḍhakī-kumbha-nikumbha-vyoṣa-rohiṣaiḥ

NB: *vyoṣa* and *rohiṣa* are in the next stanza in the Tibetan version.

Uttaratantra vii. 22–23a

ćha-ba gsum daṅ ro-ḫi-ṣe[42]
mur-ba[43] *rća-mkhṛis bu-di-kha*
ḫa-ti pi-pi-liṅ daṅ ni
ma-du-yan-te thal-tres gñis
lcaṅ-ma daṅ ni ći-tra-ka
źo ni gñis gñis mar bre gaṅ
de-bźin sṅa-mahi gśer ṛjas bskol

the three hot ones (*vyoṣa*), rohiṣa (*-rohiṣaiḥ*), bowstring hemp (*mūrvā*), chirata (*bhūnimba*), lemon grass (*bhūtīka*), elephant pepper plant (*śreyasī*), Indian jasmine (*madayantī*), the two (kinds of Indian) sarsaparilla (*-śārivā-dvayaiḥ*), willow (*-niculair*), leadwort (*agni*) – two drams each (*akṣāṃśaiḥ*); one prastha (*bre gaṅ*) of ghee; likewise (*tadvad*) the above(-mentioned) (*pūrvaiḥ*) liquid substances (*dravaiḥ*).

mūrvā-bhūtīka-bhūnimba-śreyasī-śārivā-dvayaiḥ
madayanty-agni-niculair akṣāṃśaiḥ sarpiṣaḥ pacet
prasthaṃ tadvad dravaiḥ pūrvaiḥ

NB: Dr G. J. Meulenbeld has drawn my attention to the fact that Sanskrit *bhūtīka* may be either a synonym of *yamānī/yavānī* (e.g., Śivadāsasena *ad Cikitsāsārasaṅgraha* i. 129) or of *sugandhitṛṇa* (Ḍalhaṇa *ad* Suśruta, Utt. 30. 193). *dhyāma* and *kattṛṇa* are said by Si. N 48 to be synonyms of *bhūtīka*. Assuming therefore that *kattṛṇa, dhyāma, bhūtīka,* and *sugandhitṛṇa*

---
[42] *ro-ḫi-śa* P
[43] *murba* P

are all synonyms of *bhūstṛṇa*, which is identified as some species of Cymbopogon (see G. J. Meulenbeld, *Mādhavanidāna* ... (Brill: Leiden, 1974), 584), I have rendered *bhūtīka* here as 'lemon grass'.
On *śreyasī* = *gaja-pippalī* see Ravigupta, Si. N 27.
śreyasī = *hasti-pippalī* Dh. N 85
agni = *citraka* Si. N 29
vetasa = *vañjula* = *nicula* Dh. N 193
lcaṅ-ma tr. *vañjula* Si., Ah.

Uttaratantra vii. 23b–24ab

hdi ni ba-yi rnam lṅa che
rjed-byed[44] *rims daṅ dmu-rjiṅ daṅ*
mćhan-par rdol-ba sel mchog yin
hor nad gźaṅ-hbrum mig-ser daṅ
skya-rbab skran daṅ lud-pa daṅ
gdon-rnams hjoms-par byed-pa yin

This (*idaṃ*) great (*mahat*) (medicament consisting in the) five items that (come) from the cow (*pañca-gavyam*) is the best (*param*) for removing (*-haraṃ*) epilepsy (*apasmāra*), fever (*jvara*), dropsy (*jaṭhara*), genital fistula (*bhagandara*) (and) overcomes (*-apaham*) swelling (*śopha*), piles (*arśaḥ*), jaundice (*kāmalā*), yellow disease (*pāṇḍu*), tumours (*gulma*), cough (*kāsa*), and demons (*graha*).

pañca-gavyam idaṃ mahat
jvarāpasmāra-jaṭhara-bhagandara-haraṃ param
śophārśaḥ-kāmalā-pāṇḍu-gulma-kāsa-grahāpaham

Uttaratantra vii. 24cd–25ab

bra-mhi[45] *śu-dag ru-rta daṅ*
śaṅ-ka-puṣpa[46] *mar rñiṅ bcas*
bskol-bahi mar ni yid gźuṅs[47] *byed*
smyo-byed bkra mi-śis-pa daṅ
rjed-byed[48] *sdig-pa hjoms-par byed*

[44] *brjed-byed* D
[45] *bhram-mhi* P
[46] *śaṅka-puṣpa* P
[47] *źuṅs* P
[48] *brjed-byed* D

The ghee (*ghṛtaṃ*) (obtained) by boiling (*śṛtaṃ*) with old (*purāṇaṃ*) ghee, Indian pennywort (*brāhmī*), sweet flag (*vacā*), costus (*kuṣṭha*), and *śaṅkha-puṣpı* makes the mind acute (*medhyam*) (and) overcomes (*-jit*) madness (*unmāda*), misfortune (*alakṣmī*), epilepsy (*apasmāra*), and evil (*pāpma*).

brāhmī-rasa-vacā-kuṣṭha-śaṅkha-puṣpī-śṛtaṃ ghṛtam
purāṇaṃ medhyam unmādālakṣmy-apasmāra-pāpma-jit

Uttaratantra vii. 25cd–26ab

hćho byed sde-ćhan sraṅ re daṅ
til-mar źun-mar bre re bsres
ho-ma bre ni bcu-drug bskol
hthuṅs-na rjed-byed-las[49] *thar byed*

If one mixes with one ounce of each (*palonmitaiḥ*) of the group of life-giving drugs (*jīvanīyaiḥ*) one prastha each of sesame oil (*taila-prasthaṃ*) (and) of melted ghee (*ghṛta-prasthaṃ*), boils (*pacet*) them in sixteen bre (*droṇe*) of milk (*kṣīra*), and drinks (the mixture), it frees from epilepsy (*apasmāra-vimokṣaṇam*).

taila-prasthaṃ ghṛta-prasthaṃ jīvanīyaiḥ palonmitaiḥ
kṣīra-droṇe pacet siddham apasmāra-vimokṣaṇam

Uttaratantra vii. 26cd

ho-ma bu-ram-śiṅ khu-ba[50]
bre bźi daṅ ni taṅ-pal-gyi
khu-ba brgyad hgyur-dag daṅ ni

If one boils (*vipācayet*) in four bre (*kaṃse*) of milk (*kṣīra*) and of the liquid (*-rasayoḥ*) from the sugar cane (*ikṣu*) and in eight times (*aṣṭa-guṇe*) as much of the liquid from wax myrtle (*kāśmarye*)

kaṃse kṣīrekṣu-rasayoḥ kāśmarye 'ṣṭa-guṇe rase

[49] *brjed-byed-las* D
[50] *khu daṅ* P

Uttaratantra vii. 27

hčho byed sde-čhan źo gñis gñis
źun-mar bre gaṅ[51] *bcas bskol blud*
des ni rluṅ mkhris-las gyur-pahi D 263b
rjed-byed[52] *myur-du sel-bar byed*

two drams of each (*kārṣikair*) of the group of life-giving drugs (*jīvanīyaiś*) with one prastha of melted ghee (*sarpiḥ-prastham*) and gives it (to the patient) to drink, that (*tat*) quickly (*kṣipram*) removes (*nihanti*) epilepsy (*apasmāram*) that has arisen due to wind and bile (*vāta-pittodbhavam*).

kārṣikair jīvanīyaiś ca sarpiḥ-prastham vipācayet
vāta-pittodbhavam kṣipram apasmāram nihanti tat

Uttaratantra vii. 28

de-bźin hjag-ma[53] *bi-da-ri*
ku-śa bu-ram-śiṅ[54] *ho-ma*
bskol-ba hthuṅs-pahaṅ de daṅ hdra
ku-sman-ta-yi[55] *khu-ba mar*
bco-brgyad hgyur daṅ śiṅ-mṅar-gyi
lde-gur[56] *bcas-pa bskol-bas ni*

Likewise (*tadvat*), milk (*payaḥ*) that has been boiled (*śṛtam*) with thatch grass (*kāśa*), milky yam (*vidārī*), kuśa grass (*kuśa*), (and) sugar cane (*ikṣu*) (and) drunk, or similarly, if one boils (*śṛtam*) (ghee) together with (an amount of) the liquid (*svarase*) from the white gourd (*kūṣmāṇḍa*) (equal to) eighteen times (*aṣṭādaśa-guṇe*) (as much as the amount) of the ghee (*sarpir*) and with the paste (*kalkam*) from liquorice (*yaṣṭī*),

tadvat kāśa-vidārīkṣu-kuśa-kvātha-śṛtam payaḥ
kūṣmāṇḍa-svarase sarpir aṣṭādaśa-guṇe śṛtam

---

[51] *ga* P
[52] *brjed-byed* D
[53] *hjag-mahi* D
[54] *phu-ram-śiṅ* P
[55] *ku-sman-na-yi* P
[56] *lde-gu* P

Uttaratantra vii. 29ab

rjed-byed[57] *sel-bar byed-pa daṅ* P 239b
blo daṅ ćhig gsal[58] *skad sñan*[59] *byed*

(these decoctions) remove epilepsy (*apasmāra-haraṃ*) and make (*-pradam*) the mind (*dhī*) and speech (*vāk*) clear and the voice (*svara*) pleasant.

yaṣṭī-kalkam apasmāra-haraṃ dhī-vāk-svara-pradam

Uttaratantra vii. 29cd–30ab

ba ni ser-skyahi mkhris-pa-yis
sna-sman btaṅ yaṅ mchog-tu phan
khyi daṅ va daṅ byi-la daṅ
seṅ-ge sogs-kyi mkhris-pa bsṅags

Moreover, if one administers as nasal medicine (*nāvane*) the bile (*pittaṃ*) from a tawny (*kapilānāṃ*) cow (*gavāṃ*) it is extremely beneficial (*paraṃ hitam*). The bile of the dog (*śva*), the jackal (*śṛgāla*), the cat (*biḍalānāṃ*), and the lion etc. (*siṃhādīnāṃ ca*) is recommended (*pūjitam*).

kapilānāṃ gavāṃ pittaṃ nāvane paraṃ hitam
śva-śṛgāla-biḍalānāṃ siṃhādīnāṃ ca pūjitam

Uttaratantra vii. 30cd–31ab

go-da[60] *sre-mo glaṅ-po-che*
ba-laṅ dred daṅ pri-śa-tahi
mkhris-pa til-mar bskol-ba dag
lus bsku snar ni blugs-nahaṅ[61] *phan*

Sesame oil (*tailaṃ*) that has been boiled (*sādhitaṃ*) in the bile (*pitteṣu*) of the varan (*godhā*), the weasel (*nakula*), the elephant (*-nāgānāṃ*), the ox (*-gavām*), the bear (*ṛkṣa*), and the bull (*pṛṣata*), if it is smeared on the body (*abhyaṅge*) (or) poured into the nose (*nasye*) is also beneficial (*śasyate*).

[57] *brjed-byed* D
[58] *bsal* P
[59] *sñaṅ* P
[60] *go-ta* P
[61] *blud-nahaṅ* P

godhā-nakula-nāgānāṃ pṛṣata-ṛkṣa-gavām api
pitteṣu sādhitaṃ tailaṃ nasye 'bhyaṅge ca śasyate

NB: On *nakula* see G. J. Meulenbeld, *Mādhavanidāna*, 480-481.

Uttaratantra vii. 31cd–32cd

hbras-bu gsum daṅ ćha-ba gsum
nas-ćhig hkhus thal ko-ñon-ćhe
pha-ni-ja-ka[62] *sra-rći pog*
'a-pa-marga ka-rañjahi
sa-bon til-mar ra-gcin daṅ
bcas-pa bskol-ba snar blugs-paham[63]
phye-ma sna-nas pus-pahaṅ phan

Sesame oil (*tailaṃ*) together with goat urine (*basta-mūtre*) when boiled (*vipācitam*) with the three fruits (*triphalā*), the three hot ones (*vyoṣa*), the alkali extracted from burnt barley (*yava-kṣāra*), the Himalayan pine (*pītadru*), sweet marjoram (*-phaṇijjakaiḥ*), resin of the sal tree (*śryāhva*), rough chaff tree (*apāmārga*), and the seed of Indian beech (-*kārañja-bījais*), either poured into the nose (*nasyaṃ*) or (*vā*) blown out (*dhmāpayed*) of the nose as powder (*cūrṇaṃ*) is also beneficial (*hitaṃ*).

triphalā-vyoṣa-pītadru-yava-kṣāra-phaṇijjakaiḥ
śry-āhvāpāmārga-kārañja-bījais tailaṃ vipācitam
basta-mūtre hitaṃ nasyaṃ cūrṇaṃ vā dhmāpayed bhiṣak

NB: *pītadru* cf. *pītadruma* = *sarala* Dh. N 111. See Jäschke on *ko-ñon-ćhe.*

The rendering of *śryāhva* by *sra-rći pog*, which is the regular rendering of *sarja-rasa*, is surprising as *śryāhva* is presumably the same as *śrīvāsaka*, resin of the Himalayan pine (*pītadru*). A synonym of *śrīvāsaka* is *dadhi-nāma*, which in Si. xv. 16 is rendered *pog dkar-po*. There appears to be considerable uncertainty in the rendering of the various resins.

Uttaratantra vii. 33

sre-mo[64] *hug-pa sprehu daṅ*
bya-rgod khyi rta bya-rog sbrul
mchu[65] *daṅ sgro daṅ rtug-pa-yi*
dud-pas hdi-la bdug-par bya

---

[62] *pha-nid-ja-ka* P
[63] *blug-paham* P
[64] *sre-ma* P
[65] *chu* D

In this (*asya*) (case) one must fumigate (*prayojayet*) (the patient) with the smoke (*dhūpam*) from the beak (*tuṇḍaiḥ*), wing (*pakṣaiḥ*), and dung (*purīṣaiś ca*) of the weasel (*nakula*), owl (*ulūka*), monkey (*mārjāra!*), vulture (*gṛdhra*), dog, horse, crow (*kāka*), and snake (*ahi*).

nakulolūka-mārjāra-gṛdhra-kīṭāhi-kāka-jaiḥ
tuṇḍaiḥ pakṣaiḥ purīṣaiś ca dhūpam asya prayojayet

NB: *khyi rta* 'dog, horse' must originally have been a transcription of Sanskrit *kīṭa*!

Uttaratantra vii. 34

til-mar sgog-skya bcas-paham
ho-ma ñehu-śiṅ bsten-nahaṅ[66] *phan*
bra-mḫi-ham[67] *ru-rtahi khu-baham*
śu-dag sbraṅ-rćir ldan-pahaṅ phan

Moreover, if one keeps to (*śīlayet*) sesame oil (*taila*) containing garlic (*laśunaṃ*) or (*vā*) milk (*payasā*) (and) asparagus (*śatāvarīm*), it is beneficial. The liquid (*rasaṃ*) from Indian pennywort (*brāhmī*) or from costus (*kuṣṭha*), or sweet flag (*vacāṃ*) containing honey (*madhu-saṃyutām*) is beneficial.

śīlayet taila-laśunaṃ payasā vā śatāvarīm
brāhmī-rasaṃ kuṣṭha-rasaṃ vacāṃ vā madhu-saṃyutām

Uttaratantra vii. 35

nad-gźi[68] *mñam-du hkhrugs-pa-las*
lus daṅ sems-la brten hgyur nad
skyes-par gyur-pa gaṅ yin de
rjed-byed[69] *gnad ni chen-por gnas*

That (*eṣa*) epilepsy (*apasmāro*) which (*yaj*) is a disease that has arisen (*jāyate*) due to the humours (*doṣaiḥ*) having been equally (*samaṃ*) disturbed (*kruddhair*) (and) is based on body (*śārīra*) and mind (*-mānasaiḥ*) is located (*-samāśrayaḥ*) in the large vital point(s) (*mahā-marma*).

samaṃ kruddhair apasmāro doṣaiḥ śārīra-mānasaiḥ
yaj jāyate yataś caiṣa mahā-marma-samāśrayaḥ

[66] *bsten yaṅ* D
[67] *bḫraṃ-mḫi-ham* P
[68] *nad-bźi* P
[69] *brjed-byed* D

Uttaratantra vii. 36

de-bas gso dkah hdi-la ni
bcud-kyi[70] *len-gyis gso-bar bya*
des ñen me daṅ chu-la sogs
ya-ṅa-ba-las rtag-tu bsruṅ[71]

Therefore (*tasmād*) in the case of this (*enaṃ*) (disease which is) difficult to cure (*duś-cikitsyam*), one must treat (*upācaret*) (the patient) with an elixir (*rasāyanair*). One must constantly (*sadā*) protect (*pālayet*) (the patient who is) oppressed by that (*tad-ārtaṃ*) from terrible (*viṣamāt*) fire and water etc. (*agni-toyāder*).

tasmād rasāyanair enaṃ duścikitsyam upācaret
tad-ārtaṃ cāgni-toyāder viṣamāt pālayet sadā

Uttaratantra vii. 37

thar-pa-na ni yid hkhrul-bas
khyed-kyis hdi-ltar byas-so źes
mi-brjod yul ni yid hoṅ-bas
ñams-pahi[72] *sems ni brta-bar*[73] *bya*

If (the patient) has become rid (*muktaṃ*) (of epilepsy), one must not speak (*na brūyād*) thus (*iti*) (to him): 'You (*tvam*) acted (*kṛtavān*) in this way (*itthaṃ*) due to your mind having been disturbed (*mano-vikāreṇa*).' One must strengthen (*bṛṃhayet*) (his) damaged (*kliṣṭaṃ*) mind (*ceto*) by (means of) things (*viṣayair*) that are agreeable (*iṣṭaiḥ*).

muktaṃ mano-vikāreṇa tvam itthaṃ kṛtavān iti
na brūyād viṣayair iṣṭaiḥ kliṣṭaṃ ceto 'sya bṛṃhayet

Colophon

yan-lag brgyad-pahi sñiṅ-po bsdus-pa-las
phyi-mahi gnas-kyi lehu-ste bdun-paho

From the eight-membered (*aṣṭāṅga*) collected (*saṃhitāyāṃ*) heart (*hṛdaya*), the seventh chapter (*adhyāyaḥ*) on the last topic (*uttara-sthāne*).

---

[70] *bcud-kyis* D
[71] *sruṅs* P
[72] *mñam-pahi* P
[73] *brtan-par* P

iti śrī-vaidya-pati-siṃhagupta-sūnu-śrīmad-vāgbhaṭa-viracitāyām aṣṭāṅgahṛdaya-saṃhitāyāṃ ṣaṣṭhe uttarasthāne 'pasmārapratiṣedho nāma samāpto 'dhyāyaḥ

yan-lag brgyad-pahi sñiṅ-po bsdus-pa-las
hbyuṅ-pohi[74] *gdon gso-bahi yan-lag rjogs-so*

From the eight-membered (*aṣṭāṅga*) collected (*saṃhitāyāṃ*) heart (*hṛdaye*), the member (*tantraṃ*) on healing the elemental demons (*bhūta*) is finished (*samāptam*).

ity aṣṭāṅga-hṛdaye bhūta-tantraṃ tṛtīyaṃ samāptaṃ

[74] *hbyuṅ-pohi* om. P

Chapter 5

Vaiḍūrya

Marianne Winder

The Tibetan Medicine Buddha

THE COLOUR OF THE GEM *vaiḍūrya* plays a great role in Tibetan medicine. The Medicine Buddha is called *be-du-rya hod-kyi rgyal-po*, or 'King of the *Vaiḍūrya* Light'. In the *Saddharmapuṇḍarīka* of about AD 200 he is only called 'King of Healing'. But in a Chinese medical text of AD 500 to 600, the *Sūtra on the Merits of the Fundamental Vows of the Master of Healing* in Hsüan Tsang's *Tripiṭaka* version, he is called the '*Vaiḍūrya* Radiance *Tathāgata*'.[1] The Chinese word is *liu-li*. In Tibetan *vai-ḍu-rya* or *be-ḍu-rya* and other variant forms remain untranslated loan words. According to Jäschke's *Tibetan-English Dictionary*,[2] *be-du-rya* means 'azure stone, lapis lazuli'. It quotes *Dzanglun* (i.e., *hdzaṅs-blun*), a collection of legends, in which are mentioned the *Vaiḍūrya dKar.po*[3] 'White *Vaiḍūrya*' and *Vaidūrya sṄon.po*[4] 'Blue *Vaiḍūrya*', which are titles of works on astronomy–astrology and on medicine, respectively. The *Tibetan–English Dictionary* of Chandra Das says:[5]

> *bai-ḍu-rya* – malachite or chrysolite. There are three descriptions ... the yellow lapis-lazuli called *Mañjuri* [sic], the green lapis-lazuli called *Sugata*, the white lapis-lazuli called *Sūnya* [sic].

[1] Raoul Birnbaum, *The healing Buddha* (London: Rider, 1979), 151.

[2] H. A. Jäschke, *A Tibetan-English dictionary*, reprint of 1881 edition, (London: Routledge and Kegan Paul, 1977), 371.

[3] Short title of *phug-lugs rćis-kyi legs-bśad mkhas-pa'i vaiḍur dkar-po'i do-śal dpyod-ldan sñiṅ-nor.*

[4] Short title of *gso-ba rig-pa'i bstan-bcos sman-bla'i dgoṅs-rgyan rgyud-bźihi gsal-byed bai-ḍūr sṅon-pohi mallika.*

[5] Rai Sarat Chandra Das, *A Tibetan–English dictionary* (Calcutta: Bengal Secretariat Book Depot, 1902), 877.

Mañjuri is probably an allusion to the Yellow Mañjuśrī, *Sugata* 'having fared well' is easily associated with green, the colour of growth, and the colour white with *Śūnya* 'empty'. However, there is no such thing as a white, green or yellow lapis lazuli. The colour blue is not mentioned by Chandra Das. The works called 'White *Vaiḍūrya*' and 'Blue *Vaiḍūrya*' to which can be added a book called 'Yellow *Vaiḍūrya*' on history do not seem to mean 'lapis lazuli'. Even the title 'Blue Lapis Lazuli' would not make sense because of the tautology, as lapis lazuli can have no other colour. Jaques André and Jean Filliozat compare the meanings of *vaiḍūrya* in nineteenth century dictionaries and come to the conclusion that the early nineteenth century ones favoured the meaning 'lapis lazuli',[6] and that those near the end of the nineteenth century preferred 'cat's eye'.[7]

Beryl, cat's eye or lapis lazuli?

What, then, does *vaiḍūrya* mean? Etymologically it is related to Pāli *veḷuriya* and Prākrit *veḷuriya, verulia, velurya* and *veḷulia.*[8] Prākrit *verulia* became Greek βερυλλιον whence came English 'beryl'.[9] While Greek βερυλλιον and, from there, English *beryl* were derived from Prākrit *verulia*, the Persian and Arabic words *billaur, ballūr* and *bulūr* meaning 'crystal or beryl' were also borrowed from India, but according to Alfred Master, they are not derived from Sanskrit *vaiḍūrya* or Pāli *veḷuriya.*[10] He does not suggest a Prākrit form from which they could be derived. 'Crystal' can be a generalised term for 'beryl' because the beryl occurs in crystalline form.

The meaning of the Sanskrit word *vaiḍūrya* is also 'beryl' according to Mayrhofer.[11] To corroborate his opinion he quotes A. Master who gives a chronology of the occurrence of *vaiḍūrya* and its Prākrit and Pāli forms and asserts that the

[6]For example Horace Hayman Wilson, *Dictionary, Sanskrit and English* (Calcutta: Education Press, 1819.

[7]*L'Inde vue de Rome. Textes latins de l'Antiquité relatifs à l'Inde* (Paris: Belles Lettres, 1986), 371–372, note 216.

[8]Richard Pischel, *Comparative grammar of the Prākrit languages*, translated from the German by Subhadra Jhā, 2nd edition, (Delhi: Motilal Banarsidass, 1965), 173. § 241 gives various Prākrit forms.

[9]J. Halévi, 'Mélanges etymologiques', *Mémoires de la Société Linguistique*, xi (1900), 82, thinks that the Prākrit form *velurya* is a corruption from Greek βερυλλιον, diminutive of βερυλλος 'beryl' and that this word of Greek origin was imported into India either during the campaigns of Alexander the Great or later. This view does not hold water because the word *vaiḍūrya* is found in Sanskrit sources of as early as the *Adbhuta Brāhmaṇa* of 650 BC.

[10]Alfred Master, 'Indo-Aryan and Dravidian, Section II', *Bulletin of the School of Oriental and African Studies*, xi (1943–46), 304–307.

[11]Manfred Mayrhofer, *Kurzgefaßtes etymologisches Wörterbuch des Altindischen. A concise etymological Sanskrit dictionary* (Heidelberg: Winter, 1980), iv, 267.

evidence for the meaning 'beryl' is conclusive for all of them.[12] But he mentions[13] that Mallinātha[14] of the fifteenth century identifies *vaiḍūrya* with lapis lazuli, and that Apte followed his example.[15] He also mentions that Sten Konow[16] and A. C. Woolner[17] translate Prākrit *veḷuria*, *verulia* as 'cat's eye', and Dines Andersen does the same with Pāli *veḷuriya*.[18] The passage in which Mallinātha explains *vaiḍūrya* as lapis lazuli connects it at the same time with the meaning of 'cat's eye' as follows:[19]

> The women are afraid of the rays of the moon coming through the window, which are reflected on the *vaiḍūrya* walls and therefore *biḍālekṣaṇabhīṣaṇābhyaḥ*

which Buddruss explains as 'frighten like cat's eyes' and Master translates as 'make terrible cat's eyes'. Thakkura Pheru translates *vaiḍūrya* in this context as 'chrysoberyl' or 'cat's eye' saying that Māgha's use clearly indicates the chatoyancy of *vaiḍūrya*.[20] Perhaps the difference in the dates is significant: Māgha wrote his work during the seventh century AD and Mallinātha's commentary is of the fifteenth century. Louis Finot translates *vaiḍūrya* as 'cat's eye' because of the passage in Buddhabhaṭṭa's *Ratnaparīkṣā*, 200, which says that the *vaiḍūrya* shows such a variety of brilliances that it gives the impression of flashing sparks.[21] The passage in the *Karpūramañjarī* which Konow interprets as 'cat's eye' is taken by Lanman to mean 'beryl'.[22] Böhtlingk and Roth translate *vaiḍūrya* as 'beryl' without explaining why.[23]

---

[12]Master, loc. cit., 305.

[13]Ibid., 304.

[14]Kolāchala Mallinātha, *Commentary on Māgha's Śiśupālavadha*, iii. 45. (Bombay: Nirnaya Sagar Press, 1923).

[15]Vaman Shrivram Apte, *Sanskrit English dictionary*, revised edition, (Bombay: Gopal Narayen, 1957–59).

[16]Rājaśekhara, *Rājaçekhara's Karpūramañjarī*, edited by Sten Konow, with notes and translation by Charles Rockwell Lanman, (Cambridge (Mass.): Harvard University Press, 1901).

[17]A. C. Woolner, *Introduction to Prākrit*, 3rd edition, (Lahore: Motilal Banarsidass, 1939), § 58, pp. 24, 228.

[18]Dines Andersen, *Pāli Reader*, 4th edition, (Copenhagen: Gyldendal, 1935).

[19]Quoted from George Buddruss, 'Zum Lapis Lazuli in Indien', *Studien zur Indologie und Iranistik*, v/vi (1980), 6.

[20]Thakkura Pheru, *Rayanaparikkhā, a Medieval Prakrit Text on Gemmology*, translated by S. R. Saṇma, (Aligarh: 1984), 67–68, verse 94. Pheru's reference to Kālidāsa's *Kumārasambhava*, i. 24 (fifth century AD) suggests the crystals of beryl. Pheru's book was not accessible to me, and I am indebted for this and other references to Dr Arion Roşu.

[21]Louis Finot, *Les lapidaires indiens*, (Paris: Bouillon, 1896), xlv–xlvii and 43.

[22]Cf. note 16.

[23]Otto Böhtlingk, and Rudolph Roth, *Sanskrit-Wörterbuch*, (St. Petersburg: K. Akademie der Wissenschaften, 1855–75).

In the Pāli canon

Looking for *veḷuriya* in the Pāli Canon we find in *Dīghanikāya*, ii. 84:[24]

> Just, O King, as if there were a *veḷuriya* gem, bright, of the purest water, with eight facets, excellently cut, clear, translucent . . .

Now, a lapis lazuli is opaque, and the whole purpose of this passage is to show that a coloured thread going through a translucent gem can be clearly seen, comparing it to a purified mind recognising the truth easily. Lapis lazuli is a rock and does not form crystals. The beryl is six-sided but the writer of this passage and similar ones may have regarded the two ends as two more sides. Otto Franke says to this passage that in other passages eight-sided columns are mentioned made of *veḷuriya* and that the listeners' ears may have got attuned to this so that the idea of eight facets are an assimilation to this habit of thinking.[25] There is also the association of the Eightfold Path.

> *Vinayapiṭaka*, ii. 12 has:[26]
> You are not, O Bhikkhus, to use bowls made of gold, silver, set with jewels, or made of beryl, crystal, copper, glass, tin, lead, bronze.

Max Müller's note 1:

> It is clear from verses 192–196 of the 13th chapter of the *Rājanighaṇṭu* written by Narahari in the 13th century (or according to B. Laufer, the 15th) that at that time *vaiḍūrya* meant 'cat's eye'. But it is uncertain that that was the only meaning . . . at the time when this passage was composed.

I shall come back to the *Rājanighaṇṭu* later.

> *Saṃyuttanikāya*, i. 643 has:[27]
> Even as a beautiful, illustrious berylstone of eight facets, well polished, when laid on an orange coloured cloth shines and glows and blazes . . .

---

[24] Translated by T. W. Rhys Davids, *Sacred Books of the Buddhists*, vol. ii, reprint of 1899 edition, (London: Pāli Text Society, 1973), 87.

[25] *Quellen der Religionsgeschichte*, (Göttingen: Kgl. Gesellschaft der Wissenschaften, Religionsgesch. Kommission, 1923), 77, note 4.

[26] Translated by Max Müller, *Sacred Books of the East*, vol. xx, (Oxford: Clarendon Press, 1885), 82. I. B. Horner also translated *veḷuriya* as 'beryl' in *Cullavagga*, 5th Khandhaka, 'On Minor Matters', *Sacred Books of the Buddhists*, vol. xx, (London: Luzac, 1952), 152.

[27] Part I, chapter ii, section 3, *The Divers Sectaries Suttas*, 9, translated by Caroline A. F. Rhys Davids, (Oxford: Oxford University Press, 1917), 89.

Mrs. Rhys Davids' choice of stone seems right since the implication is that the gem is transparent and has facets.

> *Aṅguttaranikāya*, iii. 70, 24 has:[28]
> Within this *cakkavāla* [sphere] there are pearls, gems, cat's eyes ... all these are not worth one sixteenth part of the merit resulting from a fast with eight vows.

Here again is the pre-occupation with the figure eight. Nyānatiloka's German translation has Türkisen for *veḷuriya*.[29]

> *Aṅguttaranikāya*, ii. 19, 8 has:[30]
> Lord, the mighty ocean has many and diverse treasures; there is the pearl, the crystal, the lapis lazuli (*veḷuriya*), the shell, quartz, coral, silver, gold, the ruby and cat's eye (*masāragalla*).

E. M. Hare's note to *veḷuriya*: 'the colour of bamboo, of the acacia flower' must be taken from a Pāli commentary. Here I thought I would find out what colour *veḷuriya* was: bamboo when young is usually dark green but turns into yellow wood after one year, and the acacia flower is white or yellow. This was inconclusive until I read the passage in the *Rājanighaṇṭu*:[31]

> The cat's eye can be recognised from three types of sheen, that is, when it slightly shimmers like a bamboo leaf, shines strongly like a peacock's neck or has the reddish-brown appearance of the eye of cats.

Apart from the fact that my favourite cat would object to the latter description, this seems to be a standard comparison unless it has been lifted out of the Pāli commentary used by Hare. The comparison with a bamboo is probably due to a conventional false etymology which associates *veḷuriya* with Pāli *veḷu* or *veṇu*, both meaning 'bamboo'. E. M. Hare, in spite of his note, 'the colour of the acacia flower', translates *veḷuriya* as 'lapis lazuli'. The reason for this is not far to seek. At the end of the enumeration in the *Aṅguttaranikāya* a new gem has appeared, the *masāragalla*, which Hare translates as 'cat's eye'.

While the *Rājanighaṇṭu* compares the sheen of the cat's eye to that of the bamboo leaf,[32] Hare's note to the passage in the *Aṅguttaranikāya* compares the colour of the

---

[28] *Tikanipāta, Mahāvagga*, translated by Edmund Rowland, reprint of PTS 1885 edition, (Galle: J. Gooneratne, 1913), 235.

[29] *Die Reden des Buddha aus dem Ang£ttara-Nikāya. Inhalt: Einer–bis Dreierbuch* ..., 2nd edition, (München: Oskar Schloss, 1923), 348.

[30] *Aṭṭhanipāta, Mahāvagga*, translated by E. M. Hare, (London: Luzac, 1935), 137.

[31] *Die indischen Mineralien. Narahari, Rājanighaṇṭu, Sanskrit und deutsch herausgegeben von Richard Garbe* (Leipzig: S. Hirzel, 1882), xiii. 194.

[32] Garbe, *Die indischen Mineralien.*

veḷuriya, translated by him as 'lapis lazuli', to a bamboo.[33]

The *Rājanighaṇṭu* is a compilation of various works. Verse 194 combines the comparison to a peacock's neck with a comparison to the eye of a cat, and therefore in that passage clearly means the 'cat's eye' gem. In verse 216 in chapter 13, the lapis lazuli is described and also compared to a peacock's neck as follows:[34]

> That lapis lazuli must be regarded as genuine and auspicious which is without white flecks, is blackish or dark blue, smooth, heavy, pure, shining and like a peacock's neck.

This description of lapis lazuli corresponds to the mineralogical facts. The white flecks are caused by calcite. Here five Sanskrit words are translated by 'lapis lazuli', but not *vaiḍūrya*.

The comparison of *veḷuriya* to a peacock's neck in Hare's note[35] can be substantiated with a passage in Jātaka no. 32, the *Naccajātaka*:[36] 'peacock, your neck in hue like lapislazuli . . . ' This translates *veḷuriyavaṇṇupanibhā*. Pāli *nibhā* means 'lustre', and *vaṇṇa*, Sanskrit *varṇa*, does not have to mean 'colour' but just 'beauty, appearance'. So the passage could equally mean, 'peacock, your neck has more lustre than the appearance of beryl'. The *Rājanighaṇṭu* may have borrowed the simile from the *Jātaka*.

Now, while Chalmers translated *veḷuriya* in Jātaka no. 32 as 'lapis lazuli', H. T. Francis and R. A. Neil, the translators of volume three, still under Cowell's editorship, translated in Jātaka no. 419 *veḷuriya* as 'emeralds':[37]

> *idam suvaṇṇakāyūraṃ muttāveḷuriyā*
> Here is a golden necklace and emeralds and pearls.

In volume four of the same edition, translated by W. H. D. Rouse, in Jātaka no. 463, the word *veḷuriya* is translated as 'coral':[38]

> *tasmiṃ pana samudde vaṃsarāgaveḷuriyaṃ*
> Now, this ocean was full of coral the colour of bamboos.

---

[33] Hare (tr.), *Mahāvagga*, 137.

[34] Ibid., 13,216.

[35] Hare (tr.), *Mahāvagga*, 137.

[36] Translated under the editorship of E. B. Cowell by Robert Chalmers, (Cambridge: Cambridge University Press, 1895), i. 84.

[37] *Sulāsajātaka*, (Cambridge: Cambridge University Press, 1897), 262.

[38] *Suppārakajātaka*, (Cambridge: Cambridge University Press, 1901), 89.

Rouse's note says: 'the scholiast explains that the sea was red, like the reeds called 'scorpion-reed' or 'crab-reed', which are red in colour'. He adds that the haul was coral, which is also the word used at the end of the story (*pavālo*). In fact, on the next page the sequence of precious substances found in the ocean, itself a fanciful notion, is:[39] diamonds, gold, silver, emeralds, *vaṃsarāgaveḷuriyaṃ*'; at the end of the passage it is: 'gold, silver, jewels, corals (this time *pavāla*), and diamonds.' Thus 'emeralds and *veḷuriya* the colour of bamboo' was replaced by 'jewels and corals'.

The *Dhammapada* is believed to be an early text. It is mentioned in the *Milinda-pañha* which belongs to the beginnings of the Christian era. The commentary to it is called *Dhammapadāṭṭhakathā* and is attributed in its colophon to Buddhaghosa which fixes its date to about AD 400 even if Buddhaghosa was not himself the author. In the part commenting on *Sahassavaggo*, viii. 3, the line *ime suvaṇṇakāyūrā sabbe veḷuriyā-mayā* is translated by Eugene Watson Burlingame as, 'Take these golden bracelets, all set with beryls'.[40]

The *Milindapañha*, i. 267 has an enumeration of precious substances in which *masāragallaṃ veḷuriyo* are juxtaposed.[41] I. B. Horner translates the two words as 'cat's eyes, lapis lazuli'.[42] Here is the same situation as in the *Aṅguttaranikāya*. Again, *veḷuriya* is translated as 'lapis lazuli' because *masāragalla* is 'cat's eye' or 'beryl'.

The Dictionary of the Pali Text Society renders *masāragalla* as 'a precious stone, cat's eye' and compares Sanskrit *masāra* 'emerald' and Sanskrit *galva* 'crystal'.[43] Childers' Pāli Dictionary quotes the *Abhidhānappadīpika* as saying that the *masāragalla* is a stone produced in the hill of Masara (otherwise unknown).[44] Note 10 by E. M. Hare to the *Aṅguttaranikāya* passage explains *masāragalla* which he has translated as cat's eye, as a 'variegated crystal.'

There does not seem to be any necessity for *masāragalla* to be regarded as 'cat's eye'. Recapitulating, one can say that the translators of Pāli usually rendered *veḷuriya* as 'cat's eye' or 'beryl', except when mentioned together with *masāragalla* which for unknown reasons came to be translated as 'cat's eye', and then *veḷuriya* was translated as 'lapis lazuli'.

---

[39]Ibid., 90.

[40]*Buddhist Legends Told from the Original Pāli Text of the Dhammapada Commentary*, (Cambridge (Mass.), Harvard University Press, 1921), 229.

[41]Edited by V. Trenckner, 1928 reprint of PTS edition, (London: Royal Asiatic Society, 1880), 267.

[42]Translated by Isaline B. Horner, *Sacred Books of the Buddhists*, vol. 23, (London: Luzac, 1963), 85.

[43](Chipstead: Pali Text Society, 1925), ii. 249.

[44]Robert Caesar Childers, *A dictionary of the Pali language*, reprint, (London: Kegan Paul, 1974).

Something very special

For Sanskrit, Monier Williams' dictionary says:[45]

> *Vaiḍūrya* – a cat's eye gem; at the end of a compound anything excellent of its kind.

This may well be the clue to the change in interpretation in Chinese and Tibetan: because lapis lazuli seems to be something very precious to the Chinese and the Tibetans they want to give this meaning to *vaiḍūrya* which is to express something very special though different from 'diamond' which in Sanksrit is *vajra.* Berthold Laufer maintains that not only *liu-li* was the Chinese word for *vaiḍūrya*, but that the whole word was *pi-liu-li* which occurs on a Han bas-relief and is a phonetic transcription of the Sanskrit word.[46] This is borne out by Stanislas Julien's list of loan words from the Sanskrit where, indeed, the syllable no.1374, *pi*, is shown to correspond regularly to Sanskrit *vai*, and *liu* corresponds to Sanskrit *rū*, and *li* to Sanskrit *rya.*[47] It seems not unlikely that in some Sanskrit dialect the word was *vairūrya* from which the Prākrit form *verulia* was derived. The 'cat's eye' is called in Chinese *mao tsing* 'cat's essence'. Laufer does not favour the 'lapis lazuli' translation though that is advocated by the books of Eitel[48] and F. Porter Smith,[49] which he quotes.

Chrysoberyl and aquamarine

Isidorus of Seville (560–636) mentions that beryl comes from India and is pale green, but that in chrysoberyl, i.e., cat's eye, a gold-coloured lustre can be observed.[50] Laufer decides it should be 'chrysoberyl' because this stone has an opalescent sheen. He also remarks: 'How could the Tibetan authors distinguish blue, green, white and yellow *vaiḍūrya* if the word should denote the "cat's eye"?'[51] Thus, the cat's eye' can be of only one colour and always has a sheen, while the beryl can

[45](Oxford: Oxford University Press, 1899), 1021.

[46]Publication 154, Anthropological series, volume x, (Chicago: Chicago Field Museum of Natural History, 1912), 111.

[47]Stanislas Aignan Julien, *Méthode pour déchiffrer et transcrire les noms sanscrits qui se rencontrent dans les livres chinois* (Paris: Imprimerie Imperiale, 1861), 168.

[48]E. J. Eitel, *Handbook of Chinese Buddhism* (London: Trübner, 1888), 191.

[49]F. Porter Smith, *Contributions towards the Materia Medica of China* (London: Trübner, 1871).

[50]*Etymologiae*, xvi. 7. 5–7: *Beryllus in India gignitur, gentis suae lingua nomen habens, viriditate similis smaragdo, sed cum pallore ... Chrysoberyllus dictus eo quod pallida eius viriditas in aureum colorem resplendeat. Et hunc India mittit.*

[51]Laufer, op. cit. in note 46, 111.

be of many colours and without a sheen though it may have a sheen as Laufer's 'chrysoberyl'. There are yellow, green and white beryls, and the blue beryl is the aquamarine. It must be due to this that the Tibetan doctor Yeshi Donden and his translator Kelsang Jhampa were using the phrase 'King of Aquamarine Light' for the Medicine Buddha.[52]

Chinese interpretations

The Chinese *pi-liu-li* usually appears just as *liu-li* because the Chinese are as fond of abbreviating as are the Tibetans. Édouard Chavannes is cautious in the 1912 volume of his *Cinq cents contes et apologues*: 'des parures de *vaiḍūrya* (*lieu-li*), d'or et d'argent'.[53] But by 1921 he has made up his mind: 'des parures de béryl, d'or et d'argent'.[54] Demiéville in 1924 thinks it designated a purely mythical substance.[55]

E. Burnouf in his translation of an incomplete version of the *Saddharmapuṇḍarīka* from the Sanskrit enumerates the seven precious substances *suvarṇa, rūpya, vaiḍūrya, sphaṭika, lohitamukti, açmagarbha, musāragalva* [sic], interpreting them as 'gold, silver, lapis lazuli, crystal, red pearls (connecting *mukti* with *mukta*), emerald, cat's eye'.[56] W. E. Soothill in his translation of the *Saddharmapuṇḍarīka* from the Chinese, has gold, silver, lapis lazuli, moonstones, agates, coral, amber'.[57] In his note, Burnouf informs us that he is following the *Abhidhānappadīpika* in using 'lapis lazuli', and that, according to A. Rémusat, *musāragalva* means to the Chinese a blue and white stone, perhaps 'ammonite'.[58]

Babylonian appreciation of lapis lazuli

A recent author dealing with Chinese scriptural accounts on the Medicine Buddha, in translating texts from the Chinese *Tripiṭaka*, consistently translates *liu-li* with 'lapis lazuli'. Raoul Birnbaum in his *The Healing Buddha*,[59] gives the reason for his choice,

[52] *The Ambrosia Heart Tantra, with annotations by Yeshi Donden*, translated by Jhampa Kelsang, (Dharamsala: Library of Tibetan Works and Archives, 1977), 15 and *passim*.

[53] Édouard Chavannes, *Cinq cents contes et apologues extraits du Tripiṭaka chinois et traduits en français*, 4 vols., (Paris: E. Leroux, 1910–34), iii. 362, no. 500.

[54] Chavannes, *Contes et légendes du Bouddhisme*, (Paris: Bossard, 1921), 151.

[55] Paul Démieville, review of Hong-Tchang Lapidarium Sinicum, *Bulletin d'école Française d'Extrême-Orient*, xxiv (1924), esp. pp. 276–283. John Irwin in his article 'The Lāt Bhairo at Benares (Vārāṇasī)', *Zeitschrift der deutschen morgenländischen Gesellschaft*, cxxxiii (1983), 328, f.n. 20, subscribes to this opinion.

[56] *Le Lotus de la Bonne Loi* (Paris: Imprimerie Nationale, 1852), 319–320.

[57] *The Lotus of the Wonderful Law* (Oxford: Clarendon Press, 1930), xiv. 187.

[58] Burnouf, *Bonne Loi*, 319–320.

[59] London: Rider, 1979, 60.

saying the Gandhāra is near the only source of lapis lazuli in the ancient world (i.e., Afghanistan) and that 'these images are noted for their emphasis on the depiction of light and flames emanating from the form of the Buddha.' As lapis lazuli is opaque dark blue it is not the best colour to depict light or flames, although dark blue pervaded with golden rays often appears on thankas as the back curtain or back plate of a deity. The gold flecks in lapis lazuli which are caused by pyrite were the reason why it was highly prized by the ancient Babylonians who compared them to the stars in the night sky.[60] The etymology of *lapis lazuli* directs us also to Persia. The word occurs first in the fourteenth century as a compound of Latin *lapis* 'stone' and Mediaeval Latin *lazulum* from Arabic *lāzaward* from Persian *lāzhuward* 'lapis lazuli'. From this was derived the Sanskrit word *rājavarta* for 'lapis lazuli'. About this, the *Laghuratnaparīkṣā*, verses 19–20, says: 'it is without white spots and the colour of a peacock's neck'.[61] According to the *Rājanighaṇṭu*, xiii. 215, *rājavarta* used against bile diseases is soft and cool, while *vaiḍūrya*, according to *Rājanighaṇṭu*, xiii. 193, is warm. The English word *azure* goes back to the same Arabic word *lāzaward* through Old French and Old Spanish, omitting the initial *l* which was mistakenly regarded as an Arabic article.

Conclusion

In conclusion, then, it seems that *vaiḍūrya*, *veḷuriya* and *liu-li* mean 'beryl', and that Pāli *veḷuriya* is interpreted as 'lapis lazuli' when juxtaposed with Pāli *masāragalla*, while Chinese *liu-li* and Tibetan *be-ḍu-rya* are often translated as 'lapis lazuli' because lapis lazuli was an extremely rare and special stone which could only be obtained from Afghanistan before the rocks near Lake Baikal were discovered, and because it resembled the night sky with its stars, the most exalted symbol of the divine.

If 'beryl' translates *vaiḍūrya*, and the Medicine Buddha is traditionally surrounded by a blue radiance, it would have to be called 'blue beryl radiance.' According to Dongthog's *New Light English–Tibetan Dictionary* the Tibetan word for 'aquamarine' is *pu.shka.ra*, a loan word from a Sanskrit word for 'blue lotus'.[62] But as a blue beryl is an aquamarine, 'aquamarine radiance' still seems to be the best translation for Tibetan *be.du.rya.hod.* Why *puṣkara* is the Tibetan word for 'aquamarine' is another question. Is the colour of the blue lotus aquamarine?

---

[60] Ernst Darmstädter, 'Der babylonisch–assyrische Lasurstein', in *Studien zur Geschichte der Chemie, Festgabe für E. O. von Lippmann* (Berlin: J. Springer, 1927), 2.

[61] Edited by Louis Finot, in *Les lapidaires indiens* (Paris: E. Bouillon, 1896), 201.

[62] T. G. Dongthog, (Dharamsala: Library of Tibetan Works and Archives, 1973), 21.

Chapter 6

Études āyurvédiques III. Les carrés magiques dans la médecine indienne*

Arion Roşu

L'ĀYURVEDA, QUI EST UNE MÉDECINE RATIONNELLE dans son enseignement fondamental, comporte aussi, bien que rarement, des pratiques magico-religieuses, dont Caraka indique par deux fois la liste (*Sūtra* xi. 54 et *Vimāna* viii. 87). D'après l'auteur classique, les remèdes surnaturels tels que les formules sacrées (*mantra*), les amulettes (*oṣadhi* et *maṇi*), etc., remontent à l'*Atharvaveda*, pour lequel les médecins doivent montrer une dévotion particulière (*Sūtra* xxx. 21). Dans l'histoire de la médecine indienne traditionnelle, les prescriptions magiques concernent surtout la naissance et l'accouchement ainsi que les maladies nerveuses ou mentales, les possessions démoniaques infantiles et les morsures des bêtes venimeuses.[1]

La thérapeutique indienne non médicale utilise non seulement les incantations ou formules magiques (*mantra*) mais aussi les diagrammes rituels (*yantra, maṇḍala*) d'un emploi sensiblement plus rare. A cette dernière catégorie se rattachent les carrés magiques, que l'on ne rencontre pas plus de quatre fois dans la littérature

---

[0]* *Études āyurvédiques* I et II dans *Indologica Taurinensia*, vi (1978), 255–260 et *Sanskrit and world culture* (Berlin: Akademie-Verlag, 1986), 586–594. Le présent article est tiré d'une ample étude sur 'Les carrés magiques indiens et l'histoire des idées en Asie', à paraître dans *Zeitschrift der Deutschen Morgenländischen Gesellschaft*, cxxxviii (1988).

[1] Voir notre mémoire sur '*Mantra* et *yantra* dans la médecine et l'alchimie indiennes', *Journal Asiatique*, cclxxiv (1986), 203–268.

āyurvédique, dę Vṛnda avant l'an mille jusqu'à Trimallabhaṭṭa au milieu du XVIIe siècle.[2]

Un carré magique d'ordre *n* se présente comme un échiquier dont les cases formées par *n* lignes et *n* colonnes portent des nombres entiers de l'unité au carré de *n* disposés de sorte que leur somme soit constante à l'horizontale, à la verticale et parfois même, dans les figures parfaites, suivant les diagonales.[3] Formé de neuf cases, le carré magique d'ordre *3* (le premier nombre impair qui en est susceptible), que décrivent les recueils āyurvédiques, est le plus anciennement attesté en Chine (IVe siècle av. J.-C.) et se retrouve dans la littérature arabe, médicale ou ésotérique, avant la fin du premier millénaire, ainsi que chez Agrippa de Nettesheim, occultiste allemand de la Renaissance.

Littérature āyurvédique

En cas d'accouchement difficile, le populaire compendium *Siddhayoga*, composé par Vṛnda vers 900, prescrit un *mantra* expulseur (*cyāvana*), qui remonte à Suśruta (*Cikitsā* xv. 6–8), d'après le glossateur Śrīkaṇṭhadatta. Répétée sept fois, la formule consacre l'eau que, selon une tradition encore vivante en Inde, doit absorber la parturiente, qui regarde en même temps un diagramme eutocique, qualifié de merveilleux (*āścarya*) et utilisé comme talisman. Le carré magique qui le constitue est composé de nombres disposés de façon que l'on retrouve la constante *30* non seulement dans les deux directions, horizontale et verticale, comme semble l'indiquer le terme sanskrit *ubhaya-triṃśaka*, mais aussi suivant les diagonales.[4] Il faut noter parmi les mots-chiffres le terme *nāḍī*, qui correspond ici à *16*, et ne figure pas avec

[2] La datation des auteurs médicaux, notamment celle de Vṛnda, d'après P. V. Sharma, *Āyurveda kā vaijñānika itihāsa* (Varanasi: Chaukhambha Orientalia, 1975), *passim.* Cf. du même auteur, 'Reassessment of the date of Niścalakara and related medical authors', *Annals of the Bhandarkar Oriental Research Institute,* lvii (1976), 78. Pour fixer la date probable des auteurs āyurvédiques qui intéressent le présent article, voir aussi la contribution magistrale de G. J. Meulenbeld, 'The surveying of Sanskrit medical literature', dans G. J. Meulenbeld (éd.) *Proceedings of the International Workshop on priorities in the study of Indian medicine* (Groningen: Rijksuniversiteit te Groningen, 1984), 39 et 51: Vṛnda (800–950), Cakrapāṇi (avant 1050–1100) et Vaṅgasena (1050–1100).

[3] Cf. *Dictionnaire des mathématiques* (Paris: Presses universitaires de France, 1974), 454–455.

[4] Vṛnda, *Śrīmad-Vṛndapraṇīto … Siddhayogaḥ,* éd. Hanumanta Śāstrī Pādhye, (Poona: Ānandāśrama, 1894), lxv. 18–19 (p. 503–504):

jalaṃ cyāvana-mantreṇa saptavārābhimantritam |
pītvā prasūyate nārī dṛṣṭvā cobhaya-triṃśakam || *18* ||
nāḍy(16) *-ṛtu*(6) *-vasubhiḥ*(8) *pakṣa*(2) *-dig*(10) *-aṣṭādaśabhir*(18) *eva ca* |
arka(12) *-bhuvana*(14) *-abdhi*(4) *-sahitair ubhaya-triṃśakam āścaryam* || *19* ||

cette acception dans la lexicographie moderne.[5] Cependant le poète Bhavabhūti confirme cette valeur numérique de *nāḍī* dans le drame *Mālatīmādhava* (v. 1), quand il fait état du soi (*ātman*) de Śaktinātha au milieu de seize vaisseaux, dont les glossateurs médiévaux donnent la liste en s'inspirant du Yoga tantrique: *iḍā, piṅgalā, suṣumnā*, etc.[6]

Dans son commentaire *Kusumāvalī*, Śrīkaṇṭhadatta cite au XIIe siècle Cakrapāṇi (1050 ap. J.-C.) pour la description complémentaire du carré magique à la constante *15* (*ubhaya-pañcadaśa*), que l'on trouve représenté avec le carré d'ordre *3* à la constante *30* dans l'édition du *Siddhayoga*. L'éditeur Hanumanta Śāstrī Pādhye reproduit les dessins d'après un manuscrit portant le texte, avec variantes, qui décrit les deux *yantra* (fig. 1).[7]

8	*3*	*4*
1	*5*	*9*
6	*7*	*2*

16	*6*	*8*
2	*10*	*18*
12	*14*	*4*

Figure 1: *Carré magique d'ordre 3 à la constante 15 et 30, employé pour l'accouchement difficile. D'après le Siddhayoga (Poona, 1894), 504.*

A la différence de Vṛnda, Cakrapāṇi donne la teneur du *mantra* expulseur qu'il emprunte à Suśruta (*Cikitsā* xv. 6–8),[8] avec de légères modifications, et reprend ensuite le texte du *Siddhayoga*, qu'il complète avec la composition du carré magique d'ordre *3* à la constante *15*, supposé lui aussi faciliter la parturition (*sukha-sūti-kṛt*).[9]

[5]Cf. B. Datta et A. N. Singh, *History of Hindu mathematics*, i, (Lahore: Motilal Banarsi Das, 1935), 56. Sur la prédominance du nombre *16* dans la culture indienne, voir J. Gonda, *Change and continuity in Indian religion* (The Hague: Mouton, 1965), 115–130.

[6]Bhavabhūti, *Mālatīmādhava, with the commentary of Jagaddhara*, edited by M. R. Kale, 3rd edition, (Delhi: Motilal Banarsidass, 1967), v. 1 avec les commentaires *ad loc.* de Jagaddhara et de Pūrṇasarasvatī, éd. K. S. Mahādeva Śāstrī, (Trivandrum: Government Central Press, 1953). Cf. S. Gupta, D. J. Hoens et T. Goudriaan, *Hindu Tantrism* (Leiden: Brill, 1979), 168.

[7]Vṛnda, *Siddhayoga*, 504, note. Un ouvrage récent reproduit les deux figures carrées mais tournées à droite de 90°: G. U. Thite, *Medicine: its magico-religious aspects according to the Vedic and later literature* (Poona: Continental Prakashan, 1982), 62.

[8]Traduction et commentaire de la formule suśrutienne, dans J. Filliozat, *Étude de démonologie indienne. Le Kumāratantra de Rāvaṇa* ... (Paris: Imprimerie nationale, 1937), 31–34. L'auteur traite de la thérapeutique de l'accouchement difficile, mais il n'aborde pas la question des carrés magiques.

[9]Cakrapāṇidatta, *Cikitsāsārasaṃgrahāparanāmā Cakradattaḥ* ... *Cakrapāṇiviracitaḥ*, éd. Jayadeva Vidyālaṃkāra, (Lahore: Motilal Banarsidass, 1925), lxiii. 10 (p. 624–625): *ihāmṛtaṃ ca somaś ca citrabhānuś ca bhāmini* | ...

vasu$^{(8)}$ *-guṇa*$^{(3)}$ *-abdhy*$^{(4)}$ *-eka*$^{(1)}$ *-bāṇa*$^{(5)}$ *-nava*$^{(9)}$ *-ṣaṭ*$^{(6)}$ *-sapta*$^{(7)}$ *-yugaiḥ*$^{(2)}$ *kramāt* |
sarvaṃ pañcadaśa dvis tu triṃśakaṃ nava-koṣṭhake || *10* ||

On lira *nāḍī* au lieu de *nārī* dans la composition du carré à la constante magique *30*.

D'après le commentateur Śivadāsasena, Cakrapāṇi suit ici la pratique (*vyavahāra*) introduite par les auteurs de recueils médicaux (*saṃgraha*) depuis Vṛnda, qui recommande la septuple récitation du *cyāvana-mantra* pour consacrer l'eau que doit absorber la femme en travail, alors que le classique Suśruta prescrit à la parturiente l'écoute (*upaśṛṇuyāt*) de cette formule d'accouchement heureux (*Cikitsā* xv. 5). On inscrit les nombres dans les neuf cases (*koṣṭha*) des deux carrés (un seul chez Vṛnda) établis par le *Cakradatta*. Suivant les explications du commentaire médiéval, on dessine les deux figures carrées au milieu d'une coupe évasée (*śarāva*) qu'on doit faire voir à la femme enceinte (*garbhiṇī*), après avoir rendu un culte à l'amulette (*saṃpūjya*).[10]

En accord avec ses devanciers, Vaṅgasena fait état au XIIe siècle, en cas de dystocie, du même *mantra* expulseur de Suśruta (*Cikitsā* xv. 6–8) et du carré magique à la constante *30*, que décrivent Vṛnda et Cakrapāṇi. Il prescrit, outre un onguent accoucheur, une seconde formule, empruntée à Caraka (*Śārīra* viii. 39), et que l'on doit, au moment de l'accouchement (*prasava-kāla*), prononcer sept fois à l'oreille de la parturiente.[11]

Vers 1650, un autre compilateur médical, Trimallabhaṭṭa, recourt dans la *Bṛhadyogataraṅgiṇī* (cxl. 44–55) au carré magique d'ordre *3* afin de remédier à la dystocie, notée par *(vi)mūḍhagarbha*, et pour laquelle il fait intervenir, en plus des remèdes naturels, deux *mantra* expulseurs: le premier, suśrutien et déjà cité, rappelle les charmes védiques, tandis que le second, tardif, évoque un vers de Hārīta. La formule ancienne consacre l'eau que doit absorber la femme en travail; celle-ci regardera en même temps le diagramme, appelé *yantra* ou *cakra*, représentant le même carré à la constante *30*. Le second *śloka*, que l'on récite en répandant des grains de riz non cassés, comporte quelques variantes par rapport au texte de Hārīta (voir n. 21).

La *Hārītasaṃhitā*, dont la rédaction tardive daterait du XIIe siècle,[12] donne une longue formule magique d'heureux accouchement (*sukha-prasava*), précédée du *śloka* mentionné, et utilise également un *yantra* eutocique portant inscrits, sur une feuille d'*āḍhaka* (*Cajanus cajan*), plusieurs germes phoniques d'inspiration tantrique (*aiṃ hrāṃ hrīṃ hrūṃ hraiṃ hroṃ hrauṃ hraḥ*). On doit présenter ce talisman à la parturiente et

---

[10] Śivadāsasena *ad loc.*: *ete nava koṣṭhān kṛtvā tad-abhyantare lekhyāḥ | vṛnde tu ubhaya-triṃśakam apy uktam | etad dvayaṃ śarāva-madhye likhitvā saṃpūjya darśayitvayam || 10 ||*

[11] Vaṅgasena, *Cikitsāsārasaṃgraha*, éd. R. K. Rai, (Varanasi: Prācya Prakāśan, 1983), strī-rogādhikāra, 223–229 (p. 673–674). Pour le nombre *4*, l'auteur préfère le terme *veda* au mot *abdhi* de Vṛnda.

[12] P. V. Sharma, 'The Pseudo-Ḥārīta Saṃhitā', *Indian Journal of History of Science*, x (1975), 7.

le déposer sur son lit.[13] Mais la grande *Yogataraṅgiṇī*, au lieu de ce diagramme courant, prescrit le carré magique à la constante *15* et *30* (*ubhaya-triṃśaka*).[14] La version abrégée de ce recueil ne retient que la variante *30*, qualifiée de diagramme suprême (*yantram uttamam*).[15]

Si les indianistes connaissent depuis Colebrooke[16] le chapitre sur les carrés magiques intitulé *bhadragaṇita* dans le traité mathématiques *Gaṇitakaumudī*,[17] composé en 1356 par Nārāyaṇa Paṇḍita, ils ont jusqu'à présent ignoré les carrés numériques de l'Āyurveda. La présence de ces tableaux de nombres dans la littérature médicale sanskrite avant l'an mille nous conduit à rectifier la chronologie des carrés magiques indiens. En effet leurs premières traces archéologiques, supposées du XIe siècle,[18] sont plus récentes que la première mention āyurvédique d'un carré magique à vertu eutocique chez le médecin Vṛnda vers 900, que l'on peut proposer comme *terminus a quo* dans le domaine des carrés magiques indiens.

Sources non médicales

Les témoignages archéologiques, tous localisés dans l'Inde du Nord, attestent l'intérêt pour le carré magique d'ordre *4*, utilisé, jusqu'à l'époque moderne, à des

[13] *Hārītasaṃhitā*, éd. Jīvānanda Vidyāsāgara, (Calcutta: Siddheśvara, 1894), iii. 51 (p. 287–288): *prasavopāya-mantrauṣadhāni.*

[14] Trimallabhaṭṭa, *Bṛhadyogataraṅgiṇī*, éd. Hanumanta Pādhye Śāstrī, (Poona: Ānandāśrama, 1913–1914), cxl. 44–55 (vol. ii, p. 914–915), illustré du carré magique d'ordre *3* à la constante *30* et *15*, dont Trimallabhaṭṭa donne la composition suivante:

kalā(16)*-rasa*(6)*-aṣṭabhiḥ*(8) *pakṣa*(2)*-dig*(10)*-aṣṭādaśabhiḥ*(18) *kramāt* |
arkaiś(12) *ca bhuvanair*(14) *vedair*(4) *ubhaya-triṃśakaṃ vadet* || *52* ||
gaja(8)*-agni*(3)*-vedāḥ*(4) *śaśi*(1)*-bāṇa*(5)*-khe'ṭā*(9) *rasa*(6)*-adri*(7)*-pakṣā*(2)
navakoṣṭha-madhye |
prasūti-kāle likhitaṃ gṛhītvā sukhena nārī-prasavo 'tiśīghram || *55* ||

[15] *Yogataraṅgiṇī*… *Trimallabhaṭṭena viracitā*, éd. Gaṅgāviṣṇu Śrīkṛṣṇadāsa, Khemarāja Gupta, (Bombay: Śrīveṅkaṭeśvara, 1888), lxxv. 36–41 (p. 291). Dans cette version abrégée, l'auteur a inversé l'ordre des vers du *mantra* suśrutien. Le texte imprimé est illustré de la figure du carré d'ordre *3* à la constante *30*, dont les neuf nombres ont une suite différente de celle que présente la figure du meme carré dans l'édition de la *Bṛhadyogataraṅgiṇī* (vol. ii, p. 915.). Sur les huit configurations possibles du carré magique d'ordre *3*, voir W. Ahrens, 'Studien über die "magischen Quadrate" der Araber', *Der Islam*, vii (1917), 190.

[16] *Algebra, with arithmetic and mensuration, from the Sanscrit of Brahmegupta and Bháscara*, translated by H. Th. Colebrooke, (London: J. Murray, 1817), 113, note.

[17] Nārāyaṇa Paṇḍita, *The Gaṇita Kaumudī*, éd. Padmākara Dvivedī, 2 vol., (Benares: Government Sanskrit College, 1936–1942). Sur les carrés magiques indiens et les méthodes de leur composition selon Nārāyaṇa, voir S. Cammann, 'Islamic and Indian magic squares' II, *History of Religions*, viii (1969), 271–290.

[18] H. Hargreaves, *Annual progress report of the superintendent: Hindu and Buddhist monuments, Northern Circle for the year ending 31st March 1916* (Archaeological Survey of India), 3.

fins de magie blanche aussi diverses que la chance dans les affaires et la guérison des maladies.[19] Raghunandana en fait état vers 1500 dans la section astrologique (*Jyotistattva*) de son vaste traité *Smṛtitattva.* D'après ce juriste bengali, l'action du carré magique de seize cases que l'on doit regarder ou porter sur soi, se modifie selon la constante magique, caractérisée par une vertu particulière, thérapeutique ou autre: *20* agit comme contrepoison, *32* hâte l'accouchement, *50* chasse les esprits mauvais et *72* rend féconde la femme stérile.[20] Le carré magique d'ordre *4* avec la constante *32* se retrouve à notre époque dans les croyances populaires du Bengale. En effet, d'après certaines prescriptions rituelles, on fabrique une amulette portant inscrit un tel carré magique, qu'on doit attacher, en même temps qu'un *mantra* expulseur, dans les cheveux de la parturiente. La formule, qui rappelle un charme d'accouchement heureux de Hārīta (III. 51), est la suivante:[21]

> *asti godāvarī-tīre jambhalā nāma rākṣasī* |
> *tasyāḥ smaraṇa-mātreṇa viśalyā garbhiṇī bhavet* ||
> 'Sur les bords de la Godāvarī demeure la *rākṣasī* nommée Jambhalā, dont la simple évocation en pensée procure la délivrance à la femme enceinte.'

Le *śloka* concernant Jambhalā remonte vraisemblablement au traité astrologique *Rājamartaṇḍa*, attribué au roi Bhoja (XIe siècle). Ce vers a été repris au XVIe siècle par le ritualiste et juriste Raghunandana du Bengale dans le *Jyotistattva* / *Jyotiṣatattva*, que mentionne le lexique moderne *Śabdakalpadruma*, s.v. Jambhalā, avec une légère variante au premier hémistiche: *samudrasyottare tīre jambhalā nāma rākṣasī.*[22]

Le nom de Jambhalā, qui rappelle l'homonyme masculin Jambhala, connu du tantrisme bouddhique, se réfère à une ogresse du tantrisme hindou. Sous son aspect bénéfique, elle est réputée favoriser la grossesse chez les femmes stériles qui murmurent son nom avec vénération.[23] Le chapitre intitulé *grastabālacikitsā* de l'*Uḍḍīśa-*

---

[19] *Panjab Notes and Queries*, i (1884), notes 462 et 537.

[20] G. A. Grierson 'An American puzzle', *Indian Antiquary*, x (1881), 89–90.

[21] Voir A. K. Sur, *Folk elements in Bengali life* (Calcutta: Indian Publications, 1975), 23–24 (texte aimablement communiqué par le Dr Rahul Peter Das, Hambourg). Cf. *Hārītasaṃhitā* (Calcutta: Siddheśvara, 1894), 288, cité par J. Filliozat, *Le Kumāratantra de Rāvaṇa*, 33. Le texte commence ainsi:

> *himavad-uttare kūle surasā nāma rākṣasī* |
> *tasyā nūpura-śabdena viśalyā gurviṇī bhavet* ||
> 'Sur le versant nord de l'Himalaya demeure la *rākṣasī* nommée Surasā; le son de ses anneaux de chevilles procure la délivrance à la femme enceinte.'

[22] Cf. O. Böhtlingk et R. Roth, *Sanskrit-Wörterbuch*, III, 42: *samudrasyottaratīre jambhalā nāma rākṣasī.*

[23] Voir S. Sen, 'On Yakṣa and Yakṣa worship' dans J. Ensink et P. Gaeffke (éds), *India Maior. Congratulatory volume presented to J. Gonda* (Leiden: Brill, 1972), 192–193. C.f. M.-Th. de Mallmann, *Introduction à l'iconographie du tântrisme bouddhique* (Paris: [s.n.], 1975), 195–197.

tantra, attribué à Rāvaṇa, présente Jambhalā dans le rôle malfaisant d'une *yoginī* qui possède les enfants.[24]

Au moyen âge, les hymnes jaina, prakrits[25] et sanskrits,[26] qui évoquent les carrés magiques témoignent eux aussi de la diffusion des diagrammes numériques, ignorés dans les Āgama du Sud mais dont traitent plusieurs textes tantriques du Nord, principalement le *Śivatāṇḍava*, commenté au XVIIe siècle par le même Nīlakaṇṭha qui a expliqué le *Mahābhārata*.[27]

Les carrés magiques se sont maintenus en Inde sous les princes moghols, dont les attaches culturelles persanes en favorisaient l'usage. Au XVIIe siècle l'envoyé extraordinaire de Louis XIV auprès du roi de Siam Phra Narai apprenait sur la route des Indes la méthode qu'employaient les brahmanes de Surat pour composer des carrés magiques.[28] Soizante-dix ans plus tard, Anquetil-Duperron, arrivé à Surat, retrouve les diagrammes numériques dans les textes mazdéens et chez les musulmans de l'Inde occidentale.[29] Dans la même région que le port Surat, la ville de Nasik prête son nom aux carrés magiques qu'élabora après 1850 le missionnaire anglais A. H. Frost,[30] à une époque où les descriptions ethnographiques de l'Inde du Nord font référence aux carrés numériques.

Croyances populaires

Parmi les remèdes superstitieux W. Crooke mentionne au siècle dernier dans l'Inde du Nord deux carrés magiques, dont l'un, d'ordre *3* à la constante *15*, est contre le mauvais oeil et l'autre guérit la stérilité chez la femme. L'auteur indique à ce titre un carré magique d'ordre *4* à la constante *73* (et non *72* prescrit avec la même indication dans le *Jyotistattva*), qui est figuré sur une croûte de pain destinée à nourrir un chien noir, animal attribué au dieu Bhairava, donneur de fécondité.[31]

---

[24]Voir J. Filliozat, *Le Kumāratantra de Rāvaṇa*, 67.

[25]H. R. Kapadia, 'A note on Jaina hymns and magic squares', *Indian Historical Quarterly*, x (1934), 140–153.

[26]H. R. Kapadia, *A history of the Sanskrit literature of the Jainas*, ii, 1, (Baroda: Pragati Printing Press, 1968), 392–397 (en gujarātī). Mlle Nalini Balbir nous a signalé ces pages, dont Mme Usha Colas nous a donné la traduction.

[27]Détails sur les données archéologiques et littéraires dans notre article déjà cité, *Zeitschrift der Deutschen Morgenländischen Gesellschaft*, cxxxviii (1988).

[28]Simon de La Loubère, *Du Royaume de Siam*, ii, (Paris: J. B. Coignard, 1691), 295–359.

[29]A. H. Anquetil-Duperron, *Zend-Avesta* (Paris: N. M. Tillard, 1771), i, 1, DXXVII–DXXVIII et i, 2, XXVIII.

[30]A. H. Frost, dans *Encyclopaedia Britannica*, 11th edition, xvii (1911), 310a–313a (s.v. magic square).

[31]W. Crooke, *The popular religion and folk-lore of Northern India*, I, (London: A. Constable, 1896), 159–160.

La tradition des diagrammes numériques reste encore vivante parmi les guérisseurs de l'Inde du Nord, où une récente enquête de sociologie médicale, menée dans la région de Bénarès, relève l'emploi d'un carré magique d'ordre *3* dans le traitement du paludisme,[32] mais non dans l'accouchement selon la prescription traditionnelle. Cet emploi nouveau montre l'étendue possible des prodédés médico-magiques, confirmée par d'autres témoignages du Rasaśāstra. C'est ainsi que l'anneau talismanique que recommande le *Rasendracūḍāmaṇi* (x, 79–82), peut hâter l'accouchement, mais aussi guérir la colique ou le mal d'yeux. Le carré magique composé de neuf cases prescrit de nos jours contre la fièvre paludéenne sera dessiné sur une feuille de figuier sacré (*pippala*)[33] et enveloppé dans une pièce de tissu avant d'être attaché au bras droit du malade.

Tradition islamique

Le carré magique d'ordre *3*, connu dans la tradition islamique sous l'appellation de sceau d'al-Ġazālī,[34] est attesté pour la première fois avant le Xe siècle, vers la même époque, dans les textes āyurvédiques (*Siddhayoga*) et dans la littérature arabe, qu'elle soit médicale (*Firdaus al-ḥikma*, achevé en 850)[35] ou ésotérique (Corpus attribué à Ǧābir, daté du IXe ou du Xe siècle).[36] Les trois auteurs, aussi bien le médecin indien que le savant persan et l'alchimiste arabe, prescrivent ce talisman à la parturiente si elle éprouve de la difficulté à accoucher. On doit cependant remarquer, outre les modalités différentes d'emploi, que les deux carrés islamiques présentent la constante magique 15, alors que la figure numérique de Vṛnda comporte la somme 30, reprise par d'autres auteurs āyurvédiques du XIe au XVIIe siècle.

Quoi qu'il en soit, le problème reste entier quand il s'agit d'établir, pour l'invention ou l'emploi de ce carré magique à vertu eutocique, la priorité d'une civilisation

---

[32] K. P. Shukla, *Traditional healers in community health* (Varanasi: Gomati Krishna Publications, 1980), 150.

[33] Cf. Mahīdhara, *Mantramahodadhi*, éd. et trad. hindī Śukadeva Caturvedī, (Varanasi: Prācya Prakāśan, 1981), xx, 114–115, (p. 644), qui décrit un *yantra* fébrifuge, tracé avec le suc de la plante *dhuttūra*, réputée abaisser la température.

[34] *Encyclopédie islamique*[1], iv, 1140a.

[35] A. Siggel, 'Gynäkologie, Embryologie und Frauenhygiene aus dem "Paradies der Weisheit über die Medizin" des Abu Hasan 'Alī b. Sahl Rabban aṭ-Ṭabarī', *Quellen und Studien zur Geschichte der Naturwissenschaften und der Medizin*, viii (1941), 1–2, 253–254.

[36] M. Berthelot, *La chimie au moyen âge* (Paris: Imprimerie nationale, 1893), vol. iii, *L'alchimie arabe*, 118 (texte arabe) et 150–151 (traduction française). Cf. P. Kraus, *Jābir ibn Ḥayyān. Contribution à l'histoire des idées scientifiques dans l'Islam*, ii, (Le Caire: Imprimerie de l'Institut français d'archéologie orientale, 1942), 73, note 1.

sur l'autre. L'écart dans le temps entre les trois textes mentionnés, arabes et sanskrit, est trop réduit pour que l'on puisse, s'il y a emprunt, discerner le modèle et la direction de l'influence. Certaines sources sont même difficilement datables. Le IXe siècle retenu pour le *Siddhayoga* n'est pas plus assuré que pour le document alchimique du Corpus ǧābirien.[37] En effet, on place parfois le compilateur Vṛnda, habitant du Bengale, à la fin du Xe siècle.[38] Cette datation gagnerait en vraisemblance si le diagramme médical était réellement un emprunt aux musulmans qui avaient déjà à l'époque envahi le sous-continent indien par la conquête du Sind, étendue jusqu'à Multan sur l'Indus supérieur.[39]

La thèse diffusionniste suscite une certaine réserve chez les historiens des mathématiques, enclins à accepter un parallélisme de raisonnement plutôt qu'une influence historique caractérisée. Pour eux, le carré magique d'ordre *3* fait appel à une arithmétique élémentaire, qui peut être conçue indépendamment dans plusieurs aires de culture. La diffusion des carrés magiques en Asie peut s'être limitée, dans certains cas, à la connaissance que de telles figures peuvent exister sans que pour autant des modèles aient été diffusés.[40]

Les deux traditions, indienne et arabe, ont cependant contribué ensemble, dans le prolongement de spéculations divinatoires et numérologiques chinoises, au développement des carrés magiques, qui se sont répandus au moyen âge à Byzance[41] et en Europe. Cet art qui a commencé par être une pratique talismanique en Asie est devenu, à partir du XVIIe siècle, le sujet d'une recherche savante chez les mathématiciens occidentaux.[42]

Summary

Magic squares in Indian medicine

Hitherto, the importance of *āyurvedic* literature in the chronology of Indian magic squares, of which the origin remains controversial in the history of Oriental ideas, has been ignored.

Represented on archaeological monuments of north India from the eleventh century onwards, magic squares pertain to Hindu Tantric tradition, which describes them as ritual numerical diagrams (*aṅkayantra*), a subject that has not yet been studied by Indologists.

[37] *Encyclopédie islamique*^{2}, ii, 367b–368a.

[38] G. J. Meulenbeld, *The Mādhavanidāna and its chief commentary* (Leiden: Brill, 1974), 426–428.

[39] I. Prasad, *L'Inde du VIIe au XVIe siècle* (Paris: E. de Boccard, 1930), 62–67.

[40] Communication personnelle de M. Philippe Demonsablon, mathématicien.

[41] P. Tannery, *Le traité de Manuel Moschopoulos sur les carrés magiques,* texte grec et traduction, dans *Mémoires scientifiques*, iv, (Toulouse: E. Privat, Paris: Gauthier-Villars, 1920), 27–60.

[42] A. Aubry, 'Les carrés magiques. Aperçu historique', dans E. Cazalas, *Carrés magiques au degré n* (Paris: Hermann, 1934), 7–15.

One has further to emphasize the presence of numerical diagrams among the magical prescriptions of Indian medicine in the medieval period. As early as about AD 900, the treatise on therapy called *Siddhayoga* had already prescribed a magic square of the third order for its eutocic virtue. The mention of the same childbirth charm is also found in the Arabic medical literature as early as AD 850 (*Paradise of Wisdom*).

Chapter 7

On *Mādhavacikitsā*

Johannes Laping

IN HIS VALUABLE TRANSLATION of the *Mādhavanidāna* published in 1974, Meulenbeld put together whatever information was available at that time on the existence of another text of Mādhavakara, namely the *Mādhavacikitsā*.[1] The three MSS known to be in existence at that time are (or were) available in the:[2]

1. Library of H. H. the Maharaja of Bikaner,
2. Bhandarkar Oriental Research Insititute, Poona, and
3. Collection Cordier of the Bibliothèque Nationale of Paris.

During the half-year tenure of a Visiting Fellowship at Utkal University in Bhubaneswar, Orissa, in the winter of 1983–1984, I came across some more information about this text and its author. I am putting together this information for the use of other scholars who are interested in this text.

At present, the manuscript collection of the Orissa State Museum, Bhubaneswar, contains approximately 500 MSS dealing with *āyurveda*. There is only an alphabetical catalogue, edited by Nilamani Mishra, and published already in 1961, to chart these treasures.[3] A descriptive catalogue is now in preparation. Amongst these MSS are numerous ones under the authorship of Mādhavakara, or the titles

[1] G. J. Meulenbeld, *The Mādhavanidāna and its chief commentary. Chapters 1–10. Introduction, translation and notes* (Leiden: Brill, 1974), 8–10.

[2] For exact references, see Meulenbeld, ibid.

[3] *An alphabetical catalogue of Oriya & other manuscripts in the collection of the Orissa State Museum, Bhubaneswar* (Bhubaneswar: Orissa State Museum).

of which are reminiscent of the known works of this author. In the search for MSS of the *Mādhavacikitsā*, I took a close look at a few of those MSS which appeared to contain the *Mādhavacikitsā*. The additional MSS are as follow:

4. Accession no. 'Ay 348'. The authorship has been given by the cataloguer as Mādhava. A clear title for the MS is missing; it has therefore been catalogued in standard form as 'Vaidyaśāstra'.

   Folios 1–180 contain this text which is concluded by an Oriya colophon which gives this title and the author's name as Mādhavakara. The MS contains 48 more folios with a text called *Paryāyamuktāvalī*. The folios measure ca. 36.5 × 3 cm., with 3–6 lines on each side and 50–60 letters to a line. The script is Oriya, the language is Sanskrit and Oriya. It is in a fairly good condition. The Oriya colophon at the end of the whole MS allows us to date it to the year 1713. The MS was recovered from the village Kotapalla in Khurda subdivision, Puri District. The text begins with *raktapitta, rājayakṣma, uraḥkṣatakṣīṇa, kāsa, hikkāśvāsa, svarabheda, aruci, chardi, tṛṣā, mūrccha, madātyaya, dāha, unmāda/bhūtonmāda, apasmāra,* and *vātavyādhi*. To this extent, the serialisation in this MS agrees with P. V. Sharma's analysis of the Poona MS.[4] The MS also contains a descriptive part (*nidāna*) for each disease. At the end of a chapter, the *puṣpikā* is given in the following manner:

   > *iti rogādhikārarugviniścaye ... [name of the disease] ...*
   > *nidānalakṣaṇacikitsā samāptā.*

5. Accession no. 'Ay 373'. The author is given as Mādhavakara, the text is again catalogued under the standard name 'Vaidyaśāstra'.

   The whole MS contains 337 folios, measuring 42.9 × 3.2 cm. It is partly worm-eaten. The script is Oriya, the language is Sanskrit and Oriya. It may have been written during the second half of the eighteenth century. The MS was discovered at the village of Ghoradia, P. S. Brahmagiri, Puri District. The text appears to be a compilation of various materials for the practical use of *vaidyas*. It begins with the quantities required for the preparation of medicines. Only the second half of the MS seems to contain parts of *Mādhavacikitsā*. The list of diseases dealt with in this part of the MS, which can be clearly identified as our text, comprises: *jvarātisāra, atisāra, grahaṇī, arśaḥ, mandajīrṇarogavisūcyālasyavilambikāroga, krimiroga, pāṇḍuroga, raktapitta, rājayakṣma, kāsa, hikkā, śvāsa, svarabheda, arocaka, chardi, tṛṣā,* and *mūrcchā*. This agrees with P. V. Sharma's analysis.[5] The *puṣpikā* at the end of each chapter reads uni-

[4] P.V. Sharma, *Āyurveda kā vaijñānika itihāsa*, 2nd edition, (Benares: 1981), 279.
[5] Ibid.

formly:

> *iti śrīmādhavakaraviracitaṃ rugviniścaye carakādi … [name of disease] … karmavipākanidānapathyāpathyacikitsā samāptam*

The reference to *karmavipāka* and *pathyāpathya* in MS no. 5 described above may be significant. Both the Orissa MSS characteristically also contain the *nidāna*. Whereas the Poona MS (no. 2 above) only contains *cikitsā*. In spite of many efforts, it was not possible for me to study the above two Orissa MSS in detail, nor to compare them with the Poona MS which is easily accessible.

While in Orissa, I obtained information about the existence of a few more MSS of the *Mādhavacikitsā* in that part of India.

6. A paper transcript of an old palm-leaf MS is in the possession of Kaviraj B. Das, Cuttack. I have not myself seen this MS, because at that time he had left it with a senior Sanskrit scholar, Pandit A. T. Sharma of Berhampur, Orissa, for proper editing. According to personal information from Kvj. B. Das, the text is complete from the beginning up to the section on *hṛdroga.* It contains *nidāna* and *cikitsā*, and also *daivavyapāśrayacikitsā.*

7. Another old palm-leaf MS of this text is said to be in the possession of one Mr Barapanda, senior reader at the Gopabandhu Āyurveda College, Puri. I have no further information about this MS and its contents.

There may be quite a few more MSS of the *Mādhavacikitsā* in Orissa. On the whole, Mādhava seems to be very popular in Orissa, and the *Mādhavacikitsā* in particular. From the fact that numerous MSS of the works of Mādhava exist in the state, Mādhavakara is claimed as a 'son of Orissa'. According to Kvj. B. Das, he was a Brahman scholar and physician at the time of the Bhaumakara dynasty of Orissa, which had its capital at what is modern Jajpur, about 40 km north-east of Bhubaneswar. The imperial Bhaumakaras were in power from the early eighth to the early tenth century AD. During this period a transition took place from the Buddhist religion to Śaivism. The surname 'kara' is said to apply in Orissa to Brahmans, Khetriyas and weavers. In Bengal, however, it applies only to the caste of barbers. Epigraphical records of the Bhaumakaras mention patronage given to medical science.

From Dr R. N. Dwivedi, former professor of the Āyurveda College of Benares Hindu University, I learned about the existence of two more MSS of the *Mādhavacikitsā*:

8. in the Rajasthan Oriental Research Institute, Jodhpur, and

9. in the State Library of Jammu, Jammu-Tawi.

No further information about these MSS is available at present.

Most attention has been directed so far towards the Poona MS. One Dr P. Kishore of the C. R. I. (Āy.), Bhubaneswar, has been working on this MS alone. Dr H. S. Pandey, presently director of the Āyurveda College in Puri, is said to be working on the MSS from Poona and Jodhpur (no. 8) under the guidance of Dr R. N. Dwivedi. The Jodhpur MS appears to be a transcript from the Poona MS. Dr D. Wujastyk, London, has drawn my attention to editorial work on the Poona MS done by one Mr K. M. Dugar from Bombay.[6] None of these efforts has been completed and published so far.

I have myself studied in detail only a very small part of the Poona MS, namely the chapter on *krimiroga*. The Poona MS contains only *cikitsā*, and the material found in the chapter on *krimiroga* is not very original. There are parallels with much earlier or slightly later literature such as the *Suśrutasaṃhitā*, the *Siddhasāra*, Vṛnda and Cakradatta.

A detailed concordance concerning this subject will be given in a forthcoming publication on *krimiroga*.

[6] Address: 15 Aljabriya Court, 69 Marine Drive, Bombay 20.

Part II

Colonial interactions

Chapter 8

The relationship of Indian and European practitioners of medicine from the sixteenth century

T. J. S. Patterson

THE EARLIEST CONTACT between Indian and European practitioners of medicine came through the Spice Trade. There had been a demand in Europe for spices from the East since Roman times. The cargoes of spices always contained a high proportion of substances which were used medicinally. From the beginning of the sixteenth century traders from Europe set out to capture a share of this lucrative trade. The Portuguese were the first in India; by 1510 they were established on the west coast, with their capital at Goa. The Dutch followed in 1595, making the centre of their empire in the East Indies. The English East India Company set up its first trading post in India in 1608. With the success of the first English expeditions the import of drugs into England increased markedly: the proportion of drugs imported from outside Europe in 1588 was 14%, in 1621 48% and in 1669 70%, of which the majority had come from India and the East Indies.[1]

From the seventh century AD Arabs trading along the west coast of India had brought about a considerable interchange of medical information. The Arab physicians of the tenth and eleventh centuries had a wide knowledge of Indian medicine, which they incorporated into their writings. These were translated into Latin in the

[1] R. S. Roberts, 'The early history of the import of drugs into Britain', in F. N. L. Poynter, *The evolution of pharmacy in Britain* (London: Pitman Medical, 1965), 165.

thirteenth century and became the standard texts in Europe. In this way some Indian knowledge reached the West in the Middle Ages. But Indian medical works were written in Sanskrit, so that much of this remained unknown in Europe until the end of the eighteenth century, when the first translations into European language were made.[2]

From the ninth century there were Indian physicians at the Arab courts, and some of the features of Arab medicine began to filter back into India. This increased with the repeated Muslim invasions of India, which started in the eleventh century, and continued up to the establishment of the Moghul Empire by Babur in 1526. With the rising power of the Muslims their system of medicine, *yūnānī tibb*, began to compete with *āyurveda*, although there was little conflict between the Hindu and Muslim physicians; each would borrow from the other's pharmacopoeia when necessary. In spite of these interchanges *yūnānī* was the medicine of the ruling class, and came to be the main practice in the cities and in the palaces and courts of noblemen; *āyurveda* continued mainly in country districts and among the poor. This was the position of medicine in India when the European traders arrived at the beginning of the sixteenth century.

The Portuguese in India

In the first half of the sixteenth century little was known in Europe about tropical diseases. The first known European writer on the subject was Garcia d'Orta of Portugal, the most distinguished European physician in the East in the sixteenth century. His *Coloquios dos simples, e drogas he cousas mediçinais da India* . . . , or 'Colloquies on the drugs of India,' printed in Goa in 1563, was the third book printed in India, the earliest on medicine in India, and the first European work on tropical medicine.[3] There were relatively few European physicians in the country, and d'Orta's services were widely in demand. He had a large practice among the rich Indians, and here he came into consultation with the local physicians, from whom he always tried to learn as much as he could of their methods. At these consultations he encountered the same problems that European physicians and surgeons of other nations were later to record: even if an Indian might express a wish to be treated in the European way, his own physicians might oppose this. He might defer to them as the local customs were too strong, but he might also consult d'Orta

[2] S. N. Sen, 'Scientific works in Sanskrit, translated into foreign languages and vice versa in the 18th and 19th century A.D.', *Indian Journal of History of Science*, vii (1972), 44.

[3] C. R. Boxer, *Two pioneers of tropical medicine: Garcia d'Orta and Nicolás Monardes* (London: Wellcome Historical Medical Library, 1963).

in secret. Sometimes d'Orta would find it difficult to persuade his patient that his diagnosis and treatment were preferable to those of the local physicians; it was only to be expected that the local practitioners would have greater experience of local diseases.

Among the prominent members of the Portuguese community there was much praise for Indian physicians, who acquired great prestige by their successful cures, and were granted special privileges. There was clearly a good deal of interchange of medical ideas: d'Orta acknowledged how much he had learned from the Indians by coming to know the Indian physicians well, and discussing clinical problems and drugs with them. He had tried out many of the Indian drugs on himself, and found great benefit from some of them. If he was uncertain about the action of any drug he took the advice of the Brahmins, and he was prepared to transfer his patients to the local practitioners if they were not recovering under his regime. The Indians were also quick to learn from the Portuguese: to be guided by the appearance of the urine, to bleed patients, and to use various European medicines.[4] But by the beginning of the seventeenth century some of the Portuguese physicians were denouncing the Indian doctors as faith-healers, and in 1618 the municipal council of Goa made a decree that nobody could practise medicine or surgery without taking an examination by the Chief Physician and Surgeon. They also limited the number of Hindu practitioners to thirty. It seems that the licence to practise was for European medicine only.[5]

The Dutch in the East Indies

The most distinguished Dutch physician in the East in the seventeenth century was Jacobus Bontius (1592–1631), although his works were not published until 1658 in Amsterdam, and only translated into English in 1769. He made a comprehensive study of tropical conditions and tropical diseases, discussing living standards and the health and hygiene of Europeans in the tropics. He studied local plants and their medical properties, and added many new drugs to the pharmacopoeia, extolling the herbal knowledge of the local women; if he himself was ill, he would 'rather trust himself to one of them . . . '.[6]

[4]D. V. S. Reddy, 'Medicine in India in the middle of the XVI century', *Bulletin of the History of Medicine*, viii (1940), 61.

[5]J. M. de Figueiredo, 'Ayurvedic medicine in Goa according to European sources in the sixteenth and seventeenth centuries', *Bulletin of the History of Medicine*, lviii (1984), 225.

[6]D. Schoute, *Occidental therapeutics in the Netherlands East Indies during three centuries of Netherland settlement (1600–1900)* (Batavia: Neth. Indies Publ. Hlth. Serv., 1937).

The English East India Company

For the first half of the seventeenth century the numbers of the English East India Company in India were relatively small. Their trading activities were concentrated on the coast, and they had little contact with people inland. Any contacts were superficial because of the language barrier. Their factories were often poorly manned and difficult to defend; they had to obtain the favour of the local rulers for trading facilities, and, at first, for protection. They had little experience of living and working in tropical conditions, and, at first, they brought their European habits with them: they continued to wear heavy uniforms and ceremonial dress, they insisted on eating huge meals of animal protein, and, a major problem for all time in India, they drank alcohol in even larger quantities than at home – not only from the impressive stores that they brought with them, but also various local brews, which were not only very potent but also toxic. It was soon recognised that these were all powerful factors in inducing and exacerbating tropical diseases, and comparisons were made with the lightly clad Hindu, who could carry heavy loads in the heat, who lived abstemiously on vegetables, and, in the higher castes, was forbidden alcohol. There were many exhortations to the Europeans to modify their habits, and there were frequent edicts, but with little effect. These warnings were reinforced by the chaplains who were impressed by the piety of the Hindus, and urged the men to copy their example.

The early traders faced formidable medical problems, and, at first, they were eager to learn anything they could from the local medical practitioners.[7] The merchants' accounts recorded incidental medical details, but this was mostly at the level of folk medicine – the local remedies that were used for the local diseases – and the remedies that they had tried out on themselves and found effective. John Marshall, a factor in Bengal 1668–77, gave an accurate account of Hindu medicine which he had learned from local practitioners in Pattana. He was not a doctor, but a trader in an isolated post, and he seems to have had very little access to any European medical advice. He gave many examples of local prescriptions, often of multiple ingredients, as purges, and for the treatment of stone, snake and scorpion bites, fevers, wounds and bruises, toothache, colic, French pox, disorders of the guts, sore eyes, gout, worms, barbers, ague, dropsy and epilepsy. He had tried a number of these himself, and he noted which of them 'probate per J. M. to bee good'.[8] Mis-

[7]K. K. Roy, 'Early relations between the British and Indian medical systems', in *Proceedings of the XXIII International Congress of the History of Medicine* (London: Wellcome Institute of the History of Medicine, 1974), i, 697.

[8]Shafaat Ahmad Khan (ed.), *John Marshall in India: notes and observations in Bengal, 1668–1672* (London: OUP, 1927).

sionaries also brought about important medical contacts in the early days. They carried medicines, and they took the trouble to learn the local languages.

All the trading companies sent out surgeons with their expeditions, but they had little experience of tropical diseases, and they brought their European methods with them: heroic bleeding and purging, and the excessive use of mercury. Slowly they recognised that this treatment could only be survived by a full-blooded soldier newly arrived from home, and that it was very dangerous for the emaciated, yellowing merchant who had been any length of time in the tropics. When they began to treat Indians, they found that they also withstood this regime very poorly. The early trading posts were often short of surgeons, who died as often as their patients, and it took at least a year before a replacement could arrive from Europe. This shortage led to the employment of Indian physicians where necessary, and this became official policy for the English East India Company in the first half of the seventeenth century. The English authorities in India even went so far as to suggest that English surgeons might not be necessary, if local practitioners were available.

They were also short of European drugs, which were often lost or damaged on the voyage out, or decayed in the heat. They set out to learn as much as they could about local drugs from the Indian practitioners, and they studied the local plants for their medicinal properties. It became the policy of the English Company that Indian diseases were best treated by Indian methods. The budgets from the early times always included an allowance for 'country' medicines. Towards the end of the seventeenth century Company physicians and surgeons, such as John Fryer and Samuel Browne, began to make extensive collections of Indian medicinal plants, sending the plants and their seeds to James Petiver for his collection formed for the Royal Society.[9]

Faced with a continuing high mortality the Europeans noticed that Indians were relatively immune to some of the local diseases. This led to the policy of 'indianisation': the attempt to make the blood of the European more like that of the Indian, and so make him more resistant to Indian disease. This had been started by the Portuguese, by bleeding their men, and then feeding them exclusively on Indian food. The English at first copied this idea, but only starved their men, without bleeding, before filling them up with local food. But there were soon objections to this practice when it was found that Europeans were more resistant to injury than Indians, and that their wounds healed more quickly.[10]

---

[9] J. Petiver, 'An account of some Indian plants', *Philosophical Transactions of the Royal Society of London*, xx (1698), 313.

[10] N. Chevers, 'Surgeons in India – past and present', *Calcutta Review*, xxiii (1854), 217.

The eighteenth century

By the end of the seventeenth century the English, with their greater sea-power, had defeated both the Portuguese and the Dutch. As they became more powerful their dependence on Indians and Indian medicine began to change. They had always found it hard to distinguish between trained *āyurvedic* and *yūnānī* physicians and the much larger numbers of practitioners of folk-medicine, regarding them all as part of one system. The dramatic and extravagant behaviour of the folk-practitioners played a part in the increasingly poor opinion of Indian medicine in general that developed towards the end of the seventeenth century. They were also puzzled by the Indian concern for the health of animals compared to their carelessness of human life, with the provision of hospitals for animals of all sorts, but none for humans. The travellers who reached India by sea landed in the area of Surat and Cambay, where the Jain religion was predominant, and they assumed that this pattern extended over the whole of India. With increasing experience of tropical diseases the English became increasingly scornful of Indian medicine. John Fryer, the most distinguished physician in the East India Company in the seventeenth century, was in India for nine years from 1673. In his account, published in 1698, he gave a full description of Indian medicine, which he had learned from local practitioners, but he was very critical of what he regarded as their 'ignorance and malpractice'.[11]

In the eighteenth century the English (now the British) East India Company steadily increased its military and political power, defeating the French on land by 1762, and becoming the largest and most powerful trading company in the East. For the greater part of the eighteenth century most Europeans were contemptuous of Indian medicine and science. Indian medicine continued on traditional lines, and there was no longer any enthusiasm to learn from it. Contact with Indian physicians was now mainly at Courts of rulers and the houses of noblemen, who requested consultation with European practitioners, particularly when some surgical operation was required, for the Indians had no general surgeons at this time. The head of a princely house would have several physicians on his staff, *āyurvedic* and *yūnānī*, and often a number of European physicians and surgeons.

The wars with the French in India from 1740 led the Company to develop a regular army with a regular medical service. In 1764 the medical officers in Bengal were organised into the Bengal Medical Service, followed by similar arrangements in Madras and Bombay. This was the start of the Indian Medical Service, which

[11]John Fryer, *A new account of East India and Persia, being nine years' travels, 1672–1681, edited . . . by William Crooke* (London: Haklyut Society, 1909–15).

continued until Independence in 1947. For its armies the Company began to recruit Indians, and Company surgeons became responsible for their health – the first time that Europeans had had direct medical care of Indians in any number. The first hospital, opened in Madras in 1664, was for Europeans only. The first hospital for Indians (for soldiers in the Company's service only) was not opened until 1760, and the first for Indian civilians in 1792. These civilian hospitals were often founded by individual Company surgeons.

There had always been unofficial training schemes for Indians employed with the Company's medical services. At first this was the work of individual surgeons, who would teach Indians the rudiments of nursing and pharmaceutical techniques. They were mostly employed as nurses and dressers, and, later, as compounders of drugs. When trained, they were given responsibility for much of the day-to-day care of patients. There were many tributes to their skill and good service, particularly as nurses. After a period in a hospital, a competent dresser or compounder would be given a certificate of proficiency by the surgeon-in-charge, and his name would then be added to the payroll, and he became eligible for a pension on the same terms as other Company employees. With recruitment of increasing numbers of Indian troops it became necessary to employ Indian dressers for attachment to each native regiment. Most of the sepoys were high-caste Hindus, whose rules forbade them to accept food or drugs that had been handled by a European. Each native battalion, therefore, had one or more 'Black Doctors' (as they were officially called) to prepare and administer the drugs prescribed by the European medical officer.

The Enlightenment

The period from the late eighteenth century to the early part of the nineteenth was a time of great social, political and industrial change in Europe. There was a sudden interest in Indian history and culture. Sanskrit works, particularly on astronomy, mathematics and medicine, were translated into European languages for the first time. Stimulated by Sir William Jones, who was in Calcutta from 1783–1794, Europeans learned with astonishment of the antiquity of Indian culture, its science and its medicine. Jones urged that there was a great deal to be learned from Indian medicine, and that its herbs and drugs should be collected and studied. There was a general revival of interest in Indian medicine, at a time when Europeans had nothing new to offer for the treatment of tropical diseases. This enthusiasm for Indian medicine led many Europeans in India to consult the local practitioners about their own diseases – it being reasoned that the Indians had far greater experience of tropical diseases than a surgeon newly out from England. It became official Company policy to require its surgeons to note any treatment by an

Indian that might be useful. If anything strange or unknown cropped up in medical or veterinary practice no treatment was to be undertaken until the local authorities had been consulted, and the local remedy evaluated. The necessary drugs and herbs were to be collected, so that they could be sent into the general hospitals for clinical trial. If successful, the Company undertook to publish and circulate the results, so that new methods would be widely diffused. This was the time of the start of the great botanical collections by Company surgeons and others, and the ordering of this knowledge into the first Indian pharmacopoeias. The publication of this botanical knowledge, and the correspondence between interested collectors, led to the formation of the first medical societies and the publication of the first medical journals.[12]

Inoculation (with human material) against smallpox had long been practised in India. Holwell, in his account to the College of Physicians in 1767, said 'since time out of mind', and he commended the Indian technique and its success.[13] Lymph for vaccination (cow-pox) reached India in 1802. But there was considerable resistance. The people felt that if they were exempt from smallpox their cattle would get it. The higher castes and their families objected to any treatment from another caste, or, worse, from a European. Vigorous programmes were set up to train high-caste Indian vaccinators, and to start by convincing the chiefs and respected elders in the villages.

There was very little surgery practised by Indians at this time. Indian surgery, which had been so highly developed under Suśruta (*c.* 100 BC), had steadily declined since then, persisting in scattered families, handing down a particular craft from father to son, often in conditions of great secrecy. There were three of these operations in particular: cutting for stone, couching for cataract and grafting skin for deformities of the face. The technique of cutting for stone was the 'low lithotomy', also well known in Europe from the earliest times. The cataract operation was the one that had been described by Suśruta. In the early part of the nineteenth century Company surgeons regarded it as worth studying, with a view to training simple practitioners to carry out the procedure in areas where no European skills were available. The results could be very satisfactory, but there was a high rate of complications, and the method was superseded by techniques introduced from Europe. In the third operation, skin grafting, the Indians showed great skill, and

[12] A. Neelameghan, *Development of medical societies and medical periodicals in India 1780 to 1920* (Calcutta: Oxford Book & Stationary Co., 1963).

[13] J. Z. Holwell, *An account of the manner of Inoculating for the Small Pox in the East Indies* . . . (London: Becket and De Hondt, 1767). Reproduced in *Indian science and technology in the eighteenth century: some contemporary European accounts*, edited by Dharampal, (Delhi: Impex India, 1971), 143–163.

reports of their success, which reached Europe towards the end of the eighteenth century, were the starting point for the modern speciality of plastic surgery.

This renewed interest in Indian medicine was part of a general feeling that such an advanced state of Indian civilisation should not be interfered with. Europeans should leave it alone, but learn all they could from it. As part of this policy the East India Company set up, towards the end of the eighteenth century, colleges and medical schools for Indians to study the sciences, including medicine, in the vernaculars. Most of the teachers were from the Company's medical service. The course was for three years, with teaching in Sanskrit and Urdu, and clinical training at the general hospitals.

Westernisation

During the first half of the nineteenth century, however, the drive for 'westernisation,' both secular and religious, had been growing. The only course for India was thought to lie in abandoning Indian ways, and arranging for all education to be on western lines. This resulted in a complete reversal of the earlier liberal attitude of Europeans to Indian culture, including medicine. In 1833 the Grant Committee reported that the Indian medical colleges should be abolished, and all support for Indian medicine withdrawn. Only western medicine should be taught, and all teaching should be in English. This was reinforced by the adoption of English as the official language of India in 1835. Increasing numbers of medical schools were then set up on western lines, and in 1839 the first Indian students graduated from the new Calcutta medical school. These medical schools were designed primarily to turn out medical officers of subordinate grade for the army. The first Indian universities were founded in 1857, but there was relative neglect of the teaching of science, and Indians complained that there were very limited facilities for independent research.

After 1835 there was no official support for Indian medicine. There was some support by individuals, and small local schemes were set up to make use of Indian practitioners, when it was realised that theirs was the only medicine that could reach many of the villages. But these schemes carried no general or official support, and most Europeans became increasingly opposed to Indian medicine. Teaching of Indian medicine was now confined entirely within the family. The middle and richer classes of Indians came to make increasing demands for modern medicine.[14]

[14] William Campbell Maclean, *Diseases in tropical climates: lectures delivered at the Army Medical School* (London: Macmillan, 1886).

The practitioners of Indian medicine were following the same lines as the classical authors of a thousand years before, but were responsible for the treatment of the greater part of the population, particularly in the rural areas. This treatment could be expensive, and although the poor might prefer Indian medicine they often had to accept free treatment and attendance from Europeans. Between 1912 and 1917 a number of Medical Acts set up Medical Councils in the various provinces, and laid down qualifications for registration of medical practitioners which excluded traditional physicians, and made it illegal for a registered practitioner to be associated with Indian medicine.[15]

The establishment of Indian medicine

But from 1920 increasing Indian nationalism began to carry Indian medicine with it. The Government of Madras set up the first Committee on Indigenous Systems of Medicine in 1923. In 1944 the Bhore Committee – the Health Survey and Development Committee – was set up to look at the future of the health services. Its recommendations, in 1946, only dealt with modern medicine. But support for Indian medicine had been steadily increasing, and the Bhore report was widely criticised. As a result of this, the Committee on Indigenous Systems of Medicine (under Col. Sir R. N. Chopra) was set up, reporting in 1948. It urged support for Indian medicine and its integration with western medicine, particularly to teach the student those aspects of western medicine that were not part of Indian medicine. The committee was asked to go further and consider the synthesis of all the medical systems of India. They concluded that such a synthesis would not be easy, and would be time-consuming, but that it was not only possible, but practicable and essential. In 1969 the Central Council for Research in Indian Medicine and Homeopathy was established with particular responsibility for the evaluation and standardisation of traditional drugs. In 1971 the Central Council of Indian Medicine was set up to regulate the standards of education and to control practice in the traditional systems. Since then the various systems of Indian medicine – *āyurveda* and *siddha*, *yūnānī*, homeopathy, yoga and naturopathy – have had official support, with Central Government and local State funds, in parallel with modern (European) medicine.

[15]Patrick Hehir, *The medical profession in India* (London: Oxford Medical Publishers, 1923).

Chapter 9

'A Pious Fraud': The Indian claims for pre-Jennerian smallpox vaccination

Dominik Wujastyk

ONE OF THE GREATEST TRIUMPHS of medical science in recent times has been the final eradication of smallpox. This was achieved through the widespread use of vaccination, a procedure discovered and promoted by Edward Jenner (1749–1823), whose name will forever be remembered as that of one of mankind's foremost benefactors. The discovery of vaccination was published by Jenner in 1798 in his epoch-making book *An inquiry into the causes and effects of the Variolæ Vaccinæ*. The story of Jenner's discovery has often been told: in essence, his insight was as follows.

It was well known before Jenner's time that *inoculation* against smallpox could provide immunity to the disease. A person would be infected with the smallpox virus, through a scratch in the skin, and after suffering a mild dose of the disease, would be immune to further infection. Smallpox inoculation – this deliberate infection of a person with a the smallpox virus – has a long and interesting history in the Orient, and was brought to England from Constantinople by Lady Mary Wortley Montague in 1717. Although effective, it was a dangerous and controversial procedure, because the inoculated person could develop a more serious and even lethal case of smallpox. It was also dangerous because the inoculated person, even if suffering only a mild attack himself, was still very infectious to others. Thus, unless the simultaneous inoculation of a whole locality could be coordinated, the infection could spread inadvertently, causing a genuine epidemic.

Jenner's unique contribution was to notice that a person inoculated with the cow-pox virus, instead of smallpox, would develop a mild case of cow-pox, and recover a few days later. But this person would then be immune to smallpox, although strangely not to cow-pox itself. Cow-pox was a harmless disease, whose symptoms were a rash and a slight fever. It was commonly caught by milkmaids from spots on the udders of cows. For this reason Jenner coined the term 'vaccination,' from the Latin *vacca*, 'a cow'. Since Jenner's discovery, vaccination has spread all over the world, giving today's total freedom from the terrible scourge of smallpox.

Imagine, then, the astonishment of a doctor visiting Sri Lanka in late 1984 who, while browsing through the tourist brochures in his hotel room, came across the following tidbit of medical history:[1]

> The earliest documents of Indian medicine are found in the Vedas (Books of Knowledge) compiled at least as early as 1000 B.C. To quote one example of the precedent nature of this knowledge, cowherds on the subcontinent were practising a kind of immunization against smallpox long before Jenner – as the following text from the Book of Dhanwantari indicates:
>
> "Take the fluid of the pock on the udder of the cow ... upon the point of a lancet, and lance with it the arms between the shoulders and elbows until the blood appears; then, mixing the fluid with the blood, the fever of a mild form of small pox will be produced."

The passage cited quite clearly describes vaccination, as opposed to inoculation. If true, it would seriously undermine Jenner's historic reputation, and upturn one of the most cherished facts in the history of medicine.

It might be tempting to dismiss the passage out of hand: after all, tourist brochures are not famous for their verity. But the above citation is by no means the first time pre-Jennerian vaccination has been claimed for India. The author of the above passage also raised the same point at an international conference in Sri Lanka in 1982,[2] but the claims go back almost as far as vaccination itself, and fascinating public debates on the subject took place between prominent physicians in several newspapers and journals throughout the nineteenth and early twentieth centuries. The reason that so many eminent men allowed themselves to become embroiled in the question is that from the earliest appearance of the claim it has been accompanied by several quotations in the Sanskrit language, attributed to an ancient medical author, clearly describing vaccination. Furthermore, these Sanskrit

[1]Personal communication from Dr W. Gordon (26/2/1985), whose experience this was. The brochure in question is unfortunately no longer traceable, but Dr Gordon had the presence of mind to copy out the passage cited, from an article by Sanjiva Wijesinghe.

[2]The Edinburgh College Conference. Personal communication (16/11/1982) from Professor C. B. Perry, Chairman of the Jenner Trust.

passages appear in authoritative dictionaries and reference books, lending support to the idea that vaccination is indeed part of India's ancient science. What then is the truth behind these claims, and how did the idea of pre-Jennerian smallpox vaccination in India develop? Let us first trace the growth of the idea, and then analyse the trustworthiness of its roots. Finally we shall speculate on some possible reasons for the birth of the idea.

Calvi Virumbon and the *Madras Courier* of 1819

The main origin of the idea that vaccination was known to ancient Indian medicine is a newspaper article which appeared in the *Madras Courier* on Tuesday January 12th 1819. Copies of this issue of the *Madras Courier* are almost unobtainable today. After extensive searching a single damaged copy was located in the library of the Asiatic Society of Bombay and; through the kindness of the Society's librarian, a microfilm copy of this is now deposited in the library of the Wellcome Institute in London. The article in question, written as a letter to the editor, is signed 'Calvi Virumbon,' and dated 2nd January 1819.

The author of the letter began with a discussion of what the 'works in general use among the Hindu Medical Practitioners' had to say about spasmodic cholera, an epidemic of which had recently afflicted Madras. Virumbon claimed that the then modern treatment of that disease, 'if not borrowed from the Hindus, is closely correspondent with that indicated in their medical writing.' He supported his claim with quotations from Sanskrit, Tamil and Telugu texts, describing the preparation of medicinal compounds to combat the symptoms of spasmodic cholera.[3]

After this discussion, Calvi Virumbon turned to the matter of smallpox vaccination, which interests us here. His words, quoted in full, were as follow:

> As my examination of the Vaidya Sástras has been casual and may never be repeated, I shall here notice a fact, which will add another to

[3]Virumbon said he was citing a work called *Chintámani* (i.e., *Cintāmaṇi*) by Dhanvantari, with a Telugu commentary. The only works which might fit this description are the *Yogacintāmaṇi* attributed to Dhanvantari in some manuscripts, e.g., Bhandarkar Oriental Research Institute, Pune, India, MS 371/1882-83 (*Descriptive catalogue of ... manuscripts*, xvi, no. 157) and Harṣakīrti's *Yogacintāmaṇi*. No copy of the former work was accessible to me, but the catalogue describes a short, undistinguished work on *āyurveda*. Harṣakīrti's work has many recensions, and the verses Virumbon quotes do not appear in the editions available to me. Virumbon attributed the Tamil passages to one text called *Yugamuni Chintámani* (probably *Yūkimuni Cintāmaṇi* – GJM), and another called *Careisel-munmúru* (probably *Karical-munnūṟu* – GJM) which is attributed to Agastiyer (i.e., Agastya). He also referred to a myth which 'is to be read, either in Sanscrit or Tamil, in the Jayána-Vásish'tam.'

the many proofs of the truth of the Wise man's adage, that – "There is nothing new under the Sun." It is that the Inoculation for the Cow-Pox was known of old time to the Hindu Medical writers. To substantiate this statement, it is necessary only to refer to the *Sactéya Grantham*, attributed to Dhanwantari, and, therefore, undoubtedly an ancient composition. In this work, after describing nine several species of the Small-pox, of which three (one, A´lábhi, being the confluent kind) are declared incurable, the Author proceeds to lay down the rules for the practice of inoculation; from this part the following extracts are taken, of the first of which the original is given in the English character for the satisfaction of the Sanscrit Scholar, and of the other for the sake of brevity translations only.

TEXT.

D,hénu stanya ma'súchì va Naránàn cha ma'súchicà.
Taj jalam báhumúlàt cha `sastrán téna grĭhitavàn.
Báhumúlè cha `sastráni rect' òtpatti caráni cha.
Taj jalam ṙecta militam spótaca jwara samb,havah.

Translation.

Take the fluid of the pock on the udder of a Cow, or on the arm between the shoulder and elbow of a human subject, on the point of a lancet, and lance with it the arms between the shoulders and elbow until the blood appears; then mixing the fluid with the blood, the fever of the Small-Pox will be produced.

Translation.

The Small-Pox produced by the fluid from the udder of a Cow, (Góstany' òdacam) will be of the same gentle nature as the original disease, not attended by fear, nor requiring medicine; the diet may be according to the pleasure of the patient, who may be inoculated once only, or two, three, four, five, or six times. The pock when perfect should be of a good colour, filled with a clear liquid, and surrounded by a circle of red. There will, then, be no fear of the Small-Pox as long as life endures. When inoculated with the fluid from the udder of a Cow, some will have a slight fever for one day, two, or three days, and with the fever there will sometimes be a slight cold fit. The fever will, also be attended by a round swelling in the arm-pits and the other symptoms of the Small-Pox, but all of a very mild nature. There will be no danger, and the whole will disappear in three days.

I am, Sir,

Your obedient servant,
Madras, 2d January, 1819. CALVI VIRUMBON.

Within months, Virumbon's letter was reported in the *Asiatic Journal*, a London publication, under the heading 'Traces of vaccination in Hindoo medical writers'.[4] The editor of the *Asiatic Journal* noted that the former part of Virumbon's letter 'contains a learned exposition of the *spasmodic cholera* ... [which], though exceedingly curious, we cannot at present find room to insert. The subject incidentally introduced merits all the prominence it will receive by being detached.' Virumbon's passage concerning vaccination, as given above, was then reproduced in full, thus bringing the news to Europe.

Two years after that, the report was cited as authoritative by Henri Marie Husson in an article on vaccination in the *Dictionaire des sciences médicales*, a major survey of the state of medical knowledge in France at that time. Husson had the following to say about the history of vaccination:[5]

> On vient de découvrir dans le *Sancteya Grantham*, ouvrage shanscrit, attribué à d'Hauvantori, ouvrage, par conséquent, très-ancien, des preuves que l'inoculation de la vaccine était connue des auteurs indous, qui, dans les temps reculés, ont écrit sur la médecine. L'auteur décrit neuf espèces de petites véroles, dont il reconnaît que trois sont incurables. Il indique les règles suivantes à observer pour l'inoculation:
>
> "Prenez le fluide du bouton du pis d'une vache ou du bras d'un homme entre l'épaule et le coude sur la pointe d'une lancette, et piquez-en les bras entre l'épaule et le coude jusqu'à ce que le sang paraisse, le fluide se mêlant avec le sang, il en résultera la fièvre de la petite vérole.
>
> "La petite vérole produite par le fluide tiré du bouton du pis de la vache, sera aussi bénigne que la maladie naturelle. Elle ne doit pas occasioner d'alarmes, et n'exigera pas de traitement médical. Le malade suivra la diète qui lui conviendra; il pourra ètre inoculé une seule fois ou deux, trois, quatre, cinq et six fois. Le bouton, pour ètre parfait, doit ètre d'une bonne couleur, rempli d'un liquide clair et entouré d'un cercle rouge; on ne doit pas craindre alors d'ètre attaqué de la petite vérole pendant tout le reste de la vie.

---

[4] *The Asiatic journal and monthly register for British and foreign India, China, and Australia* (July 1819), 27f.

[5] *Dictionaire des sciences médicales*, edited by F. P. Chaumeton and F. V. Mérat de Vaumartoise, (Paris: C. L. F. Panckoucke, 1812–1822), lvi (1821), 391f.

> "Quand l'inoculation a lieu par le fluide provenu du bouton du pis d'une vache, quelques personnes ont une fièvre légère pendant deux ou trois jours, et quelquefois il s'y joint un léger accès de frisson.
>
> "La fièvre est aussi accompagnée de gonflemens ronds aux aisselles, et d'autres symptômes de la petite vérole, mais d'une nature très-bénigne. Il n'y a aucun danger, et le tout disparaît en trois jours."

This is a direct, though unacknowledged, translation of Virumbon's letter to the *Madras Courier*. The mistakes of '*Sancteya*' for '*Sactéya*' and 'd'Hauvantori' for 'Dhanwantari' suggest that the report may be at second hand, although the first may be an an attraction to 'sancta,' suggesting a Hindu holy book, and the second is a natural reaction of a French speaker to a proper name beginning with the non-phonemic initial /dh/.

The author of the *Dictionaire* article continued with two further items of interest concerning Asiatic smallpox. The first concerned Nawaub Mirza Mehady Ali Khan's report of vaccination in Bengal before Jenner's time, and the second related a story about vaccination amongst the peasants of Persia.

A Brahmin from Oude and a Doctor of Bisnopore

The story told by Nawaub Mirza Mehady Ali Khan first appeared in the *Asiatic Annual Register* of 1804, under the title, 'Curious Discovery on the Antiquity of Vaccination in India'.[6] In introducing the story, the editor of the journal stated that he was presenting a 'translation of a written memorandum from the Nawaub Mirza Mehady Ali Khan,' for the attention of those who had the 'opportunity and ability' to investigate the matter further. The Nawab, he claimed, had long been resident at Benares. The editor, who took the memorandum at its face value as proof of pre-Jennerian vaccination, was much exercised by the difficulty of reconciling what he called the 'modern degeneracy' and 'predjudices' of the Indian character, with their great scientific achievements in ancient times. Ironically, he attributed the 'neglect' with which he felt classical Indian learning was treated to the influence of 'foreign sway' in India: presumably he meant pre-British foreign sway. To be fair, however, Macaulay's Minute was still thirty years off, and in 1804 British opinion still strongly favoured traditional learning in India. The full text of the Nawab's memorandum ran as follows:

---

[6] *The Asiatic Annual Register, or, a view of the history of Hindustan, and of the politics, commerce and literature of Asia*, edited by Lawrence Dundas Campbell, (1804), 98f.

Translation of a written Memorandum from
the Nawaub Mirza Mehady Ali Khan

During the period of my abode in the district of Benares, my eldest son being taken ill of a bad kind of the small pox, and my friends interesting themselves for my comfort and his relief, one of them, named Slookum Chund, a Hindu, pointed out to me that there was in the city of Benares, one Alep Choby, a Brahmin from Oude, whose practice was chiefly confined to this malady. Him, therefore, I lost no time in sending for to the town of Gahzeepoor, where I dwelt; and he arrived on the ninth day of the eruption; on seeing which, he observed that if the eruption had not taken place he would have endeavoured to facilitate and render it easy; but that now it was too late. On asking Choby what his process was, he said, "From the matter of the pustule on the cow, I keep a thread drenched, which enables me, at pleasure, to cause an easy eruption on any child; adoring, at the same time, Bhowanny, (who is otherwise called Debee, Mata, and Seetla, and who has the direction of this malady) as well in my own person as by causing the father of the child to perform the like ceremonies; after which, I run the drenched string into a needle, and, drawing it through between the skin and flesh of the child's upper arm, leave it there, performing the same operation in both arms, which, always ensures an easy eruption; on the first appearance of which the child's father or guardian renews his worship to Bhowanny; and as the animal this goddess rides on, is an ass, it is customary for such parent or guardian to fill his lap with grain, which an ass is sent to eat up – which observances ensure the propitious direction of Bhowanny, so that only a very few pustules make their appearance; nor does any one die under this process!" Thus far did I learn from Alep Choby.

Upon referring on this subject to a native, well versed in the learning and customs of the Hindus, he told me that the practice thus described by Choby was not general among them; but confined to those who were attached to the worship of Bhowanny and adored her with implicit faith; and upon my asking the person, whether he was aware how the matter of the pustule got from the cow, and whether all cows had such pustules, or only those of a certain description? he answered, that on these points he possessed no information; but had certainly understood that the cows had these pustules break out on them, and that from the matter thereof children were infected; acknowledging, however, that he spoke not this much from ocular knowledge, but from report.

This report, appearing in 1804, predates the *Madras Courier* letter by fifteen years, and seems to be independent of it. However, the evidence is suspicious because the method of vaccination using a thread was that specifically used by the British.[7] The mixture of genuine vaccination with the various practices associated with the worship of the goddess strongly suggests a native inoculator who has been taught the new practice of vaccination.

The above report may be related in some way to another report that was published by Shoolbred the following year, since both reports emanated almost simultaneously from the Bengal Presidency:[8]

> An old Bramin of Barrasset, very well learned, looked over several Shanscrit books, but he could not find that the disorder called *Gow Bussunt*, or cow small-pox, was capable of being communicated; nor could he find that any of the *Dhununturries* ever considered it to have been applicable to the prevention of small-pox.
>
> The doctors and all old men of Bowannypore say, that they never heard such a thing in their lives. Two of the doctors carefully looked over the *great* medical book, called *Neydan*, but they could not find any where, that it was ever considered by any of the *Chickutchucks* in former times as capable of being communicated to the human subject.
>
> A farmer, about fifty years old, residing in the district of Burdwan, says, that about fifteen years ago all his cows and bullocks were affected with this disorder, and they all died, except one of the cows who had the disorder on the teats only; when a Doctor of Bisnopore, having heard that all his cows and bullocks were dying by the *gow bussunt*, came to his house, and after living three days at his house (until the disorder on the teats was ripened) he took the *peeb* out of the *gow bussunt* on a little bit of cotton, saying, that he would innoculate a child of a great man with it, as it would not put him into the danger of the small-pox, but a very strong fever for three days, and thereby he would be freed from the danger of the small-pox while he would live.

As Shoolbred said, this report contained 'something both for and against the probability of the vaccine disease being known in India.' With characteristic scepticism,

[7] See, e.g., John Shoolbred, *Report on the progress of vaccine inoculation in Bengal, from the period of its introduction in November, 1802, to the end of the year 1803: with an appendix submitted to the medical board at Fort William*, reprint of the Calcutta 1804 edition, (London: Blacks and Parry, 1805), 87.

[8] Schoolbred, *Report on the progress of vaccine*, 59f.

he added that, 'It is more than probable ... that the above account ... was suggested by the questions of the person who made the enquiry.' However, both these reports stand as puzzles in the history of vaccination, although it must be noted that they both postdate the introduction of vaccine into India, and are probably, for reasons outlined at the end of this essay, to be considered the products either of conscious vaccination propaganda or of early rumours or reports of the new method of vaccination.

Bruce on the Persian evidence

The second item of interest referred to by the *Dictionaire*, about vaccination among the peasants of Persia, goes back to a letter from a W. Bruce, translated in Gay-Lussac's *Annales de chimie et de physique*,[9] earlier published in *The Asiatic Journal* for June 1819, though written originally in March 1813.[10] The *Asiatic Journal* version was as follows:[11]

Cow-pox in Persia – similar Disease in Milch Sheep
Extract of a letter from W. Bruce, Esq. resident at Bushire,
to W. Erskine, Esq. of Bombay.

> "When I was in Bombay, I mentioned to you that the cow-pox was well known in Persia by the Eliaats, or wandering tribes. Since my return here I have made very particular inquiries on this subject amongst several tribes who visit this place in the winter to sell the produce of their flocks, such as carpets, rugs, butter, cheese, &c. Their flocks during this time are spread over the low country to graze. Every Eliaat that I have spoken to on this head, of at least six or seven different tribes, has uniformly told me, that the people who are employed to milk the cattle caught a disease, which, after having once had, they were perfectly safe from the small-pox. That this disease was prevalent among the cows, and showed itself particularly on the teats, but that it was more prevalent among and more frequently caught from the sheep. Now this is a circumstance that has never, I believe, before been known; and of the truth of it I have not the smallest doubt, as the persons of whom

[9] *Annales de chimie et de physique*, edited by Joseph Gay-Lussac, Dominique François Jean Arago, et al., (1819), 330–331.

[10] The *Annales* provide the date of the letter, noting that it was published in the *Mémoires de la Société de Bombay*. This can hardly refer to the *Asiatic Journal*, and the letter must therefore have first appeared in a Bombay publication, though it is not known which at present.

[11] *Asiatic Journal* (1819), 646f.

> I inquired could have no interest in telling me a falsehood; and it is not likely that every one whom I spoke to should agree in deceiving, for I have asked at least some forty or fifty persons. To be more sure on the subject, I made more particular inquiries of a very respectable farmer who lives about 14 miles from this, by name Malilla (whom Mr. Babington knows very well), and who is under some obligations to me; this man confirmed very thing that the Eliaats had told me, and further said, that the disease was very common all over the country, and that his own sheep often had it. There may be one reason for the Eliaats saying that they caught the infection oftener from the sheep than the cow, which is, that most of the butter, ghee, cheese, etc. is made from sheep's milk, and that the black cattle yield very little, being more used for draught than anything else."

It is certainly not impossible that these shepherds could have evolved for themselves a working method of vaccination. After all, the milkmaids of Gloucestershire had done exactly this in the late eighteenth century, and it was an acquaintance with this fact that had originally spurred Jenner to investigate the phenomenon. As Baron described:[12]

> He [the young Jenner] was pursuing his professional education in the house of his master at Sodbury: a young country-woman came to seek advice; the subject of small-pox was mentioned in her presence; she immediately observed, "I cannot take that disease, for I have had cow-pox." This incident riveted the attention of Jenner. It was the first time that the popular notion, which was not at all uncommon in the district, had been brought home to him with force and influence.

However, it would have to be established reliably that the disease of cow-pox was present naturally in Persia at the time in question, and perhaps even today.

French and Italian encyclopaedias

The French *Dictionaire des sciences médicales*, quoted above (p. 125), was the first of a rash of Medical encyclopaedias published in France in the first half of the nineteenth century, which sought to reproduce in the field of medicine the success which Diderot and the other Encyclopédistes had achieved in the previous century with

[12] John Baron, *The life of Edward Jenner with illustrations of his doctrines, and selections from his correspondence* (London: H. Colburn, 1827), 121f.

the controversial but highly successful *Encyclopédie.*[13] In common with the practice of all Encyclopédistes, the writers of later works copied a great deal of material from their predecessors. In this way, Virumbon's report about vaccination in ancient Indian texts was propagated through a whole series of works in French and Italian, throughout the nineteenth century. Thus, from Husson's article in the *Dictionaire des sciences médicales* of 1821 it was natural that the report would also appear in the fifteen volume abridgement of the *Dictionaire* which began to appear even before the sixtieth and last volume of the *Dictionaire* itself was published. The *Dictionaire abrégé des sciences médicales* noted that:[14]

> ... la vaccine était connue sous d'autres noms dans l'Inde, et dans plusieurs contrées de l'Europe, notamment en Languedoc, lorsque l'Anglais Edouard Jenner, d'immortelle mémoire, mis sur la voie par une idée lumineuse du Français Rabaut-Pommier, fixa l'attention de l'Europe sur la propriété antivariolique du cow-pox inoculé à l'homme.

The *Dictionnaire de médicine*, published in twenty-one volumes between 1821 and 1828, also noted:[15]

> Il paraît, du reste, que l'inoculation de la vaccine était pratiquée dans l'Inde dès la haute antiquité, comme le prouve un passage du *Sancteya grantham*, ouvrage manuscrit, attribué à d'Hauvantori.

This *Dictionnaire* also reported Bruce's letter from Bashir about vaccination in Persia. This latter version of these reports reached an Italian readership when they were translated into Italian in the *Dizionario classico di medicina interna ed esterna*, a fifty-six volume encyclopaedia published between 1831 and 1846. The Italian version read as follows:[16]

> Sembra, per altro, che l'inoculazione della vaccina praticata fosse nell'India sin dalla più remota antichità, siccome lo prova un passo del *Sancteya grantham*, opera manoscritta, a d'Hauvantori attribuita.

---

[13]See, e.g., Robert Lewis Collison, *Encyclopaedias: their history throughout the ages* (New York: Hafner, 1964), *passim.*

[14]*Dictionaire abrégé des sciences médicales ... par une partie des collaborateurs* ([Paris]: C. L. F. Panckoucke, 1821–1826), xv (1826), 377f.

[15]*Dictionnaire de médicine,* edited by Nicolas Philibert Adelon, (Paris: Bèchet, 1821–1828), xxi (1828), 148.

[16]*Dizionario classico di medicina interna ed esterna,* translated from the French by M. G. Levi, (Venezia: Giuseppe Antonelli, 1831–1846), xlvii (1839), 431f.

Once again reference was also made to Bruce's letter.

While the *Dizionario classico* was being published in Venice, the *Encyclographie des sciences médicales: Répertoire général de ces sciences au XIXe siècle* was being published in Brussels. This syncretistic combination of earlier French, English and German encyclopaedias, produced in thirty-one volumes between 1841 and 1845, also reported on the ancient Indian science of vaccination:[17]

> *Historique et origine de la vaccine.* – Un passage du *Sancteya Grantham*, ouvrage sanscrit attribué à d'Hauvantori, prouve que l'inoculation de la vaccine était pratiquée dans l'Inde à une époque déjà très-reculée.

The spelling of 'Sancteya' and 'd'Hauvantori' shows that all these passages go back to Husson's *Dictionaire des sciences médicales* article of 1821.

Moving into the second half of the nineteenth century, the *Nouveau Dictionnaire de médicine et de chirurgie pratiques*, published in forty volumes between 1864 and 1886, reproduced yet again the report concerning ancient Indian vaccination:[18]

> D'après Husson, une description très-fidèle de l'opération de la vaccination, qu'il a trouvée dans un vieil ouvrage sanscrit, le *Sancteya Grantham*, attribué à D'Havantari, ferait remonter la connaissance de la vaccine à une époque beaucoup plus reculée. D'après les renseignements des voyageurs, cette pratique n'était pas inconnue en Perse (Bruce) et dans l'Amérique du Sud (Humboldt).

At least this time there is explicit mention of Husson, although the suggestion is clearly that Husson himself discovered the Sanskrit passages in question.

Finally, one year after the above passage appeared, the *Dictionnaire encyclopédique des sciences médicales*, published in Paris, repeated the story yet again:[19]

> Certains modes opératoires employés déjà pour l'insertion du virus vaccin paraissent renouvelés de pratiques usitées dans l'Inde, où, d'après les descriptions précises du Sancteya Grantham, ouvrage sanscrit attribué à d'Hauvantori, la vaccine était déjà connue à une époque

[17] *Encyclographie des sciences médicales: Répertoire général de ces sciences au XIXe siècle* (Bruxelles: Société Encyclographique des sciences médicales, 1841–1845), xxx (1845), 184.

[18] *Nouveau dictionnaire de médecine et de chirurgie pratiques*, directeur de la rédaction: le docteur Jaccoud, (Paris: J. B. Baillière et fils, 1864–1886), xxxviii (1885), 1.

[19] *Dictionnaire encyclopédique des sciences médicales*, edited by J. Raige-Delorme, A. Dechambre (1864–1885) and L. Lereboullet (1886–1889), with L. Hahn, 100 vols (Paris: Asselin, Labé, Masson, 1864-1889), fifth series (U–Z), ii (1886), 167.

> très-reculée. "Prenez le fluide du bouton du pis de la vache ou du bras d'un homme entre l'épaule et le coude sur la pointe d'une lancette et piquez'en les bras entre l'épaule et le coude jusqu'à ce que le sang paraisse; le fluide se mêlant avec le sang, il en résultera la fièvre de la petite vérole, etc." (Husson, *Dictionnaire* [sic] *des sciences médicales*).

It had been pointed out by Baron in 1827 that the French, and in particular Husson, were trying to undermine Jenner's achievement by claiming French precedence for the discovery.[20] The repeated assertion of an ancient Indian knowledge of vaccination in these encyclopaedic works would seem to be part of the same general argument.

The early British medical historians: Shoolbred and Baron

John Baron, whom we have already had reason to quote, wrote the earliest major biography of Jenner.[21] In it, he noticed the French citation of 'Dhawantari' (*sic*) and the Sancteya Grantham,[22] and referred it to its source in the *Madras Courier* for 1819. He noted that as a description of the technique of vaccination it was very deficient, and went so far as to claim that the description given by the Sanskrit passages had,[23]

> ... the appearance of a delineation which had been made, not from original observation, but from materials obviously acquired from other sources and put together with studied ambiguity, the writer having been more anxious to maintain the semblance of antiquity than to convey precise information on a point of infinite importance.

Baron went on to point out that the discovery of vaccination was of greater importance to the 'inhabitants of the East' than to almost any other peoples in the world and that it was inconceivable that vaccination could have been practised in India without its knowledge being universally diffused. In spite of his scepticism on the

---

[20] Baron, *Life of Edward Jenner*, 543–555.

[21] See note 12 above.

[22] Baron, *Life of Edward Jenner*, 555. Baron also noted that, 'The subject [i.e. ancient Indian vaccination] was mentioned many years ago in the Bibliotheque Britannique.' If this is a reference to genuine vaccination, then it is very important. Unfortunately, the copy of *Bibliothèque Britannique* deposited in the British Library was destroyed in the war, and I have been unable to check the reference.

[23] Ibid., 556.

subject, Baron took some pains to check further into the matter by consulting one of the most eminent Orientalists of his day. From Sir John Malcolm, a leading political figure in early nineteenth century British India, and a scholar and historian of substance, Baron learned the following facts:[24]

> On the introduction of vaccine inoculation into India it was found that the practice was much opposed by the natives. In order to overcome their prejudices the late Mr. Ellis, of Madras, who was well versed in Sanskrit literature actually composed a short poem in that language on the subject of vaccination. This poem was inscribed on old paper, and said to have been *found*, that the impression of its antiquity might assist the effect intended to be produced in the minds of the Brahmins while tracing the preventive to their sacred cow.[25]
>
> The late Dr. Anderson, of Madras, adopted the very same expedient in order to deceive the Hindoos into a belief that vaccination was an ancient practice of their own.

Baron noted that if smallpox had been known in India at the time it would have been unnecessary for Ellis and Anderson to have composed these tracts, and added that no one disputed the fact that smallpox *inoculation* was frequently practiced in India before the introduction of vaccination, but that 'there is no proof whatever that they employed vaccination.'

Baron continued with a description of a similar attempt to prove the antiquity of vaccination in India which took place in Bengal. Baron's description was presumably also passed to him from Sir John Malcolm, who in turn seems to have drawn his observations at least partly from Shoolbred's account, which was as follows:[26]

> Mr. Gillman, surgeon to the 8th Regiment Native Infantry, stationed at Bareilly, making enquiries on this subject, got possession of a Shanscrit manuscript, which was said to contain an account of the inoculation with matter originating in the cow, for the purpose of destroying the susceptibility to small-pox. This manuscript Mr. Gillman sent down

[24] Ibid., 557.

[25] In the index to his *Life of Edward Jenner*, Baron gives Ellis the initials J. A. It is probable that this is a mistake for Francis Whyte Ellis (*d.* 1819) who was a leading Sanskrit and Tamil scholar in Madras at the time, and an active fellow member of the Literary Society of Madras, where Sir John Malcolm attended his lectures (see the *Asiatic Journal*, vii (June 1819), 643a). On F. W. Ellis see *Dictionary of National Biography*, edited by L. Stephen and S. Lee, 22 vols, (London: Smith, Elder & Co., 1908–1909), vi, 694a–694b: the details of this entry were debated in the *Madras Mail* of May and June, 1905 (see below, pp. 149ff.).

[26] Schoolbred, *Report on the progress of vaccine inoculation*, 54ff.

> to Mr Munro at Calcutta, in April last, by whom it was submitted to the perusal of a gentleman of distinguished eminence in Shanscrit literature, who gives the following account and translation of it:
>
> "The leaves sent by Mr. Gillman contain an extract from a work entitled *Sud'hasangraha*, composed by a physician named *Mahádéva*, under the patronage of *Rájá Rájà sinha.*[27] This extract contains a chapter on the *Masúricá*, (in Hindi called *Masuria*, or *Masooría*,) which is, I believe, a sort of chiken-pox. Towards the end, the author seems to have introduced other topics; and immediately after directing leeches to be applied to bad sores, he proceeds thus:
>
> "Taking the matter (pùya) of pimples (granthi,) which are naturally produced on the udders of cows, carefully preserve it; and, before the breaking out of the small-pox (sitala,) making, with a small instrument, a small puncture, (like that made by a gnat,) in a child's limb, introduce into the blood as much of that matter, as is measured by the fourth part to a *Racti*; thus the wise physician renders the child secure from the breaking out of the small-pox."
>
> "If this passage," says the translator, "has not been interpolated by the *Hindoo* physician, who communicated it to Mr. Gillman, vaccination must have been known to the *Hindus* before Dr. Jenner discovered it. Other copies of the same work should be sought and examined, to determine whether the passage be genuine."

Shoolbred expressed his doubts about the genuineness of the Sanskrit passage in question, and then continued:[28]

> Other copies of the book were therefore sought for, and luckily procured ... When the extract in question was collated with other copies of the *Sud'hasangraha* procured in Bengal, nothing of the passage relating to vaccination was to be found in the latter, and I accordingly obtained from Mr. Blaquiere ... the following statement of the impression he received from the collation of the two manuscripts.
>
> "I found the manuscript you sent me agreed nearly word for word with a chapter of the *Vanga Sena Chicitsa Meharnava*,[29] until the mention of the vaccination. The conclusion I formed was, that the manuscript

[27] I.e., The *Rājasiṃhasudhāsaṅgraha* of Mahādeva.
[28] Ibid., 55.
[29] I.e., the *Cikitsāmahārṇava* of Vaṅgasena (*fl.* c.1050–1100).

> was thus far a copy of the said chapter, and all beyond it, on the subject of vaccination, interpolation."
>
> The Vanga Sena Chicitsa Meharnava, mentioned above, is a chapter of the Sud'hasangraha,[30] expressly on the subject of medicine, in which it may fairly be concluded the vaccine disease would have been noticed, if at all. Mr. Foster and Mr. Bentley, two other gentlemen well acquainted with the Hindoo literature, also collated the manuscripts, with the same result as Mr. Blaquire [*sic*]; and I have their farther authority for saying, that they have examined the two most ancient and most esteemed Shanscrit books, composed professedly on the subject of Nosology, called the Needan and Churruck,[31] without being able to discover the slightest trace of a previous knowledge of the vaccine disease among the Hindoos, though they both treat largely of the small-pox under the name of *Bussunt* and *Sitala*.
>
> From the above respectable testimonies, it can scarcely, I think, be doubted, that the extract forwarded by Mr. Gillman, is an impudent forgery interpolated into a Shanscrit book, by one of those frauds so commonly and so dextrously committed by the Hindoo literati, for the purpose of supporting the claims of the Bramins to the prior possession of all kinds of science.

Baron added, when describing this incident, that:[32]

> This communication [i.e., the Gillman manuscript] was shown to Mr. Colebrooke and Mr. Blaquiere, both eminent Sanscrit scholars, and they both suspected that it was an interpolation. The first-named gentleman further adds that the original work from which the extract purports to have been taken, was not exhibited to anyone well versed in Sanskrit. I believe I may further add that Mr. Colebrooke made inquiries whilst in India, which fully satisfied him that no original work of the kind ever had existence. Sir John Malcolm has been kind enough to ascertain that no such book is to be found in the library of the East India Company.

The fact that Colebrooke could not find other copies of the *Sudhāsaṅgraha* is odd, in view of the statement by Shoolbred quoted above (p. 135) that other copies of the

[30] This is a confusion: if anything, the reverse is true.

[31] I.e., The *Mādhavanidāna* and the *Carakasaṃhitā*.

[32] Baron, *Life of Edward Jenner*, 559.

work were 'sought for and luckily procured.' It would seem that Schoolbred misunderstood the fact that Blaquiere and the other scholars involved were comparing the Gillman manuscript not with copies of the *Sudhāsaṅgraha*, but with other well known Sanskrit medical works, looking for parallel passages.

By an extraordinary piece of codicological luck, the Gillman manuscript has survived, and is now in the library of Trinity College, Cambridge.[33] It consists of a mere ten leaves, claiming to be just the chapter on smallpox taken from the *Rājasiṃhasudhāsaṅgraha*, and it came to the college as part of a collection of manuscripts originally belonging to John Bentley, who was mentioned above as one of the Sanskrit authorities in Calcutta to whom the manuscript was shown. In 1869, Theodor Aufrecht published a catalogue of the Sanskrit manuscripts in Trinity, and quoted the verses purporting to describe vaccination. They run as follow:[34]

> *usrāstaneṣu sargeṇa graṃthayaś ca bhavaṃti ye* |
> *teṣāṃ pūyaṃ samāgṛhya rakṣaṇīyaṃ prayatnataḥ* | |
> *śītalāvikṛtaiḥ pūrvaṃ pratīke bālakasya tu* |
> *vidhāya kṣudraśāstreṇa maśakakṣatravatkṣataṃ* | |
> *praveśayitvāsṛji pūyayaiva raktaiś caturyāṃ śamitaṃ vipaścit* |
> *bhiṣaktamo nirbhayataḥ mupaiti* [sic] *śiśau* | . . .

The translation of this passage, as quoted by Schoolbred and reproduced above (p. 135), is a fair rendition. Aufrecht noted that these verses of the *Rājasiṃhasudhāsaṃgraha* were 'open to the suspicion of modern authorship.' Twenty-two years later, in a major survey of all Sanskrit manuscripts then known to exist in catalogued libraries worldwide, Aufrecht noted two further complete copies of the *Rājasiṃhasudhāsaṅgraha*, both in the Maharaja of Bikaner's private library, the Anup Library, in Rajasthan.[35]

Before finishing his excursus into the Indian reports concerning vaccination, Baron made the following summation, kinder in its judgement of motives than Shoolbred's:[36]

[33]Trinity College MS R. 15. 86. The last leaf of the MS has, in a copperplate hand: 'The Forgery of the Hindus respecting the Cowpock-innoculation [sic].'

[34]Th. Aufrecht, *A catalogue of Sanskrit manuscripts in the library of Trinity College, Cambridge* (Cambridge: Deighton, Bell, 1869), 25. The passage ends abruptly in mid verse, with marks of a lacuna.

[35]T. Aufrecht, *Catalogus catalogorum*, 3 vols, (Leipzig: German Oriental Society, 1891–1903), i, 502a. These manuscripts are each about six hundred leaves long, and steps have been taken in an attempt to obtain copies of these texts for a fresh comparison with the Gillman manuscript.

[36]Ibid., 559.

> From these statements it must be apparent, that the well meant devices of those who attempted to propagate Vaccination in India, have lead to the belief that the practice was known to the Hindoos in earlier times.

Whatever may be the truth about the Gillman manuscript, Sir John Malcolm's testimony and opinions concerning the composition of Sanskrit works on vaccination by Ellis and Anderson are not be taken lightly. As noted, Sir John knew Ellis personally, and Dr James Anderson, formerly Physician General at Madras, was very well known to all.[37] If Sir John says that they composed such works, then it is highly likely that they did so. This fact would not need to be stressed, were it not for the heated debate which broke out on this issue in 1905 (see pp. 146ff. below). To understand the motives of these men, in producing the vernacular vaccination tracts, it is necessary to understand the resistance that faced the early vaccinators in India.

The introduction of vaccination into India

Working from the journals of the day it is possible to piece together something of the atmosphere of the time when smallpox vaccination was first introduced into India, and some of the activities of men like Ellis and Anderson who recognised its value and sought to spread vaccination by any means.

A short time after Jenner's discovery of the value of cow-pox inoculation, work began on carrying the cow-pox virus across the world, so that people everywhere could benefit from the new technique.

The first attempt by Jenner to send the lifesaving cow-pox lymph to India failed: at the end of 1799 he sent copies of his book together with a quantity of lymph to India on the ship *Queen*. Unfortunately this vessel was burnt on the coast of South America in 1800 and so never reached India.[38] It was later realised that, in any case, the lymph could not have retained its properties for the duration of a sea voyage to India. Following a suggestion by Jenner, an attempt was next made to form a human chain of cow-pox carriers. A number of people volunteered to

[37] A gentleman named Anderson was secretary of the Madras Literary Society at the time of Ellis's lectures, and presided over the meetings (*Asiatic Journal* (1819), 643a), but must have been different from the Dr James Anderson to whom Malcolm probably refers, and who died in 1809 (*Dictionary of National Biography*, i, 382a; Baron, *Life of Edward Jenner*, 423f.).

[38] See Thomas Christie, *An account of the ravages committed in Ceylon by Small-pox, previously to the introduction of vaccination; with a statement of the circumstances attending the introduction, progress, and success, of vaccine inoculation in that island* (Cheltenham: J. and S. Griffith, 1811), 17; *British Medical Journal* (May 1896), 1267a.

be vaccinated one after another during a sea voyage from England to Ceylon via Bombay. Records are not complete, but it seems that this attempt to transmit cow-pox vaccine to India also failed. Vaccine finally reached India overland by way of Vienna, Constantinople, and Baghdad. From Baghdad a vaccinated child was sent to Basra and from that child's arm various vaccinations were successful. Lymph from these vaccinations was continued in weekly succession and towards May 1802 some of it was sent on board the ship *Recovery* to Bombay. There, on the 14th of June 1802, a Dr Scott produced successful cow-pox on the arm of a three year old child called Anna Dusthall.[39] The *Asiatic Annual Register* of 1803 reported the successful introduction of cow-pox vaccine to India the previous year as follows:[40]

Cowpox

> Aug. 7th [1802]. The introduction of the cow pox at Bombay may now be considered as having been established. From the veneration in which the animal is held by Hindus, it requires only an intimation that such a blessing was within their reach, to ensure its earliest dissemination throughout this division or class of the inhabitants of Bombay; and, to render it general, an official notification on the subject, in the different country languages, would not, we apprehend, be unattended with success. The nature and effects of the vaccine inoculation has, it appears, been explained to a few Hindus and Parsees, who have expressed an anxiety to partake of its benefits.

From Anna Dusthall in Bombay, the precious cow-pox vaccine was sent to Poona, Surat, Hyderabad, Ceylon and Madras. Attempts to transmit the vaccine to Bengal failed until Dr James Anderson, Physician-General at Madras, vaccinated a young boy of thirteen called John Cresswell on the 10th October 1802, and sent him aboard the ship *Hunter* under Captain Anderson. During the voyage to Calcutta the vaccine was kept alive through a human chain of children, and on the 17th November 1802 a fifteen year-old boy called Charles Norton arrived in Calcutta with a genuine cow-pox pustule on each arm. Through him, vaccination was established throughout Bengal.[41]

---

[39] See John Ring, *A treatise on the cow-pox; containing the history of vaccine inoculation and an account of the various publications which have appeared on that subject, in Great Britain, and other parts of the world*, 2 vols (London: Printed at the Philanthropic Reform ... by J. Richardson: 1801, 1803), 1022; Thomas Christie, *An account of the ravages*, 20–26; Sydney Price James, *Smallpox and vaccination in British India* (Calcutta: Thacker, Spink & Co., 1909), 16f.

[40] *Asiatic Annual Register* (1803), 27a. The news was reported locally by the doctors responsible, Dr Moir and Dr Scott, in the *Bombay Courier* of July 1802.

[41] Shoolbred, *Report on the progress of vaccine inoculation* (1805), 1ff., 85–93; *British Medical Journal*

Resistance to vaccination

There is contemporary evidence that in spite of the enthusiasm of the medical staff of the Indian Medical Service, there was quite a lot of resistance to vaccination in India when it was first introduced. From the start, it had been generally assumed that because vaccine was essentially a product of the cow, it would be readily received in a land where the cow was venerated. The passage quoted above from the *Asiatic Annual Register* expressed this idea, and it was even believed by Jenner himself.[42] However, it seems that this was not the case, at least not universally. Shoolbred emphasised how strongly the introduction of vaccination was opposed in Bengal, even though the vaccinators were in many cases Brahmins.[43] The following letter to Dr James Anderson, published in the *Asiatic Annual Register* gives an idea of of the issues and feelings involved in publicising vaccination in the Madras Presidency:[44]

Letter from a Bramin on Vaccine Inoculation
To J. Anderson, P.G. Madras.

Honoured Sir,

I beg leave to observe, for the information of the natives of this country, that I have perused the papers which you have published on that wonderful, healthful, and immortal vaccine matter, discovered on the nipples and udders of some cows in England, by that illustrious physician, Dr. Jenner, whereby the loathesome, painful, and fatal small pox has been prevented from seizing the many of our fellow creatures in India, as well as in Europe.

I am an eye-witness, as well as many others, that numbers of children here have been inoculated with vaccine matter, without any injury or blemish whatsoever, excepting a small spot at the place where the matter is applied, which is commonly on the arm. It is, therefore, greatly to be wished that an intimate knowledge of this wonderful discovery may be acquired by the natives of this country, so as to enable

(1896), 1267; James, *Smallpox and vaccination*, 18. The report in the *Indian Medical Gazette* (August 1802, 322) that vaccination was introduced to India through Madras is wrong, as is the report in the *British Medical Journal* (June 1899, 1341a) that vaccine was introduced to Bombay in 1804.

[42] Shoolbred, *Report on the progress of vaccine inoculation* (1805), 59; *Medical and Physical Journal* (July 1803), 93.

[43] Shoolbred, *Report on the progress of vaccine inoculation* (1805), 58f.

[44] *Asiatic Annual Register* (1805), 76.

> them to preserve the lives of the rich and honourary, as well as those of low casts.
>
> On this account, it might be useful to remove a prejudice in the minds of the people, arising from the term cow-pock, being literally translated *comary*, in the advertisement which has been published in our Tamil tongue, whereas there can be no doubt that it is a drop of nectar from the exuberant udders of the cows in England, and no ways similar to the humour discharged from the tongue and feet of diseased cattle in this country.
>
> I remain, with great respect, Honourable Sir,
> Your obedient and very humble servant,
> MOOPERAL STREENIVASACHARY [*sic*].
> December 29, 1804.

Evidently someone had bungled the translation of publicity material into Tamil, and had produced an advertisement for vaccination which generated revulsion rather than attraction to this particular product of the cow.

It also appears that the Brahmin inoculators, who had for over a century made their living from smallpox inoculation, felt that their livelihood was under threat.[45]

In 1902, the centenary of vaccination in India, a long and interesting letter to the editor appeared in the *Indian Medical Gazette*.[46] It was written by W. G. King, of whom more later, and in it he quoted from a memorial to the government by Swamy Naick, the first Chief Native Vaccinator in the Madras Presidency, outlining the many difficulties that Naick had faced as one of the earliest vaccinators in Madras. Naick reported that had he encountered very serious hazards, 'from the natural prejudice, the inhabitants in general entertained, towards this beneficial operation, together with their mistaken notions, and veneration for the small-pox.' Naick continued,

> ... And further, the operation of the cow-pox being altogether novel and an innovation, as well as totally unknown in this part of the world, the principal inhabitants of Madras, and the neighbouring out-station looked upon the undertaking with very suspicious notions, and apprehended that the English Government intended to introduce something which would tend to prejudice their religion, and other Hindu systems of worship.

[45] *Asiatic Journal* (1823), 352b.
[46] *Indian Medical Gazette* (1902), 413f.

On one occasion, Naick was even attacked by an angry mob of Armenians, 'who were ignorant of the beneficial effects of cow-pox,' and had his earring torn from his ear and stolen! One of the facts which seems, on the other hand, to have encouraged people to come forward for vaccination was that Lord Clive let his garden be used as a vaccination station.

One of the most serious hindrances to the spread of vaccination in the early years was a rumour which spread amongst the native population to the effect that the purpose of vaccination was to put a 'Government mark' on the arms of every child. When older, the male children with this mark would be sent as coolies to other British colonies, or forcibly drafted into the army. Girls with the mark would be forced into harems.[47] Another version of the rumour was that the mark was part of a census of the people with a view to imposing a new tax.[48]

The preparation of vernacular tracts

It was in order to overcome these obstacles that propaganda in favour of vaccination was distributed. As early as November 1802, less than six months after vaccine was first brought to India, John Fleming, first member of the Bengal Medical Board, wrote to the Marquis Wellesley, then Governor General, suggesting that,[49]

> To facilitate the general adoption of the practice of vaccination by the Natives, ... a notification should be published in the Persian, Hindevy [*sic*], and Bengalese languages, and also in the Shanscrit, giving ... a succinct History of the discovery, in which the curious, and to the Hindoos, very interesting circumstance that this wonderful preventive was originally procured from the body of the cow should be emphatically remarked ...

As we have already seen, the *Asiatic Annual Register's* report on the first arrival of vaccine in Bombay had suggested that 'an official notification on the subject, in the different country languages, would not ... be unattended with success'.[50]

Later, in a letter from the famous Abbé Dubois – himself an energetic vaccinator – to Dr James Anderson, written in April 1805, Dubois noted the 'distrust and other prejudices which have, till now, opposed its [i.e., vaccination's] progress ... '.[51] Dubois outlined a scheme for organising vaccinators, and went on,

[47] *Madras Mail* (11/5/1905), 4d.
[48] James, *Smallpox and vaccination* (1909), vii; *Asiatic Journal* (1826), 578.
[49] Reproduced in Shoolbred, *Report on the progress of vaccine*, 88.
[50] See p. 139 above.
[51] *Asiatic Annual Register* (1809), Chronicle, p.1.

> At the same time, if the plan I have the honour to propose were adopted, it would be necessary to have instructions circulated among inoculators, by which they should be made acquainted with the nature and several stages of the disease, and able to distinguish a genuine from a spurious case – I take the liberty to inclose a translation in Tamul, on the subject, extracted from Dr. Ring's work on vaccination, which may, perhaps, prove acceptable to you, since it contains the principles laid down by the Jennerian Society, to know the several stages of the disease, and to distinguish the genuine from the spurious cases. I got them translated into the Canara language as well as Tamul, for the usage of practitioners in Mysore, as well as in this country.
>
> Dubois, *Missionary*
> Kodivaily, near Satimungalum,
> April 25, 1805

Anderson replied in May 1805 that:[52]

> The translation of the vaccine symptoms into the Tamul and Canara languages, I consider of the greatest importance, as it can never be admitted that much good has been done, until the people are so intimately acquainted with the genuine appearances, and peculiar nature of the vaccine, as to apply to operators, or operate themselves spontaneously, and without any coercion or fee whatever, besides the desire of avoiding a more loathsome disease ... the publication of vaccine symptoms in the native languages, promises the greatest utility, that the people at large may learn to know the disease, which will naturally give them, who are any ways intelligent, an interest in everything regarding it, and gradually lead them to observe the disappearance of smallpox.

This passage from Anderson's letter may be the source of Sir John Malcolm's belief that Anderson had composed a tract on vaccination, although Malcolm may have had more personal knowledge. There is no evidence that Anderson, unlike Ellis, was a scholar of Indian languages, although in his official capacity he would have had to have known some native language(s). However, the letter to Anderson from Mooperal Shreenivasachary cited above (p. 140) proves that Anderson had,

[52] Ibid., 3f.

already by the end of 1804, published and circulated vaccination tracts in the Tamil language. Anderson also received some pamphlets about vaccination, together with a number of coloured drawings of cow-pox pustules, from Jenner himself, and distributed them throughout India.[53]

At the end of his letter to Dubois, Anderson added the following tantalising remark:

> Accounts have just reached me, that a learned Bramin has discovered, in an obsolete puranum, mythological stories of a disease similar to the vaccine.

This probably refers to the mythological accounts of *masūrikā* and *śītalā* such as had been earlier collected by Baldeus (1684)[54] or Sonnerat (1782).[55] It does not imply a knowledge of vaccination.

There is thus enough evidence from contemporary sources for us to be sure that documents about vaccination were composed in several of the languages of India and circulated widely.[56] Unfortunately, most of these documents were probably regarded as ephemera, and do not seem to have survived. However, there is a tract of this type in Marathi which does survive in the India Office Library.[57] It is a translation, made in 1812, of a treatise by Dr Thomas Coates, who was Vaccination Superintendent at Poona from 1807. The work is described as follows:[58]

---

[53] Christie, *An account of the ravages*, 17f.

[54] Philippus Baldaeus, *A true and exact description of the most celebrated East-India coasts of Malabar and Coromandel, as also of the isle of Ceylon ... Taken partly from their own Vedam, or law-book, and authentick manuscripts ...*, translated by Awnsham Churchill, (London: Printed for A. and J. Churchill, 1703).

[55] Pierre Sonnerat, *Voyage aux Indes Orientales et a la Chine fait par ordre du roi, depuis 1774 jusqu'en 1781. Dans lequel on traite des moeurs, de la religion, des sciences & des arts des Indiens, des Chinois, des Pégouins & des Madégasses; suivi d'observations sur le cap de Bonne-Espérance, les isles de France & de Bourbon, les Maldives, Ceylan, Malacca, les Philippines & les Moluques & de recherches sur l'histoire naturelle de ces pays* (Paris: L'auteur, 1782). See also James Carrick Moore, *The history of the small pox* (London: Printed for Longman, Hurst, Rees, Orme, and Brown, 1815), 26–31.

[56] Similarly, at least one tract on vaccination was translated into Chinese, published and distributed from Canton by East India Company officials. See the letter from Sir George Thomas Staunton (20/2/1806), one of the translators, published in *Letters of Edward Jenner and other documents concerning the early history of vaccination*, edited by Genevieve Miller, (Baltimore and London: Johns Hopkins University Press, 1983), 124f. Staunton gives almost identical reasons for the preparation of the Chinese tract to those given for the Indian situation: 'It would [otherwise] have proved difficult to have so quickly overcome the objections and scruples of the Chinese against every kind of innovation ...'.

[57] India Office MS Mar. A. 1.

[58] James Fuller Blumhardt, Sadashiv Govind Kanhere, *Catalogue of the Marathi manuscripts in the India Office Library* (Oxford: Published for the India Office Library at the Clarendon Press, 1950), 10.

The work is in sixty-one paragraphs (*kalam*), and comprises the following subjects:–

1. The great mortality caused by smallpox and the loathsome nature of the disease (1–12).

2. The discovery made by Dr Jenner in 1796, and the adoption of vaccination in Europe (13–19).

3. Measures taken to procure vaccine matter in India, its dispatch from Baghdad, and arrival at Bombay in June 1802, and the introduction of vaccination throughout India (20–23).

4. The introduction of vaccine from Bombay into Poona by Dr Coates in September 1803, the vaccination by him of the Maharaja's wife and of 17,056 persons in Poona and its outlying villages up to April 14, 1812 (the date of this manuscript), in addition to about 13,000 persons previously vaccinated by him in the Province of Malwa, making a total of over 30,000, not a single case having proved fatal, and no one having contracted the disease after vaccination (24–33).

5. The method and treatment of vaccination (34–50).

6. The advantages of vaccination and answers to objections raised against it (51–61). In conclusion Dr. Coates invites those who are desirous of learning how to vaccinate to stay under his tuition for a month or two.

Another work of this genre which survives, this time as a printed book, is Maclean's treatise, which was originally in Hindustani, but was translated into English, Tamil and Malayalam.[59] A later Hindī work on smallpox which incorporates a description of Jenner's vaccination is that of Jiyālālā.[60]

There can be no doubt that many such works, perhaps in pamphlet form, were in circulation from the first half of the nineteenth century onwards. It would, therefore, be natural to infer that the 1819 report by Calvi Virumbon, and the manuscripts given to Gillman in Bengal, were based, perhaps mistakenly, perhaps not, on such pamphlets.

But the Sanskrit text quoted by Virumbon can be found also in other reference works in Sanskrit. To investigate this point we shall start from a heated debate on

---

[59]William Campbell Maclean, *A treatise on the Small Pox and Vaccination ... Translated from Hindoostanee into English and Tamil by J. Shortt ... Translated into Malayalim by Ramasawmy Rajoo* (Trivandrum: Travancore Sircar Press, 1864). Catalogued in Albertine Gaur, *Catalogue of Malayalam books in the British Museum with an appendix listing the books in Brahui, Gondi, Kui, Malto, Oraon (Kurukh), Toda, and Tulu* (London: Trustees of the British Museum, 1971), 191a.

[60]Jiyālālā sāhab, *Śītalāparihāra aparanāma ārogyāmṛtabindu* (Baṃbaī: Śrīveṅkaṭeśvara.sṭīm yantrālaya, saṃvat 1962 [1905]), 5ff.

these matters that took place in 1899, and surfaced again the pages of the *Madras Mail* and elsewhere in 1905.

Lord Ampthill and the King debate

Lieutenant-Colonel Walter Gaven King of the Madras Medical Service was a leading figure in Indian medical circles, though not always, apparently, an easy man to get on with. He was made a Companion of the Order of the Indian Empire in 1899, and was distinguished for his services to the Madras Sanitary Department and to vaccination. An important institute for preventive medicine in Madras was subsequently named after him.

In April 1899, Surgeon-General Sir Charles Gordon wrote to the *Madras Mail* asking for more details about a lecture on sanitation by King, on which the paper had reported on the 18th of February. In the course of his talk, King had claimed that, 'the system of vaccination as a prevention against small-pox had been well understood by ancient Hindus'.[61] Sir Charles was aware of Calvi Virumbon's article of 1819, but sought further information on the subject. This innocent enquiry initiated a lengthy debate that raised many subsidiary issues, and is an example of the heights to which a sustained newspaper correspondence can rise, and the depths to which it can fall.

King replied to Sir Charles's query with a long article which appeared three days later.[62] In it he referred again to Virumbon's article, but went further, and drew attention to the *Āyurvedavijñāna*, compiled and published by Kaviraj Binod Lal Sen. Page 481 of this distinguished Sanskrit dictionary of medicine, said King, had exactly the same passage – in the Devanāgarī script – as that quoted by Virumbon:[63]

> *masūrikāyā utpādanavidhiḥ:*
> *dhenustanyamasūrikā narāṇāṃ ca masūrikā* |
> *tajjalaṃ bāhumūlāc ca śastrāntena gṛhītavān* | |
> *bāhumūle ca śastrāṇi raktotpattikarāṇi ca* |
> *tajjalaṃ raktamilitaṃ sphoṭakajvarasaṃbhavam* | |
> *etat dhanvantarikṛtaśākteyagranthaḥ śabdakalpadrumadhṛtaḥ* |

[61] *Madras Mail* (25/4/1899), 4.
[62] Ibid., (28/4/1899), 4.
[63] Cited from *Ayurveda Vijnanam or Hindu system of medicine*, compiled by Kaviraj Binod Lall Sen, second edition, (Calcutta, 1916), ch. 31, p. 196. The text of this quotation was kindly supplied by G. J. Meulenbeld.

King claimed that the *Āyurvedavijñāna* was published in 1750, and this appeared to predate not only Virumbon, but Jenner's discovery too. His article went on publicly to ask Sanskrit scholars to aid him in establishing the Hindu precedence in vaccination, a request he was to repeat more than once. He ended with a long and interesting account of smallpox inoculation amongst the Brahmins of Orissa.

King appears not to have known, or not to have followed, the several scholars, such as Christie, Baron, and Haas[64] who had dismissed the claims of Virumbon. Indeed, he seems throughout to have been disposed rather to believe the Hindu precedence with vaccination.

At any rate, the matter seems to have been dropped until 1905, when the King Institute of Preventive Medicine was formally opened on the 11th of March by Lord Ampthill, Governor of Madras. Lord Ampthill, who had only the year before been acting Viceroy and Governor General of India during Lord Curzon's absence in England, made a speech at the opening, in which he praised the efforts King had made to establish the Institute.[65] Ampthill also claimed for the Hindus the discovery, or at any rate an ancient knowledge, of vaccination. Apparently he put the case rather strongly, referring to Jenner's 'rediscovery' of vaccination, and referring to papers written by King.[66] Ampthill cited the Virumbon passage and went on to say that King himself had discovered the ancient Sanskrit work in question,[67] presumably a reference to King's discovery of the Virumbon passage in the *Āyurvedavijñāna*.

This was reported in the *British Medical Journal* the following month. The editor took Ampthill to task severely, citing Baron, Sir John Malcolm and all the other sources we have discussed. The editor added, 'On the question of Sanscrit scholarship at issue we are not competent to form any opinion,' but referring to Baron, noted that:[68]

> The conclusion that the boon which Jenner gave to suffering mankind had been known for many centuries to the Hindus would be irresistible were it not for a fact which is evidently not known to Lord Ampthill, nor it would seem to Colonel King. This is that there is good reason to believe that the passages quoted in proof of the claim made on behalf of the Hindus are simply what the higher critics call interpolations.

---

[64]E. Haas, 'Ueber die Ursprünge der Indischen Medizin, mit besonderen Bezug auf Susruta,' *Zeitschrift der deutschen morgenländischen Gesellschaft*, xxx (1876), 660f.

[65]*British Medical Journal* (April 1905), 806f.

[66]Ibid., (July 1905), 136a. It later came out that the 'papers' were the one King had published in the *Madras Mail* in 1899.

[67]Ibid., (April 1905), 838f.

[68]Ibid., (April 1905), 839.

The editor did not seem to be aware that King had come across an apparently pre-Virumbon citation of the Sanskrit passage. And his style was severe enough to amount to a strong personal attack on King, the more so as the article came at a time when King was at the pinnacle of his career, having an Institute bearing his name inaugurated. This attack was reported in the *Madras Mail* a month later.[69]

King responded immediately with a long, defensive letter to the *Madras Mail*,[70] and another of much the same substance to the *British Medical Journal*.[71] He sought to exonerate Lord Ampthill, saying that the latter had been speaking on the authority of King's own published views. King went on to note that he had never claimed to have been the discoverer of Virumbon's passage, but that:[72]

> ... when this book [the *Āyurvedavijñāna*] was being read aloud for plague references before me, although I do not understand Sanskrit I had become so accustomed to the sound of the original quotation that I myself called a halt in the reading, and was justified by finding that the quotation as given in the Madras Courier had again been found in a Sanskrit book.

King admitted that he had misunderstood the date of *Āyurvedavijñāna*: 1750 was what he called a 'Vikrama Sakha' date. But this is still a confusion of two eras: Vikrama, which would give a date of AD 1693, and Śaka, which would give AD 1828. However the *Āyurvedavijñāna* was not published until AD 1878, and the edition to which King refers must be that of 1888.[73] In fact, the passage quoted above (p. 158) from the 1916 edition of the *Āyurvedavijñāna* ends with an explicit attribution to the *Śabdakalpadruma*, a vast dictionary cum encyclopaedia in Sanskrit compiled by Rādhākānta Deva. King noted that he had also, by 1905, found the Sanskrit passage in the *Śabdakalpadruma*.[74] There, the verse is indeed quoted, at the start of the entry on *masūrikā*, in the following way:[75]

[69] *Madras Mail* (5/5/1905), 5.

[70] Ibid., (10/5/1905), 4.

[71] *British Medical Journal* (July 1905), 136.

[72] *Madras Mail* (10/5/1905), 4.

[73] The 1888 edition was the first fully in Sanskrit, and the first to have more than three hundred pages. If King's edition was dated 1810 Śaka and, instead of adding 78 to get AD 1888, he subtracted 57 in the belief that he was dealing with a Vikrama date, then he would have arrived at a date of 1753, which was possibly the source of his original belief that he had located a pre-Virumbon version of the text.

[74] Even the earliest, Bengali, edition of the *Śabdakalpadruma* was published in 1821, two years after the Virumbon article.

[75] Rādhākānta Deva, *Śabdakalpadrumaḥ*, re-edited by Varadāprasāda Vasu and Haricaraṇa Vasu, 5 vols, (Calcutta: Haricaraṇa Vasu, at the Baptist Mission Press, 1886-1891), iii (1887), 649b.

dhenustanyamasūrikā narāṇāñ ca masūrikā |
tajjalaṃ bāhumūlāc ca śastrāntena gṛhītavān | |
bāhumūle ca śastrāṇi raktotpattikarāṇi ca |
tajjalaṃ raktamilitaṃ sphoṭakajvarasambhavam | |
iti dhanvantarikṛtaśākteyagranthaḥ | |

Finally, King took strong objection to Baron's suggestion that Ellis composed a tract on vaccination and passed it off as ancient. To King this would have made Ellis a 'swindler' which King was hot to deny. King brings up the fact that far from perpetrating such deceits, Ellis was the scholar who had uncovered the falsity of the so called 'Ezour Vedam' which was believed by Voltaire and, through him, the King of France, to be a genuine Hindu work, whereas it was in fact composed (in good faith) by the Jesuit Roberto di Nobili in 1620.[76]

Of more importance to the vaccination issue was the remark that King had searched through thousands of pamphlets encouraging vaccination in the Vaccination Department archives, and could find no reference to the work by Ellis.[77]

To the version of King's letter which had appeared in the *British Medical Journal* was added a subsequent note by King that the edition of the *Śabdakalpadruma* in which the Virumbon passage appeared was a revised one, published later than Virumbon's article. The editor of the *British Medical Journal* attempted to close the debate gracefully, but still managed to insert a few stinging remarks which would be sure to enrage King further: 'We must frankly say that ... Colonel King does not seem to us to have cleared up the muddle'.[78]

At this point a new voice entered the debate, that of 'a Hindu Correspondent.' His first contribution appeared in the *Madras Mail* on the day after King's.[79] This correspondent was also concerned to protect Ellis's reputation. He outlined Ellis's distinguished career and added, 'To a scholar of his reputation even a "pious fraud" would have been utterly repugnant.' The correspondent went on to describe the allegations of fraud that had surrounded Whish's work on the history of Indian mathematics, when he published on the *Tantrasaṅgraha* and other works of the Kerala school of mathematics. These allegations proved to be false: Whish had in fact uncovered a school of medieval Indian mathematics so advanced that none of his contemporaries could credit it.[80] The same correspondent recorded that Abbé

[76]See, e.g., Ludo Rocher (ed.), *Ezourvedam: a French veda of the eighteenth century* (Amsterdam, Philadelphia: Benjamins, 1984).

[77]*British Medical Journal* (July 1905), 136b.

[78]Ibid., (July 1905), 137.

[79]*Madras Mail* (11/5/1905), 4.

[80]See David Edwin Pingree, *Jyotiḥśāstra: astral and mathematical literature* (Wiesbaden: Harrassowitz, 1981), 65, f.n. 62, for literature on this school.

Dubois 'drew up several addresses in the Indian languages, and he set out upon a tour to disseminate the vaccination system',[81] a fact interesting in itself, though possibly based on the letter by Dubois cited earlier (p. 142). King's critical rejoinder two days later, claiming that the *Śabdakalpadruma* was completed in 1813, six years before the Virumbon letter, fell flat.[82] For, three days after that, the same 'Hindu correspondent' returned to the pages of the *Madras Mail* with more information on Ellis, whose life had come to a sudden and accidental end in 1819. Many points were raised, with discreet scholarship, but perhaps the one most relevant to the present enquiry was that after Ellis's death his belongings and papers were auctioned off, and a report current at the time held that 'they served Mr. Peter's cook for months to kindle his fire and singe fowls!' A few of Ellis's research papers did survive, however, and were collected by Sir Walter Elliot who, on his deathbed in 1887, offered them to Dr Pope, a Tamil scholar, but these are no longer traceable, and no mention of their contents can be found. The Hindu correspondent finished with some delightfully abstruse and learned remarks about the exact date of the first edition of the *Śabdakalpadruma*.[83]

The 'Hindu correspondent' turned, three days later, to the only really worthwhile business: trying to locate a *Śākteya grantha*.[84] He was not able to throw any light on the subject.

The next day, a letter appeared in the *Madras Mail* from a certain R. P. Karkaria of Bombay, who was rightly concerned to defend the reputations of Baron, Malcolm, Ellis and Anderson.[85] Karkaria continued his article four days later with an apparent switch of direction. Rather than defend those who may have perpetrated a pious fraud, Karkaria suggested that it might be the wrong Ellis who was under discussion. He noticed that Baron's index recorded J.A. Ellis, not F.W. Ellis, and went on to show that there was another Ellis in Madras at the time who was an out-and-out scoundrel. 'Could this man ... have been the unscrupulous scholar we are in search of who fabricated the poem? At least he had the requisite moral character to do such a deed'.[86] The only trouble was that this bad Ellis was called Charles John Robert, and there was no evidence that he knew Sanskrit. Karkaria also remarked that such of Ellis's papers as reached Dr Pope were deposited at the Bodleian library.[87]

[81] *Madras Mail* (11/5/1905), 4.
[82] Ibid., (13/5/1905), 6.
[83] Ibid., (16/5/1905), 8.
[84] Ibid., (19/5/1905), 3.
[85] Ibid., (20/5/1905), 7.
[86] Ibid., (24/5/1905), 7.
[87] Enquiries show no trace of them there today.

Another voice was raised in Ellis's 'defence' a few days later. John Law, a sculptor, wrote to the paper saying that, 'there are the strongest *a priori* reasons for the belief that such action [i.e., a pious fraud] would be repugnant to his instincts.' Law's proof was to quote Ellis's gravestone, which was extremely laudatory.[88]

This finally drew another response from King. He entered into a minute examination of the phraseology of Baron's passage about Ellis and Anderson, and decided that Karkaria's reason was 'exceedingly at fault,' that Malcolm was not the source of these ideas, and that 'Baron's memory of Malcolm's statements was seriously at fault'.[89] The *Madras Mail* debate had degenerated into mudslinging, and the 'Hindu correspondent' had the last shots two days later when he published the last letter in the series.[90] It added nothing of note, but managed to insult everyone involved, except perhaps poor old Ellis.

But King had the last word, and where it mattered more: in the *Indian Medical Gazette*. There he repeated the letters he had sent to the *British Medical Journal*, so that his professional colleagues in Calcutta would know of his self-vindication.[91]

A closer look at Virumbon's verses

Scores of catalogues of Sanskrit manuscripts have been published since the Virumbon article was published. With the benefit of modern research tools such as Raghavan's *New Catalogus Catalogorum* we are today in a much stronger position to say whether such a text as the *Śākteyagrantha* by Dhanvantari ever existed.[92]

The first problem is that '*Śākteyagrantha*' is not a title proper, but an adjectival phrase. It simply means 'a book on a *śākta* topic.' And no work answering to such a description appears in the *New Catalogus Catalogorum* as being attributed to Dhanvantari.

Another fixed point in this welter of opinion concerns the verses themselves, as quoted in their earliest form by Virumbon. They are not in proper Sanskrit, as they stand, even allowing for the archaic transliteration. Sources such as the *Śabdakalpadruma* and the *Āyurvedavijñāna*, which quote them in the Devanāgarī script, normalise them. So does Umeśachandra Gupta's *Vaidyakaśabdasindhu*, which also

---

[88] *Madras Mail* (29/5/1905), 6.

[89] Ibid., (30/5/1905), 7.

[90] Ibid., (1/6/1905), 5.

[91] *Indian Medical Gazette* (June 1905), 234, 284.

[92] V. Raghavan, *et al.*, *New Catalogus Catalogorum: an alphabetical register of Sanskrit and allied works and authors* (Madras: University of Madras, 1949–).

quotes them.[93]

The first line of Virumbon's passage as given in the original *Madras Mail* article is as follows:

> D,hénu stanya ma'súchi va Naránàn cha ma'súchicà.

The words 'ma'súchi va' can only be intended to be '*masūrikā*,' and are in fact translated thus by Virumbon ('the fluid of the pock [on the udder of a cow]'). Somehow the letter *ri* has become *chi*, and *ka* has become *va*. The most obvious way this could happen would be through a wrong reading of an unfamiliar script. There is an Indian alphabet in which these particular combinations of letters are easily confused, namely Bengali. The *ra/ca* confusion would be particularly easy in this script. It is at least possible, then, that Virumbon – himself a Tamil, as evidenced by his Tamil title Calvi 'learned' – was working from an original in the Bengali script. One thing, at least is clear: the passage is not a copy of the text which was given to Gillman.

Conclusion

Two facts may, in conclusion, be brought to the fore. First, as we have seen, upon careful examination it turns out that *all* citations of these particular verses are later than 1819. Therefore they are all almost certainly to be derived from Virumbon's article.

The second fact strikes a stronger blow against Virumbon's claim itself, and against all similar claims. There is good evidence – albeit negative – that the cow-pox virus has never existed naturally in India. When vaccination first became known, it was natural that physicians in India should try to find the lifesaving virus in the local cattle. This would have obviated the great labour involved in bringing the virus all the way from England. Several attempts were indeed made to find cow-pox, and two distinguished doctors have left written reports that no such virus was found in India. The first was Shoolbred, who devoted a whole chapter of his book to the question. He describes how in July 1803 he put a series of queries about this matter, addressed to medical men and the general public, into the *Calcutta Gazette*. The query read as follows:[94]

93 Umesachandra Gupta, *Vaidyakaśabdasindhu or a comprehensive lexicon of Hindu Medical terms and names of drugs* ... (Calcutta: Girisa-Vidyāratna press, 1895), 724b.

94 Shoolbred, *Report on the progress of vaccine inoculation* (1805), 50ff.

> Query 8. Have you any authentic information that the disease called cow-pox, as characterised by Dr Jenner and other late writers, exists among cows in any part of India? Or, that the practice of transferring the disease from the cow to the human subject, and subsequently from human subject to human subject, for the purpose of preventing the small-pox, was ever adopted in any part of the country, or, that the fact, that a certain matter originating in the teats or udder of the cow possessed such a power, was ever known by the Bramins, or any other class of natives, previously to the promulgation of Dr Jenner's discovery?

Shoolbred continued:

> Now, as the Calcutta Gazette is a paper which falls into the hands of almost every European in the country, and as the queries were repeated by several of the other weekly journals, it will be readily admitted, I hope, that such an address to the public was the most likely way of drawing forth any information that might be possessed by individuals on so curious and interesting a subjects. The answers to my queries were not so numerous as might have been expected. Several gentlemen, however, did take the trouble to answer them at considerable length; but I am sorry to say, that their communications are all completely destitute of any satisfactory proof of the existence of the vaccine disease among cows in any part of India. Some of them do mention an eruptive disease of cows, which the natives, in common with other eruptive diseases, distinguish by the general name of *gootee* [i.e., *guṭī*, 'spot'], and which proves fatal to many of them. This is obviously not the disease in question, which, though troublesome in a dairy, under the idea of impurity, and from its infecting quality, is never known to kill the cow. What would be the effect of inoculating the human subject with the product of a disease which kills the brute, it is impossible *à priori* to say. The experiment, I think, is by no means desirable; though I cannot help mentioning, that it had a very narrow escape of being tried, about the time the real vaccine disease was first imported into Bengal.

Shoolbred obviously tried hard to find evidence of autocthonic cow-pox, and found none.

Another testimony to the same fact comes from the well-known and distinguished doctor Whitelaw Ainslie, who published an important article on the history of smallpox, inoculation and vaccination in 1830.[95] Ainslie also asserted that cow-pox was not known in India, although he gave no evidence of the details of his investigations into the matter.

The final piece of evidence on this point concerns the reasons for the establishment of the King Institute of Preventive Medicine. This institute, as Lord Ampthill made plain in his inaugural speech, was necessary precisely in order to make possible a constant, pure supply of cow-pox vaccine. As Lord Ampthill said, 'bovine lymph was exceedingly sensitive to the heat of the Indian climate',[96] and it was very hard to transport. All the failed attempts to bring the original supply of vaccine to India from 1799 to 1802 also testify to the same fact. So too does the testimony of Shoolbred, who devoted another chapter to the difficulty of keeping cow-pox alive in the hot, humid Indian climate.[97] The cow-pox virus was very hard to maintain in India. This, above all, argues strongly for the fact that vaccination was not known in India before Jenner.

After a survey of the facts and opinions of the case, a great deal has been clarified, but it is not certain that we are any further forward historically. On balance, it does seem likely that a 'pious fraud' was perpetrated at the beginning of the nineteenth century in Madras, Bengal, or both, and perhaps more than once, in order to popularise vaccination. The tracts so produced were, of course, not literary frauds in the normal sense, and were produced out of strong humanitarian feelings. It is natural, if this was the case, that some such documents would be found subsequently, and taken for the genuine article. On the other hand, the document that found its way to Gillman seems to have been more genuinely fraudulent in intent.

Nawaub Mirza Mehady Ali Khan's evidence is again suspicious because of the use of the thread, a common British method of vaccinating, and for the other reasons given above that militate against the existence of cow-pox in India. Bruce's evidence from Persia, however, seems harder to explain away, and may have been entirely genuine.

---

[95] W. Ainslie, 'Observations respecting the small-pox and inoculation in Eastern countries, with some account of the introduction of vaccination into India', *Transactions of the Royal Asiatic Society of Great Britain and Ireland* (1830), 52–73.

[96] *British Medical Journal* (1905), 807a.

[97] Schoolbred, *Report on the progress of vaccine inoculation*, 28–32.

Chapter 10

The establishment of 'Native Lunatic Asylums' in early nineteenth-century British India

Waltraud Ernst

a measure which undoubtedly has for its objects the protection of the Public on one hand, and the relief of the most unhappy Class of human beings on the other.[1]

THE BRITISH-INDIAN ENCOUNTER in the late eighteenth and early nineteenth century can be characterised as a period not only of repeated military and diplomatic campaigns against Indian peoples by the English, but also of the commencement of enforced consolidation of English rule in regions already annexed. The prevention of acts of violence against civilians by Indians and unauthorised Europeans was a measure as important to the maintenance and extension of colonial power as the subsequent annexation of ever more areas, and the upkeep of military law and army discipline. Thus the creation of Courts of Law, the establishment of police forces and the erection of jails were vital means of guaranteeing English power and of controlling public life. So were other, less conspicuous, measures of social control, such as the erection of public hospitals – characteristically called 'police or pauper hospitals' – dispensaries, licensed brothels, work-houses, and last but not least lunatic asylums.[2]

---

[1]The Court of Directors of the East India Company's Despatch to Bengal, Judicial Department (henceforth: Bg. Jud. D.), 25.4.1806, 45.

[2]The concept of 'social control' is here taken up merely as a heuristic device to describe the process by which a society is brought in line with what are expressly (and unconsciously) defined to

It is within this context that it was decreed by the Court of Directors of the East India Company in 1802 that lunatic asylums for the reception of both criminal and freely wandering insane Indians ought to be established in Bengal.[3] The measure had been necessitated by the authorities' concern with public peace and order, which had frequently been disturbed by mischievous Indian lunatics committing violent actions. As the Courts of Circuit in Madras and Bombay expressed a similiar worry about stone throwing and otherwise dangerous lunatics, in those Presidencies too the erection of lunatic asylums for Indians was sanctioned.[4]

By 1820 a number of lunatic asylums for the exclusive reception of Indians (and of the lowest strata of Eurasians) had been established. In the Bengal Presidency provision for the safe custody and care of mad persons had been made in Calcutta, Bareilly, Benares, Dacca, Murshidabad and Patna. Each of these institutions contained between 35 and 170 people, the establishment in the Calcutta area being the largest one. Under the Government of Madras one asylum in the capital itself as well as in Chittoor, Tiruchchirappalli and Masulipatnam respectively had been constructed, whilst Bombay secured its public nuisances in only one small institution in Kolaba.[5] In the course of the following three decades changes in the condition of confinement and in medical paradigm took place. These are reflected in routine records and official inquiries and can thus serve as one source for a description of the asylum system at work in India. These reports in their rhetoric echo the fashions of treatment and conceptualisations then dominant in England and therefore provide yet one more example of how much Anglo-Indian administration

be the ideals of a particular society. Social control operates in defence of particular group interests and is enforced by means of state control, law, education and ideology.

For a detailed discussion of various concepts of 'social control' see S. Cohen and A. Scull (editors) *Social control and the state* (Oxford: Blackwell, 1985).

[3]Bg. Jud. D., 30.6.1802, 49ff.

[4]Deputy Register to the Court of Fazdari Adalat to Govt. 5.3.1817; Consultations/Proceedings of the Governor in Council of the Presidency of Madras, Judicial Department (henceforth: Md. Jud. Proc.) 17.3.1817, 8.

See also: Letter/Despatch of Governor in Council of the Presidency of Madras to Court of Directors of the East India Company, Judicial Department (henceforth: Md. Jud. L.), 11.3.1820, 17.

[5]Medical Board to Govt., 22.7.1818; Consultations/Proceedings of the Governor-General in Council of the Presidency of Bengal, Judicial Department (henceforth: Bg. Jud. Proc.) 28.8.1818, 53.

Govt. to Register to the Court of Fazdari Adalat, 2.12.1817; Md. Jud. Proc., 2.12.1817, 5.

Military Board to Govt., 14.4.1818; Md. Jud. Proc., 9.6.1818, 2ff.

Asylum Superintendent to Medical Board, 30.10.1820; Consultations/Proceedings of the Governor in Council of the Presidency of Bombay, Military Department (henceforth: Bm. Mil. Proc.), 8.11.1820, no number (henceforth: n. n.).

(Sir) Andrew Halliday, *A general view of the present state of Lunatics and Lunatic Asylums, in Great Britain and Ireland, and in some other Kingdoms* (London: Thomas and George Underwood, 1828), 67ff.

and public affairs were modelled on English (and Irish) institutions and ideas. The white rulers' ideology and their social habits and customs were, after all, seen as unquestionably superior, and their transplantation to India was thus an inevitable corollary.

What we may expect to emerge from the complex interrelation of English ideals, the assumption of superiority over an allegedly inferior people and the consequent peremptory permeation of economic and social life with the white rulers' spirit is – in respect to mental illness – a system not only modelled upon the one extant in England but also reflecting medical doctrines derived from the European body of knowledge rather than the traditions of *yūnāni* and *āyurveda* so easily at hand in India.

The 1818 inquiry in Bengal

it will be extremely desirable
that a general enquiry should be made
into the state of all Hospitals in question.[6]

Shortly after the revelations of the 1815/16 Select Committee on the better regulation of madhouses in England, and only about one decade after the introduction of native lunatic asylums in Bengal, a committee was set up by order of the Vice President in Council to inquire into the 'state and internal management of lunatic asylums' in Bengal. The target areas for the Bengal investigation were similar to those taken up by the Select Committee in England, and in fact the resulting rules for the future management and control of the institutions had been drawn up with close reference to the English Committee's recommendations. As the Bengal inquiry had been set up in the shadow of such grievances in asylums like Bethlem Hospital as when a William Norris had been found chained to the wall for an indefinite time, and of repeatedly expressed suspicions about similar defects in asylums in India, the disclosures resulting were not expected to be of a pleasing nature.

The Medical Board of Bengal in fact opened its report with words which sound rather like an early warning of what was to come in the evidence:[7]

> On the first foundation of these Establishments, the authorities entrusted with the selection and superintendence of the Buildings, appear to have been but very imperfectly acquainted with the real nature

[6]Govt. to Medical Board, 17.3.1818; Bg. Jud. Proc. 17.3.1818, 3, 3.
[7]Medical Board to Govt., 22.7.1818; Bg. Jud. Proc., 28.8.1818, 53, 5.

> and great ends of such Institutions, without reflecting that a Lunatic Asylum, in order to answer the true meaning of the term, is not merely a place for the detention and safe custody of Individuals dangerous to the peace of Society, but a retreat, providing for the tender care and recovery of a class of innocent persons suffering under the severest of afflictions to which humanity is exposed, they seemed to think this momentous duty assigned to them satisfactorily performed if the houses pitched upon had only the bare properties of a Lockup House.

How then had the institutional provision for Indian lunatics looked during the first ten years of its existence? To respond adequately to this question, without taking the alleged psychiatric advances of the present time as the unproblematical yardstick against which to measure early nineteenth-century provision for the mad, is not easy. One is continually sailing between the Scylla of anachronistic condemnation and the Charybdis of excusing the misdemeanours and atrocities of historical agents as somehow understandable in their context. Nevertheless, an attempt will be made to describe the asylums' state and the lunatics' condition in the 1810s with reference to contemporary conceptualisations – namely with emphasis on institutional and environmental factors as well as moral management.[8]

The importance of adequate buildings

The buildings are low and damp
and not half large enough for the number of patients,
to which must be attributed the numerous deaths which occur.[9]

Contemporary medical practitioners believed in the curative effect of institutionalisation *per se*, on account of the effects of a regimented daily routine and controlled surroundings on moral stabilisation, and of adequate and promptly administered medication on physical and mental well-being. The architectural properties of the

[8]The theory of moral management had a distinct influence on early nineteenth-century psychiatric thought. The term 'moral' was not only to designate the opposite of 'immoral' and 'vice' but also of 'physical' and 'intellectual'. The moral managers held that 'insanity was independent of physical disease and was to be located in the relationship between the emotions and the will' (V. Skultans, *English Madness, Ideas on Insanity, 1580–1890* (London: Routledge & Kegan Paul, 1979), 111). They rejected methods of physical treatment and control and instead aimed at restoring the will-power of the patient.

[9]Medical Board to Govt., 21.2.1818; India Office Records: Board's Collections (henceforth: B. Coll.), 1820/1, 617, 15.373, 20.

buildings were a main constituent of such institutional management; especially their capaciousness and their capacity to allow for free circulation of air – thus preventing dampness from creeping into the edifice and subsequently through the miasmatic substances into the patients' bodies and minds. Further, cleanliness, proper drainage as well as a supply of fresh water were considered essential. In all these respects the buildings in Bengal, used as lunatic asylums, were evaluated as 'defective', even as 'highly objectionable'.

The Rasapagla Asylum near Calcutta, for example, contained on average 150 lunatics, and was the main institution providing for mischievous persons and similar public nuisances taken off the capital's streets. Not only was it described as being 'liable to very weighty objections', but it was simply said of it that 'In short ... a worse situation could not be found'.[10] Similarly, the Murshidabad Asylum which also had to serve a large catchment-area, was regarded as 'wholly unfit', the building being 'altogether a wretched place even in its best state ... and now falling to ruins'.[11]

The Patna Asylum, opened one year previously, was said to 'labour under disadvantages greater even than those pointed out' as existing in Murshidabad.[12] Whilst the building itself was 'of good masonry and in excellent repair', it was erected on low ground – close to the breeding-ground of miasmas – and was provided with bad brackish water. The death-rate consequently reached an enormous 52%.[13]

Opinions in regard to the Bareilly Asylum differed considerably. The Magistrate and the Medical Officer in charge deemed the building to be 'in excellent repair, airy, clean and ... well constructed for its purpose'.[14] The Medical Board for its part were of opinion that it was objectionable, due to wanting classification and separation of lunatics, but also because of the lack of an exercise area and its generally confined state. A total of 105 patients were being accommodated in 29 cells, out of which five were occupied by single patients; consequently four persons were confined in a cell not bigger than 10 by 8 feet.[15]

For the Benares Asylum which was stated to be 'on a scale (so) contracted and insufficient', and in addition to bear 'the appearance more of a prison than of an Asylum for Lunatics',[16] a detailed description of the premises was given:[17]

[10]Ibid.

[11]Medical Board to Govt., 22.7.1818; Bg. Jud. Proc., 28.8.1818, 53, 48f.

[12]Ibid., 59.

[13]Ibid., 59, 64.

[14]Ibid., 81.

[15]Ibid.

[16]Ibid., 71f.

[17]Ibid., 69, 71.

> The body of the place forms an area of 121 by 61 feet. Interiorly it is parted off into two Divisions only, one for the men and another for the women. The only entrance from without is by means of a porch 16 by 8 feet which opens by doors into the Men's Court Yard. This Yard is only sixty two by fifty eight feet, is of an irregular shape, and has in its centre a large well, whence issues a drain, which having in various directions traversed the whole range of the building completely encircles its external wall and at length makes its exit at the Southern boundary of the premises. The Court Yard is fronted by a tiled Verandah of 8 feet, round which 17 Cells, 13 feet by 12, and four 12 by 12 are disposed. The Cell opens externally by battened doors and iron bars and internally by doors only. They are about 12 feet high and with the adjoining Verandah are terraced all round ... The hospital is surrounded by a boundary wall of 244 feet by 205, about 12 feet in height and 16 in thickness. It appears to be removed no further than 60 or 70 feet from the body of the building. Confined as it is, several portions are occupied by an infirmary and a cook room, each measuring 57 by 12, a Chuprassie's Cookroom, and the men's privy, which by a strange anomaly has been removed away from the side to which it rightly belongs, and placed in a distant corner, facing the female ward.

Finally, and last but in no respect least, the Dacca Asylum – which was in fact a house rented for only Rs. 16 per month, providing for 30–50 lunatics – was simply stated to be a 'miserable hovel'.[18]

On the basis of this kind of information the physical state of lunatic asylums in Bengal was regarded as being defective. In a general evaluation the institutions were characterised as 'small, damp and unwholesome hovels' which were beyond all conceivable attempt at improvement. Consequently it was concluded by the Medical Board of Bengal that 'without wholly building them anew, it is not easy to propose any effectual remedies'.[19] Although the latter recommendation seems sensible, it did not see an early implementation on an improved scale.[20]

---

[18] Ibid., 35.

[19] Ibid., 6.

[20] Even at Dacca and Murshidabad, where the erection of new premises had been already under way since 1818, the design of these buildings was declared to raise strong doubts about whether they would guarantee adequate facilities.

Medical Board to Govt., 22.7.1818; Bg. Jud. Proc., 28.8.1818, 53, 47, 54.

The importance of diet

The food is perhaps too meagre
as adapted to persons in good bodily health.[21]

Apart from housing, air circulation and drainage, a well-designed, balanced dietary regime was seen as an important constituent of traditional curative and preventive medicine; the conditions in respect to food supplies were, however, insufficient and unwholesome. This defect might be closely related to the fact that it was the surgeons who supplied the food against payment of standard rates and who obviously made a good bargain for themselves in quite a few instances. The art of economising on food provisions lay in the drawing up of high provision bills which matched an equally sophisticated – though not blatantly exaggerated – diet plan, on the one hand, and the distribution of low-quality food in low quantities to the patients, on the other. The result was that in contradiction to all medical art, the surgeon provided food 'too meagre as adapated to persons in good bodily health'.[22] In the official language this system was described as,[23]

> an arrangement by which the interest of the Surgeon was put in opposition to his duty, and by which there was too much reason to believe that, on some occasions at least, the health and life (of the patients) was sacrificed to the avarice of the Surgeon.

Along with this conflict of personal interest and medical duty went the evaluation of lunatics' provision with food and other necessaries in generally contradictory terms – depending on who submitted the information. In relation to the Dacca Asylum – where the surgeon emphasised the adequacy of the food supplies – the Medical Board said:[24]

> In all that relates to the housing, accommodation, and feeding of the patients this establishment is extremely objectionable, and betrays such total unacquaintance with, and inadequacy to secure, the true objects of such institutions, as are never found except in the infancy of their progress.

---

[21] Ibid., 67.

[22] Ibid.

[23] The Court of Directors of the East India Company's Despatch to Bengal, Military department (henceforth: Bg. Mil. D.), 26.8.1818, 147. The quoted statement had been made in reference to army hospitals. However, there is little evidence to refute the assumption that the situation in civil institutions had been much different from those referred to.

[24] Medical Board to Govt., 22.7.1818; Bg. Jud. Proc., 28.8.1818, 53, 35, 40.

Similarly the surgeon of the Patna Asylum painted a much more favourable depiction of the provision he made as the purveyor of victuals to the insane than the Medical Board which had assessed the diet as being 'too meagre':[25]

> The daily allowance is 12 Chattacks of rice, 2 Chattacks of Dall, some Salt and potatoes or indigenous vegetables. No meat is served out, but Wine, Sago, Soups, Gruel, Milk and Atta are granted in Cases of Sickness or as indulgences to meet the wishes of individual patients. Each patient has a blanket, mat, and straw, and two Kummerbunds or pieces of Cloth, which are changed every second day. The sick are accommodated with *Charpoys.*

The institution's daily routine

indulging the unhappy objects ... with innocent games and other harmless means of recreation.[26]

There exist further accounts, provided by the surgeons, which describe the institutions' daily routine in almost idyllic terms – the narrative resembling descriptions of prestigious places in England, well known for their decidedly humane approach. Although their veracity may be doubted, they can be interpreted as representing part of the rhetoric in which the medical professionals themselves preferred to represent or legitimise their work to the outside world.

The routine in the Rasapagla Asylum, for example, was described as follows:[27]

> A patient is immediately upon being admitted into the Hospital bathed, carefully cleaned, and dressed. So soon as the peculiar type of insanity with which he is afflicted has been ascertained, he is placed with others in a similar condition, and as far as it is practicable, with persons of the same tribe or Caste with himself. This leads the way to their classification and thus the frantic, turbulent, and dirty patients are readily separated from the placid melancholy and convalescent ... Morning and Evening the Male and Female patients are at different periods taken out by their respective keepers and walked about in the airing grounds. Whilst they are abroad the wards are washed and scoured, and the whole of the bedding hung up and exposed to the sun ...

[25] Ibid., 67.

[26] Rules for the future management and control of the Insane Hospitals (henceforth: Rules); Bg. Jud. Proc., 28.8.1818, 55.

[27] Medical Board to Govt., 22.7.1818; Bg. Jud. Proc., 28.8.1818, 53, 26 ff.

> during the heat of the day the patients sit either in their several apartments or in the Verandah in front of them, and are allowed to amuse and employ themselves in any innocent occupation. At the fall of the evening they retire to their sleeping rooms and during the whole of the night are carefully watched by relays of keepers, who are incessantly on the move to preserve silence and prevent accidents. The patients are regularly fed twice a day. Their food consists chiefly of the articles usually eaten by persons in the same line of life with themselves but where necessary it is varied in every way likely to meet the prejudice or peculiar appetites of individual patients. Fruit and other harmless indulgences are allowed in addition to the principle meal; the diet is of course carefully adapted to the state of the bodily and mental health of the patients; for the boisterous and intractable manic it is principally or altogether made up of vegetables, whilst in the case of the feeble and emaciated melancholic, it is partly composed of animal food and wine.

The tender care of patients

The 'attentive and humane conduct of the keepers, and subordinate attendants'.[28]

The number of staff employed, their attitude and behaviour towards the patients, the measures taken for the upkeep of discipline and order, as well as for the prevention of violent actions, were further aspects seen to determine the proper management of an institution and to guarantee the proper care of its inmates. Yet there prevailed no uniform personnel policy;[29] neither was there any provision made which would have enabled a controlling board to establish how well the staff cared for the inmates and to what extent mechanical restraint and corporal punishment was being practised or abused.

In any case it would have been very difficult to establish the quality of care and humane treatment bestowed on patients, especially if one considers the ambiguity inherent in some such evaluations of services as: 'approaching as nearly to perfection as is consistant with the nature, habits, and education of Natives'.[30] Given that these carefully vague and indeterminate words originated from the mouths of surgeons and magistrates – whose opinion of 'Natives', of their nature, habits

[28]Rules; Bg. Jud. Proc., 28.8.1818, 55.
[29]Medical Board to Govt., 22.7.1818; Bg. Jud. Proc., 28.8.1818, 53, 65, 81.
[30]Ibid., 25.

and education, was not as a rule a very high one – the quality of services provided may not be expected to stand favourable comparison with public institutions for lower-class Europeans.

In fact, the provision in the Asylums for Indians was regarded by the English to be of such inferior quality that there was a great deal of resistance to the admission of Europeans into the Rasapagla Asylum. It was then argued that, 'Even were not the propriety of mixing Europeans labouring under mental derangement with Natives in the same unfortunate condition in itself very questionable, the Native Hospital, as it now stands, is in no way fitted for their reception'.[31] It was argued that neither was the Asylum roomy enough nor did it provide conveniences which were necessary for the comfort of the European. Further, there were no European servants attached, and the medical attendance was seen as being objectionable: 'it may be doubted whether, upon their removal to Russapaglah, this degree of attention [i.e., unremitting] could well be shown by the Medical Officer attached to the Native Lunatic Hospital, whose residence is at a great distance from the Asylum, and whose time is in part occupied by various other professional vocations of an equally important nature'.[32]

The vagueness of the few accounts and reports available contrasts starkly with the Medical Board's wish that the conduct of the keepers and subordinate attendants should be characterised by 'tenderness, forebearance and gentleness of demeanour'.[33] Further, it seems not to have been an easy task to reconcile the claim of providing institutional settings, judged well-adapted to the lunatics' former habits, with the reformers' demand of providing humane treatment – hence the ambiguities and contradictions. Administrators' disinterest and/or incompetence in matters of institutional management may, however, be an alternative explanation for the sometimes astonishing divergence of outcomes from stated objectives.

Kind and gentle treatment and the use of mechanical restraint

In consequence of the inquiry of 1818 the number of staff was prescribed. It was further ruled that the asylum superintendent was to guarantee the 'attentive and humane conduct of the keepers and subordinate attendants'.[34] Whilst adherence to the principle of employing a sufficient number of staff could henceforth be easily checked by auditing the pay accounts, it was still not transparent how patients

[31] Medical Board to Govt., 5.2.1821; Consultations/Proceedings of the Governor-General in Council of the Presidency of Bengal, Public Department (henceforth: Bg. Pub. Proc.), 20.2.1821, 32, no paragraph.

[32] Ibid.

[33] Rules; Bg. Jud. Proc., 28.8.1818, 55.

[34] Ibid.

were being treated as a matter of daily routine in general and in cases of furious emergencies in particular. The latter may to a certain extent be deducted from the means of appeasement said to have been in use in the 1810s.

The medical superintendent of the Benares Asylum mentioned recourse to a wide variety of restraints: 'When violent, maniacs are subjected to a course of sedative medicines, secluded in solitary cells or placed in the stocks'.[35] The first intervention might be viewed favourably in the light of today's custom of freely administering drugs, and so it was then; the second found, on grounds of the potential danger of suicide, no favour with the Medical Board; the last means was explicitly criticised. The Board made it clear that they thought the employment of stocks unnecessary, when 'such excellent means of coercion as the waistcoat or manacles can always be had so readily at hand'.[36]

It finally came to recommend that:[37]

> unnecessary coercion be never used, that irons be not employed except in extreme cases and then only manacles or light leg chains, and that where a preference is given to the strait waist coat it be used with discretion and be neither tied (too) tight or kept on (too) long.

Whilst in England the use of mechanical restraint, even in cases of violent paroxysms, remained a controversial issue during the heyday of the York Retreat's campaign for mild and gentle moral therapy, it was not questioned, let alone done away with, in lunatic asylums in Bengal. The support of mechanical restraint – in persistant disregard of the Court of Directors' preference for reformed treatment – was theoretically grounded in the assumption of the more sudden onset and more violent course of insanity amongst both Indians and Europeans when exposed to tropical climate. This argumentation lacked, however, persuasive power as it was simultaneously held that 'instances of raving madness are fortunately rare amongst the Natives of India'.[38]

Segregation in the asylum versus 'the unrestrained mixture of the Male and Female Patients.'

One special aspect of asylum management was, however, widely criticised: namely the inadequate segregation of patients in general and the improper, that is immoral, mixing of men and women in particular.

[35] Medical Board to Govt., 22.7.1818; Bg. Jud. Proc., 28.8.1818, 53, 72.
[36] Ibid.
[37] Rules; Bg. Jud. Proc., 28.8.1818, 55, no para.
[38] Medical Board to Govt., 22.7.1818; Bg. Jud. Proc., 28.8.1818, 53, 27.

The Dacca Asylum, for example, where '30–50 have been promiscuously huddled together in a hired house',[39] was described with a similar loathing to Murshidabad where 'scenes of the utmost licentiousness' prevailed.[40] The situation seems to have been so unmentionably shocking that the Board summarised the situation in Bengal by recourse to happenings less closely at hand, i.e., England, where[41]

> in the progress of the humane and useful enquiries recently instituted by the House of Commons into the history of Lunatic Asylums in England, no feature amidst the numerous scenes of gross mismanagement there brought to light, appears to have been productive of more serious consequences or to have excited deeper regret, than that of the looseness of morals consequent on the unlimited communication of bad[42] persons of both sexes,

Consequently it was suggested that due attention should be paid to the separation and 'if practicable', to the total disjunction of the male and female tranches of the establishments – a conditional suggestion which was neither very emphatic (in contrast to the above expressed indignation at indelicate occurrances) nor very likely to be generally 'practicable' within the context of the buildings' confined state.[43]

Medical treatment versus general management and discipline

Whilst medical treatment is mentioned as having been 'confined to instances of furious maniacs and of periodical violent paroxisms', consisting mainly of 'a course of sedative medicines', moral treatment was observed to have been restricted to such measures as maniacs being locked up in solitary cells or placed in irons.[44]

One medical doctor summarised the situation, saying that:[45]

> the medical management here as in other cases cannot be accurately described. It varies in a thousand ways, according to the previous habits and temperament of the patient; the causes, kind and degree of his

[39] Ibid., 50.

[40] Ibid., 35.

[41] Ibid.

[42] The 'bad' being later on rectified to 'mad' by an attentive and presumably less excitable pencil.

[43] Rules; Bg. Jud. Proc., 28.8.1818, 55, no para. In fact, the improvement of the buildings went on very slowly. For example, in regard to the repair of the Patna Asylum, even four years after the inquiry no steps whatsoever had been taken (Resolution, 18.7.1822; Bg. Jud. Proc., 18.7.1822, 2, 2.)

[44] Medical Board to Govt., 22.7.1818; Bg. Jud. Proc., 28.8.1818, 53, 72.

[45] Ibid., 89.

> malady, and its ever changing Symptoms – It may however be stated generally, that it mainly consists of attention to the amusement and the cleanliness of the patients and to the condition of their bodily health and of their bowels, in avoiding irritation, and in taking advantage where the disease of the mind seems to have originated in the state of the body, to make the removal of its cause subservient to recovery.

It may be concluded that medical treatment had been administered mainly in cases of bodily ailments – and then only sporadically – dependent on the various doctors' professional preferences and committment to the insane; and with varying success.[46] The Medical Board's reform suggestions similarly contained but a few general references to medical treatment. However, further diversification of the application of traditional medicine by frequent recourse to measures so prominent in England, such as cold and hot baths, Madeira wine and 'Europe Medicines' was recommended.[47]

It thus appears that medical treatment was regarded to be of minor importance in the management of the Indian insane. This was in fact to a great extent so not only in India. The first decades of English nineteenth-century psychiatry were characterised by a special concern for the quality of institutional provision, for the humane treatment of lunatics and the establishment of public control over the institutions which were seen to have been so prone to abuse.[48] The emphasis in India, too, lay on environmental aspects and official control of the institution's management. The Medical Board explicitly stated that the enquiry of 1818 had been one on 'general management and discipline ... rather than on the pathological history of the disorders and the remedies adapted to its several kinds of states'.[49] The medical aspect was consequently only rarely referred to.

Similarly the first responses to the reformed system which resulted from the uncovering of and inquiry into the state of affairs in the Bengal asylums referred to exactly these aspects of supervision and control. The Superintendent of the Benares Asylum, for example, maintained with satisfaction that the 'Darkness in which these places were involved' had given way to the 'firm and open light of Day'.[50] He at

---

[46] If success of treatment is measured in mortality and cure rates, the picture shown in Table 1 emerges. Tables compiled from: Medical Board to Govt., 22.7.1818; Bg. Jud. Proc., 28.8.1818, 53, 31, 51, 64; Medical board to Govt., 1.6.1821; Bg. Jud. Proc., 21.8.1821, 5 (Enclosure).

[47] Rules; Bg. Jud. Proc., 28.8.1818, 55.

[48] The 1815/16 Select Committee on the better regulation of madhouses in England and the subsequent campaigns aimed at public control of institutions and of their internal management. It was, however, not until 1842 and 1845 that consequential Acts were finally passed.

[49] Medical Board to Govt., 22.7.1818; Bg. Jud. Proc., 28.8.1818, 53, 30.

[50] Medical Board to Govt., 6.6.1821; Bg. Jud. Proc., 21.8.1821, 4, no para.

Rasapagla Asylum (1812–1817)	
average admitted annually	108
average in Asylum annually	150
average discharged cured annually	108 = 72% of total
average died annually	25 = 17% of total
Murshidabad Asylum (1817)	
admitted during the year	65
total in Asylum	127
discharged cured	39 = 31% of total
died	34 = 27% of total
Patna Asylum (1817/8)	
admitted during the year	50
discharged cured	2 = 4% of admissions
died	26 = 52% of admissions
Overall numbers for Bareilly, Benares, Dacca, Murshidabad, Rasapagla (1819/20)	
admitted	300
total in asylums	748
discharged cured	202 = 27% of total
died	62 = 8% of total

Table 1: *Success of treatment.*

the same time, however, also raised some early doubts as to the extent to which rules concerned mainly with the control of management and discipline may ensure the surgeon's diligence and devotion:[51]

> fine and noble Buildings may be erected and the best Regulations may be written in vain unless the Medical Officer fully and faithfully discharge his duty. The Medical charge of such a place is attended with a heavy responsibility, and is not suited to the habits and disposition of every practitioner.

The tone of this assessment suggests that the writer was acquainted with certain reformed approaches towards the management of the insane in England. 'Moral

[51] Ibid.

therapy' was the approach upon which the York Retreat in England had based its reformed asylum management. The institution was run by Quakers who possessed no medical expertise, but believed in the curability of insanity if only the mad were treated kindly, with attention, and as little mechanical restraint as possible. The superintendent's humane devotion and attentiveness as well as his moral influence on the lunatic's mind consequently played a key role.

Mention of the York Retreat in the context of the treatment of the insane in India seems appropriate not merely because the management in the former contrasts so evidently with the practice in the latter, nor because some surgeons in India were at least familiar with the Retreat's regime, and critical of the state of affairs in India. Rather, the Medical Board's rhetoric itself showed very strong affinity to the jargon of 'moral management'. This fact is worth mentioning because this Board could by force of its medical authority – at least at times and potentially – influence the happenings in European medicine in India. That the Board's practical achievements did, however, fall very much short of its rhetoric has to be emphasised.[52]

The limitations of 'moral therapy' in India

With the rhetoric being sometimes so far ahead of the practice, some contradictory and unconvincingly argued accounts of medical and moral treatment and theory seem inevitable. Further, there arose some difficulties specific to the Indian context. For example, keeping the insane's mind and body occupied with some activity was seen as an important prerequisite of moral treatment – a doctrine which did not seem to always have appealed to Indian lunatics. A surgeon in Bengal argued:[53]

> Employment would be most desirable, but besides their mental unfitness there are the prejudices of Cast, of which many seem perfectly sensible.

Through more or less gentle and mild persuasion such 'prejudices' were, however, at times overcome and the patients were 'indulged' with innocent games and

[52]It should be noted that renowned people in England were frequently intrigued by well-formulated reports from India. Such was the case with Sir Andrew Halliday who enthusiastically praised the provision for the Indian insane in India. Being himself engaged in campaigning for uniform regulations and strict control of English lunatic asylums he was particularly impressed by the measures of throwing the asylums in India 'open to the public, under proper regulations; and the placing at the head of each hospital, a British medical officer, of tried judgement and experience, with a fixed salary or allowance, altogether independent of the number of patients under his superintendence' (Sir A. Halliday, *A general view of the present State of Lunatics, and Lunatic Asylums, in Great Britain and Ireland, and in some other Kingdoms* (London: Thomas and George Underwood, 1828), 64.).

[53]Medical Board to Govt., 6.6.1821; Bg. Jud. Proc., 21.8.1821, 4, no para.

other 'harmless means of recreation'.[54] They were employed in the spinning of hemp, and the cultivation of rice, tea, tobacco, etc. Thereby, it was claimed, the surgeon would 'gain their confidence' and would 'reclaim them to the enjoyment and exercise of reason'.[55]

Apart from the problem of finding the right sort of employment for patients it seems to have been not so clear of what exactly the most adequate approach towards Indians' mental illness should have consisted. Whilst the lunatics were, for example, frequently referred to as deserving 'tender compassion and care',[56] the 'true method' of cure was repeatedly held to consist of a 'just medium' between 'harsh and indiscriminate confinement' and 'their jumbling together and unlimited intercourse'.[57]

However, not only did the Medical Board express its recommendations in at times contradictory or awkward terms, it also pointed expressly to the contrast between the desirable situation and that existing. The prison-like Benares Asylum, for example, was described as 'deficient in all the requisites for medical and moral treatment'; and it was even assumed that not 'much could be done towards effecting a cure of the unhappy persons under its roof'.[58] In reference to the Patna Asylum the Medical Board seemed not only to attempt to localise factors affecting cure efficiency but even to explicitly have subscribed to a consequent moral therapy approach, and the concomitant assumption that not so much the patient's body but their *mind* was to be and could be cured and that their wrongly connected thoughts might be normalised:[59]

> The contracted nature of the Institution, the particular habits and prejudices of the patients, and the limited measures of intercourse taking place between the Medical Attendants and their patients, have hitherto

[54]Rules; Bg. Jud. Proc., 28.8.1818, 55.
When for example Assistant Surgeon F. P. Strong had been accused of providing inadequate treatment and care for the Indian insane in the Rasapagla Asylum, he pointed out the various employments and amusements in which the inmates were involved: music, dancing, cards (after their own fashion); spinning, weaving, cleaning, gardening, cultivation; the inmates were said to have raised 'coffee, cotton, sugar-cane, anuath, mulberry, casaiva, tapioca, sapan-wood, alva plant (for rope making)'. It was added that 'their coffee in 1832 was highly approved by the London brokers' (Summary of Correspondence relating to the Calcutta Asylum for Insane Patients (henceforth: Summary), 30.10.1847; B. Coll., 1852, 2494, 141.296, 52.).

[55]Rules; Bg. Jud. Proc., 28.8.1818, 55.

[56]Medical Board to Govt., 22.7.1818; Bg. Jud. Proc., 28.8.1818, 53, 40.

[57]Ibid., 55.

[58]Ibid., 72.

[59]Ibid., 68.

> in this asylum as every other Insane Hospital placed under similar disadvantages acted as insuperable obstacles to the introduction of that general branch of management which looks to the recovery of the patient by the regulation of his mind and better direction of its principal trains of thoughts. The Board fear that this want of control over the volitions of the maniacs, will long prove an irremediable defect in these Institutions.

This prognosis as regards the general amenability of lunatic institutions in India to change towards the reformed treatment of the patients' mind sounds pessimistic. The factors indentified as an impediment to cure, apart from the buildings, were the restricted patient-doctor interaction and last but not least the Indians' customs and preferences. Comprised under the latter might have been not merely certain eating and drinking habits which might at times have counteracted the dietary and medication regime (i.e., meat and wine for Hindu or Muslim melancholics),[60] but also the yet unresolved problem whether the Indians' mind was at all susceptible to moral treatment.

Results of the 1818 inquiry

The investigation into the state of lunatic asylums in Bengal in 1818 had produced a report nearly as voluminous as the 1815/16 Select Committees' on the better regulation of madhouses in England. The evidence brought forward might give one an impression of a similar, more or less unmitigated gloom; and it must be said that there is little evidence to relieve this impression. The main features emerging from the inquiry in Bengal were the only moderate control of gross abuses, the rectification of the institutions' physical defects 'whenever practicable', and strongly expressed avowals to humane and moral treatment, proper gender segregation, and classification of lunatics.

The native lunatic asylums in Bengal in the 1830s and early 1840s

During the decade following the inquiry of 1818, not much of consequence seems to have happened as regards the situation of Indian lunatics confined in European institutions. The correspondence of officials charged with the superintendence of asylums is characterised by frequent reference to

[60] Ibid., 29.

the 'rules for management' laid down by the Medical Board. From the individual asylum returns not many details about the treatment can therefore be extracted. The 'light of the day' taking the former 'darkness'' place seems to have faded away and only blazed up for the composition of routine reports in the course of the 1830s and 1840s. The medical experts merely observed that adherence to the rule of control prevailed in the reports, and that they gave evidence for the smooth running of the institutions.

Although this formal procedure did presumably not affect the inmates much – for better or worse – it can be assumed that the condition under which Indian lunatics were confined varied up to the 1850s to a certain extent according to the internal management pursued by the superintendent in charge, the general state of the building and the understanding between staff and inmates. Some petty-corruption and mismanagement continued to be revealed, officially disapproved and disposed of, or forgotten about. In general though, calmness seems to have prevailed. A calmness which is highlighted by contrast with the noisy struggle of the medical professionals in India and in England during the 1830s and 1840s to consolidate their position as the exclusively responsible and authorised body of experts in the area of the healing arts. Schools of medicine were established, medical journals inaugurated and rules for qualification as surgeon or physician prescribed.[61] At about the same time the 'Orientalists' in India lost out to the 'Educationalists' who were guided by the spirit of Evangelism and Utilitarianism and succeeded in establishing European science, ideas and morals as the universal yardstick.

The impact of a gradually increasing race and class conscious atmosphere which was to take over from the earlier period of less antagonistic and openly hostile – albeit distant – European-Indian interaction or rather English non-interference in Indian customs and traditions, was not immediately felt in lunatic asylums. Firstly, they had been established only in the 1810s and had since been under the unquestioned superintendence of Europeans anyway. Secondly, the question of lunacy neither had high priority within European medicine during the first half of the century nor was it a main concern of the English officials who were busy

[61] In 1825 the first volume of the *Transactions of the Medical and Physical Society, Calcutta* was published. In 1835 the Medical College in Calcutta, was established.

pacifying new areas, settling the revenue and establishing law and police order.

The distinction between harmless idiots and the dangerously insane

Confinement of mentally ill Indians came to be restricted to cases involving breaches of the peace, namely violent threats to the European community. If one wants to trace any systematic policy during the 1830s and '40s, then one might merely find the preferential confinement of criminal lunatics and of violent people instead of 'harmless idiots'. The latter had previously tended to crowd the notoriously confined establishments and were consequently set free.

This policy could, of course, only prevail on the basis of a medical theory similarly differentiating between idiocy and insanity, and an express criterion for admission and discharge which favoured incarceration of those who did or were likely to commit acts of violence against themselves or members of the public. For example, reasons given for the decrease in the number of patients and in expenses at the Rasapagla Asylum from 1820 to 1840 had included the retention of bad cases only, and the disposal of tractable patients to their relatives, in addition to the regulation of the control system and general management improvements (see table 2[62]).

		Average admission	Total patients	Total expenditure (Rs)
Five years ending	1820	102 1/5	853	77.472
ditto	1825	103 1/5	610	44.990
ditto	1830	118 4/5	615	39.808
ditto	1835	137 4/5	624	39.437
ditto	1840	129 2/5	676	41.625

Table 2: *Number of patients and expenses, Rasapagla Asylum, 1820–1840.*

Separate cells for lunatics in provincial jails vs. extension of the asylum system

Another problem which appeared repeatedly – though one which never aroused any determined interference by Government – had been the confinement of lunatics in provincial jails. Separate cells for violent maniacs had been kept in many

[62]Source: Summary, 30.10.1847; B. Coll., 1852, 2494, 141.296, 51.

small towns which were endowed with a jail but not with an asylum.[63] This was in general not regarded as an inappropriate or disadvantageous measure. There were some complainants, however, who suggested separate premises for lunatics on grounds of the incompatability of prisoners and the insane – the inmates frequently annoyed each other.[64]

An exemplary official correspondence relating to the suggested erection of an asylum at Jabbalpur instead of jail confinement of lunatics can be cited here. The response of the Chief Secretary to Government may be seen as illustrative of the sensibly pragmatic, though narrowly bureaucratic, expense-orientated and medically uninformed approach towards lunacy which prevailed aside from reform suggestions and routine institutional management of the insane. It thus shows the wide range of controversial opinions and approaches within which measures towards the institutionalisation of the insane emerged.

The Chief Secretary forbade the proposed outlay on an asylum in Jabbalpur for the following reasons:[65]

> 1st Because he doubts the utility of such establishments generally, the good which they are capable of effecting being alloyed by equal or greater evil arising from the unnecessary removal of Lunatics from the care of their friends, and the congregating of those unhappy persons together where they are not likely to be sufficiently attended to.
> 2nd Because the same reasons which are assigned, rendering the measure desirable at Jubbulpore, are equally applicable elsewhere, where similar institutions are not allowed.
> 3rd Because the Expense will be greater, than is stated, and will always have a tendency to increase; the assurance to the contrary, being with reference to experience delusive.

This official decision against the *extension* of lunatic asylums beyond the number of institutions already existing in the bigger European stations passed the scrutiny of the Medical Board and the Court of Directors. This makes one assume that either they were indifferent to it or unaminously supported the restriction of institutional provision.

---

[63] Bg. Jud. D., 2.4.1845, 187, 228. India Public Despatch (henceforth: I. Pub. D.), 12.8.1857, 9.

[64] Agent, Sangor and Nerbadda, to Govt., 11.12.1830; Consultations/Proceedings of the Governor-General in Council of the Presidency of Bengal, Political Department (henceforth: Bg. Pol. Proc.), 31.12.1830, 20, 4.

[65] Chief Secretary to Government to Secretary to Governor General, 18.3.1831; Bg. Pol. Proc., 18.3.1831, 27, 2.

The suggestion of one central asylum

Towards the late 1840s again a suggestion for reform had been submitted to the Medical Board of Bengal, and was rejected.[66] This time the suggestion was found inexpedient due to its main idea of one *centrally* located public lunatic asylum for both Indians *and* Europeans, run on similar principles to Hanwell Asylum – the latter being the then prominent large-scale asylum in England which practised 'total non-restraint' under Dr J. Connolly.

The petitioner had just returned from England where he had visited renowned asylums and had become convinced that insanity could be cured if only it was treated quickly and within an effectively organised institution. The asylum was to be run by medical experts because only they were in a position to make correct decisions about the nature and kind of a patient's affliction and recommend adequate moral treatment and medical prescriptions.

The suggestion was not approved of – due to both its inherent disloyalty towards the medical establishment in Bengal and its outrageous plan of keeping Europeans and Indians within the same walls.[67] The separate institutions for Indians and Europeans were therefore to be continued and the idea of a reformed panopticon was not to be realised in Bengal.

The call for an investigation into the state of Native Lunatic Asylums in Bengal

The same suggestion, together with suspicions about the European superintendents' petty corruptions and highly divergent cure and death-rates in the asylums of the North-Western Provinces, led to separate investigations into the condition of both the asylums for Indians and for Europeans in the 1850s. Whilst the condition of Indian lunatics had, according to the evidence brought forward, not changed much, the way in which the investigation was approached and evaluated by the Medical Board differed considerably from the administration of the 1818 inquiry.[68]

[66]G. A. Berwick, M. D. to Govt., 5.3.1847; Bg. Pub. Proc., 26.5.1847, 12, no para.

[67]Medical Board to Govt., 20.10.1847; Bg. Pub. Proc., 21.6.1848, 6, 41: 'both facts and figures are opposed to the wholescale transplantation of the Native Lunatics of all the Provinces of Lower Bengal to Calcutta as well as the crude and incongruous scheme of assembling Europeans and Natives in one Establishment'.

[68]In fact, the investigation of the 1850s did not have the official status of a general inquiry. Rather, the authorities were asked by the Court of Directors to provide information on treatment in general and causes for deaths in particular. Consequently the investigation extended over a period of several years due to the initial unsatisfactory reports from Bengal and the North-Western Provinces and the Court's repeated demand for more detailed information.

The inquiries into the kind and the results of treatment in Native Lunatic Asylums (1852–1854)

In contrast to the earlier inquiry the investigation in the 1850s aimed at an evaluation of the modes of *treatment* practiced in certain institutions and at a specification of the *causes* which may have led to the greatly varying cure and death-rates (see Table 3[69]).[70] This change in emphasis not only in the specifica of treatment imposed on patients but also in its relative effect – instead of management and control of the institution – reflects a tendential shift in the medical professionals' preoccupation in general. In particular it had been – apart for the expenses, of course – the

	1846	1847	1848	1849	Total	Total average no. of days in the Asylum
Asthma	1		1		2	743.91
Cholera	1	5	1	3	10	248.08
Debility & exhaustion	11	9	11	8	39	33.55
Dysentery & diarrhoea	19	22	19	11	71	809.08
Dropsy		1		5	6	947.25
Drowning by falling into well		1	1		2	4,287.00
Epilepsy		9	7	8	24	614.96
Fever				1	1	415.00
Haemorrhoids				1	1	603.00
Ulcer		1	1		2	88.50
Total	32	48	41	37	168	

Table 3: *The causes of death among the inmates of the lunatic asylum at Benares for 1846 and three following years, as specified in the monthly returns.*

[69]Source: Civil Surgeon to Medical Board, 16.4.1853; Consultations/Proceedings of the Lieutenant-Governor in Council of the North Western Provinces, Public Department (henceforth: NWP Pub. Proc.), 15.6.1853, 149, Enclosure.

[70]Bg. Pub. L., 6.11.1850, 10ff.; India Pub. D., 25.8.1852, 43; India Pub. L., 8.4.1854, 53ff.

high morality and low cure rates in the Benares and Delhi Asylum in comparison to the institution in Bareilly which had alarmed the Court of Directors in London.

Uniformly bad provisions and what had been regarded to be inhumane treatment were no longer reported. Rather there came to light a varying quality of conditions, dependent on the superintendents' personal style of management and their individual committment to the fate of the insane.[71] The cure and death rates consequently nearly always went up or down whenever a new civil surgeon took over the asylum duties from his predecessor. The omission of guidelines as to the specifica of treatment and relevant criteria for cure had manifested itself in individual surgeons' arbitrary decisions as regards treatment and more or less accidental successes or failures. Due to lack of exchange of ideas and experiences amongst surgeons it had happened, for example, that an innovation was introduced into one asylum which had already proved to occasion deadly consequences in another.[72]

Admittedly the freedom from narrowly and precisely defined rules of treatment could potentially encourage experiments and new ideas. Due to the civil surgeons' being overburdened with various other medical duties in the district under their charge, their often doubtful competence and authentic vocation for the healing arts and their additional – though offically prohibited – engagement in extended private practice, trade, and land-speculation, the actual space for creativity and exchange of information was limited. Further, the material facilities available in most establishments were still very restricted and restricting.

The condition of Native Lunatic Asylums in the 1850s

Out of six institutions in Bengal and the North-Western Provinces only one, the Patna Asylum, was considered to suffer from no defects as regards the state of the building. The remaining establishments were either 'capable of considerable improvement' (i.e., Dacca, Murshidabad) or 'condemned' to be rebuilt (i.e., Benares, Delhi, Bareilly).[73] The physical state of the institutions was not regarded to be the main factor influencing mortality and cure though. Modest cleanliness was seen to prevail, too, and thus not many words were lost on it either.[74] From the surgeons'

[71] India Pub. L., 15.5.1855, 85; NWP Pub. Proc., 12.12.1854, 14; India Pub. D., 25.4.1856, 4.

[72] Introduction of a new dietary regime on reduced scale in 1844 in Benares Asylum: Civil Surgeon to Medical Board, 16.4.1853; NWP Pub. Proc., 15.6.1853, 149, 4.

Introduction of a new dietary regime on reduced scale in 1852 in Delhi Asylum: Civil Surgeon to Medical Board, 11.2.1853; NWP Pub. Proc., 15.6.1853, 150, 9.

[73] Medical Board to Lieutenant Governor, 10.10.1854; NWP Pub. Proc., 12.12.1854, 87, 2.

[74] Ibid., 13.

reports it had, however, become evident that decisions as regards diet and occupations for patients as well as the interest doctors took in their duty were vitally important.

The Benares Asylum: the vital importance of food

A good example thereof was the Benares Asylum which had an average death rate of 36% during the 1840s. Civil Surgeon J. Leekie had recently taken over charge of this asylum and was required to report on his predecessor's mode of treatment and the causes for the alarming death rate. Although he described the records in the office as 'very limited and incomplete as to the specific nature of the individual cases',[75] he succeeded in providing at least an impressive statistical account. He found that the deaths had been occasioned by similar bodily diseases to which not only the insane but any inmates of public institutions were prone in India. He concluded that the 'greater part of deaths were occasioned by Dysentery and Diarrhoea and in addition to the 81 so registered, I have reason to believe that nearly all the casualties included under the heads 'Epilepsy' and 'Debility and Exhaustion' were the immediate result of the same formidable disorders'.[76]

Leekie further found that the rate started rising to 8% in excess of that of the preceding years when the daily allowance of *atta*, the main staple food, had been reduced to nearly half the former amount in 1844. This diminished diet which had been maintained for five years had been said by the late surgeon to be 'quite sufficient'.[77]

The Medical Board consequently concluded that:[78]

> the greater mortality in the Asylum was more than to other causes owing to the difference of Dietary (regime) between this and the Asylums at Delhi and Bareilly amounting to 6 Chittacks less in the quantity of the Chief and staple Articles of food and that there was foundation for the belief that the Patients in the Benares Asylum were in consequence predisposed to the access of Disease and too weak when it comes to resist its force.

When the dietary regime was finally brought into line with the ones at use in the other asylums it appeared to have had a[79]

[75] Civil Surgeon to Medical Board, 16.4.1853; NWP Pub. Proc., 15.6.1853, 149, 2.
[76] Ibid., 3. See Table 3
[77] Ibid., 4.
[78] Ibid.
[79] Ibid.

salutary effect upon the condition of the inmates generally, and likewise formed ... one of the principal means which lead to the marked reduction in the number of deaths.

Despite these findings, the Medical Board did not, however, seem very quick in drawing any general conclusions. They abstained from ensuring that a minimum quantity of food supplies be henceforth guaranteed. It so happened, that the Civil Surgeon, newly appointed to the Delhi Asylum introduced a dietary regime on a similarly diminished scale just a few years after the Medical Board's revelation.

The Delhi Asylum: withdrawal of food as punishment

The development of the Delhi and Benares Asylums respectively had been complementary in respect not only to diet. Just when Surgeon Leekie in Benares introduced a 'most humane and gentle treatment'[80] in 1850 – which was to take over from the former 'noisy, filthy, and unmanageable state, with stocks and chains in full force', – Surgeon G. Paton in Delhi initiated some fatal reforms.[81] As Paton himself had obviously been very proud of his innovations, he submitted an elaborate and boastful report on the occasion of the investigation. Paton had studied the treatment of the insane in the Bicêtre in France and his first moves were consequently a reorganisation of the servants' establishment and stress on discipline by what he called gentle but firm means.

He started by threatening the servants with dismissal in case they did not ensure cleanliness.[82] The latter had been neglected by his predecessor who allowed the patients 'to relieve their wants in the Cells, verandahs and even (sic) in the open courts'.[83] The Indian doctor who was said to have kept the Hospital in a 'more filthy state than any other part of the Asylum' and did not find favour with Paton in some other respects as well, was immediately dismissed.[84] The diet was 'diversified', which basically aimed at allowing considerably less food for those who were 'idle, unwilling or unable' to work.[85] Similarly, tobacco was henceforth to be considered a luxury which was to be 'given as a reward for good behaviour only'.[86]

[80]Ibid., 7.

[81]India Pub. L., 6.11.1850, 10ff.; India Pub. D., 25.8.1852, 44.

[82]Civil Surgeon to Medical Board, 11.2.1853; NWP Gen. Proc., 15.6.1853, 150, 6.

[83]Ibid.

[84]Ibid., 6,8.

[85]Ibid., 9.

[86]Ibid.

As not a single patient complained of the reduction in their diet, Paton concluded that 'it is evident too much has been given before'.[87] Further, he considered the sliding nature of the scale of diet to furnish him with,[88]

> an easy and unobjectionable means by which to enforce Discipline amongst the patients ... and to encourage exertion, and to discourage idleness or malingering in Hospital.

He aimed at making the Asylum both a self-sufficient unit by employing the patients in vegetable gardening and fruit cultivation and the surrounding garden 'pleasant to look upon' by having the grounds laid out.[89]

According to his understanding of insanity, mental or physical occupation were the chief means of cure. 'It leads', he argued, 'to a diversion of the mind from its morbid channel of thought and thus favours the restoration of the faculty or faculties of the mind which have been at fault'.[90] Due to the patients lowly class, mechanical work seemed more appropriate than the otherwise desirable intellectual occupation. Especially horticulture and the cleaning of cells were therefore regarded 'most healthful' works for Indians.[91]

Paton's innovation, being expressly characterised by both 'kindness and firmness', was so successful that he stated:[92]

> I am happy to say that of 78 male patients here every one of them excepting 16 is working with a good will in the Garden.

The employment of female patients in the spinning of cotton thread was calculated to become a similar success. The superintending matron had been authorised to retail the goods, whereby she was expected to become interested in the production.[93]

Whilst the initiated industriousness of the place met with Paton's satisfaction, he greatly regretted the patients' disinclination to amuse themselves after a day's work. He maintained:[94]

---

[87] Ibid., 11.

[88] Ibid., 10f.

[89] Ibid., 14.

[90] Ibid., 16.

[91] 'It would be desirable to introduce the school master into the Asylum, but the patients are not of that class to benefit by or take advantage of intellectual improvement. Mechanical works seems most adapted for them' (ibid).

[92] Ibid.

[93] Ibid., 17.

[94] Ibid., 18.

> Natives are generally fond of kite flying, the swing or see-saw, and keeping pigeons or rabbits, but I have not seen any taste amongst the insane here, for such amusements.

As regards medical treatment he was in favour of applying 'the usual remedies' only in cases when patients were out of health. In the few cases,[95]

> Where we apprehended existence of physical Disease as the cause of insanity our chief remedies consist of Seton and Blisters in the neck, the cold duck or shower bath and warm bath and occasionally mild courses of... Tonic and aperient medicines.

Further, regular recourse was had to daily ablutions and exercise in open air; the latter of which had consisted of physical labour in the gardens.[96]

In the long run Surgeon Paton's approach of enforcing discipline and industriousness by punishment through food restriction and economic incentives was reflected in not altogether favourable cure and death rates. His rigid regime was consequently again to be followed by a more liberal one when a new surgeon took over the Civil Surgeoncy in the Delhi area.[97]

The Bareilly Asylum: the effect of increased policing and of the institutions' enhanced popularity on cure and death rates

The Bareilly Asylum which had been positively commented on when the investigation was set up,[98] showed in respect to cure efficiency a vacillating profile. Shortly after Surgeon K. Kirke had taken over the institution the mortality and cure rates followed a less favourable pattern. He attributed this statistical trend both to the improving state of the police in the district – leading to lunatics being picked up more quickly – and the increasing popularity of the institution – resulting in patients being admitted at an earlier stage of their affliction.[99] And it was in the early period of insanity, Kirke argued, that both deaths and recoveries were much more numerous than at later stages.[100] The calamity of alarming efficiency rates was thus made a virtue of and favourable sounding reasons for unfavourable rates assigned.

[95]Ibid., 19.
[96]Ibid., 12.
[97]Medical Board to Lieutenant-Governor, 10.10.1854; NWP Pub. Proc., 12.12.1854, 87, 8.
'Diet ... no complaints except at Delhi where Dr. Balfour has found it necessary to introduce a more liberal scale than the one recently in force' (ibid.).
[98]India Pub. D., 25.8.1852, 42ff.
[99]Civil Surgeon to Medical Board, 24.1.1853; NWP Pub. Proc., 15.6.1853, 151, 7.
[100]Ibid., 2f.

Kirke refrained from elaborating in any more detail on his mode of treatment – presumably a wise omission.

The results of the report on the mode of treatment and the causes of varying cure and death rates

The heterogeneity of accounts referring to frequently changing treatment patterns in but three institutions and the variety of explanatory models employed for the characterisation of insanity's nature, its course and termination all point to the wide range of theoretical emphases and practices in use. There is not much uniformity detectable in treatment, nor do the surgeons always appear to have been zealously committed to their duty.

The Medical Board, aware of this heterogeneity, made explicit in its final report the various practices by referring to details of the institutions' state and treatment. Its general evaluation of the state of native lunatic asylums in Bengal and the North Western Provinces consequently contains much more differentiated and less harmonising statements than the report of 1818. The analytical headings under which the findings were subsumed covered incidence, buildings, cleanliness, classification, restraint, treatment, employment, amusements, diet, cooking, costs, cures and mortality, and causes of mortality.[101] It is in imitation of these then preferred categories, that the state and condition of lunatic asylums in the early 1850s will be characterised here.

The *asylum population* in 1854 had been calculated to have reached a total of 1,041 (see Table 4).[102] Out of this number the majority, namely 958, were designated 'insane', whilst the remaining 63 were considered 'imbeciles'. This ratio in favour of the 'insane' reflects the admission policy of the 1830s and '40s of leaving harmless 'idiots' at large. Despite further provision for lunatics in small stations' jails it was pointed out that only a very small proportion of the insane had been cared for. Although the incidence of madness was seen to be naturally lower in 'less civilised' countries, British India was still wanting facilities for the Indian insane.[103]

However, not only was the insufficient number of asylums criticised, but also the still inadequate state of the *buildings*. A strong preference was indicated for low-cost and Indian-style institutions. The non-adoption of a design 'where a ditch took the place of walls and native huts of pucka buildings based on the principle of

[101] Medical Board to Lieutenant Governor, 10.10.1854; NWP Pub. Proc., 12.12.1854, 87.
[102] Ibid., 1.
[103] Ibid.

	Male	Female	Total
Bengal			
Rasapagla	230	59	289
Dacca	167	36	203
Patna	81	27	108
Murshidabad	43	9	52
North-Western Provinces			
Bareilly	142	34	176
Delhi	84	31	115
Benares	76	22	98

Table 4: *Lunatics confined in Native Lunatic Asylums, 1854.*

making the Asylums as little different in appearance from the houses of the patients as possible' was consequently deplored.[104]

As to *cleanliness* a 'generally satisfying' situation was said to prevail, although it was carefully added that only in Patna were no improvements required.[105]

Classification, in contrast, was judged as 'most imperfect'. The Medical Board found fault both with the lack of separation of convalescent from less improved cases, and the mixing of patients regardless of their former social position.[106] Out of seven superintendents, however, only two or three were reported to be satisfied with the classification, and to even doubt the expediency of a further separation of patients. This the Medical Board saw as proof that these surgeons 'cannot give any very great attention to the study of individual cases, or cannot be well acquainted with the treatment of Insanity'[107] – a criticism of individual surgeons which would not have been expressed a few decades earlier. Further, adequate separation and classification was obviously no longer impeded only by the buildings' confined state. The recognition of the importance of classification was even taken as an indication of medical experts' professional knowledge.

No overt disagreement now existed about the use of *mechanical restraint* – which had in the 1820s been the decisive criterion for assessing a surgeon's familiarity with reformed asylum practice. Locking up in separate cells, hand cuffs and the strait

[104]Ibid., 2.
[105]Ibid.
[106]Ibid., 3.
[107]Ibid.

waist coat were rarely reported to be in use. Only in the case of criminal lunatics were leg irons resorted to.[108]

As to *treatment* the report's tenor differed even more distinctly from the 1818 inquiry. In the latter an attempt had been made to depict the surgeons as committed advocates of mild and gentle treatment, with moral management being fully realised despite the impediments of poor housing. In 1854, in contrast, it was bluntly stated that 'moral treatment can scarcely be said to have been attempted'.[109] The reason for this was seen to lie with the fact that no European surgeon was actually resident and thereby readily available for the attentive and intensive care of patients so characteristic of moral treatment. The Medical Board even went so far as to conclude that,[110]

> under these circumstances it appears to us surprising that so much success has attended (the surgeons') efforts.

More than any medical treatment, the improved *diet* – evaluated as 'generally satisfactory' – was seen as the most effective cure.[111]

Medical intervention was still restricted to soothing prescriptions, with the therapeutic agents being not 'much used for insanity itself but rather for any diseases accompanying it'.[112] Some experiments were mentioned, though not all were reported to have been successful: acupuncture of the testicles (Bareilly) and mesmerism (Murshidabad, Rasapagla).[113]

Employment in the open air, along with good diet was regarded to be of great curative benefit. Different practices were however reported to have prevailed in the various asylums. Whilst in Rasapagla and Patna only a few patients were employed, for Delhi, Dacca and Murshidabad it was observed that 'a great deal remains to be done'. In Benares it was found impossible to 'attempt anything systematic in this respect'; Bareilly, in contrast, employed its lunatics 'extensively'.[114] Less activity and even disinterest on the patients' side was revealed in regard to another therapeutic practice, namely *amusements*.[115]

---

[108] Ibid., 4.
[109] Ibid., 5.
[110] Ibid.
[111] Ibid., 5, 8.
[112] Ibid., 5.
[113] Ibid.
[114] Ibid., 6.
[115] Ibid., 7.

A further means of cure and indicator for a patient's recovery appeared for the first time in an offical record and was even explicitly emphasised on account of its major importance: *cooking*.[116] It was held that,[117]

> the process of cooking may be made an excellent test and aid of convalescence. This is one of the few resources possessed by those who are in charge of Asylums in India; which are not enjoyed by those who treat insanes in European ones.

Contrary to this insight – which also attests to a certain attentiveness to the Indian peoples' idiosyncrasies on the Medical Board's part – the formidable resource was not fully made use of in the majority of asylums. In Patna and Delhi 'some of the best men cook for all', in Benares and Bareilly at least a few were allowed to cook their own food, whilst in Dacca no patient at all was permitted to cook.[118]

In only a few cases did relatives provide food for patients; and in even less instances did relatives contribute towards a person's maintenance in the asylum.[119] Most of the inmates were designated as 'paupers', consisting of 'nearly 2/3 of the admissions of religious mendicants, Outcastes and prostitutes'.[120] Although the cost per patient varied from place to place, it was calculated to have on average amounted to only one third of the cost of a pauper in a County Asylum in England.[121] Consideration was, however, given to the provision of improved accommodation for fee-paying private patients in the future.[122] It was argued that such a measure would not only help to save public expenses but would also enhance the prestige of the institution and thereby encourage more people to be sent to the public asylum. The latter was a prominent consideration because the number of mentally ill people at large was seen by the authorities to be an evil which needed rectification.

Cure and death rates and causes for their variance

As regards cure and mortality rates it was found that they varied considerably: from between 35% to 70% for the former, and 20% to 35% for the latter (see

[116] Ibid., 9.
[117] Ibid.
[118] Ibid.
[119] Ibid., 9f.
[120] Civil Surgeon to Medical Board, 16.4.1853; NWP Pub. Proc., 15.6.1853, 149, 5.
[121] Medical Board to Lieutenant Governor, 10.10.1854; NWP Pub. Proc., 12.12.1854, 87, 10.
[122] Ibid.

Table 5[123]).[124] Further, in comparison to English institutions a peculiar pattern

	1852		1853		1854	
	Mortality	Cure	Mortality	Cure	Mortality	Cure
Bareilly	20.17	19.74	17.94	20.92	17.82	23.91
Benares	18.98	27.78	29.55	19.70	14.59	26.48
Delhi	10.76	26.58	16.11	25.00	13.17	22.75

Table 5: *Rates of Mortality and Cure (in %) in Native Lunatic Asylums (NWP), 1852–1854.*

was detected. The mortality rate in India had been twice as high; whilst the cure rate was more favourable to the Indian institutions, with about 15% above the average in England.[125]

This phenomenon was, however, interpreted very critically by the Medical Board, which thought the cure rate for Bengal to be grossly over-stated. Although the possibility that insanity was more curable in Indians was regarded as a possibility, the Medical Board saw itself nevertheless inclined to believe that:[126]

> considering the imperfect investigation that is necessarily made of such cases, that patients must often be admitted who are not really insane and patients often be discharged who are not cured; we have a proof of the latter in what is said of the immense number of readmissions at the Rassapaglah institution.

As to the ease with which patients could be managed the Indians were regarded as much more tractable than Europeans. This fact was related to the habit of *Ganja* smoking which was seen as a *cause* of insanity in nearly half the cases and it was concluded that 'it is easy to see how the withdrawal of this stimulant will lead to recovery'.[127] This finding was contrasted with 'Europeans' chronic habits of drinking' which were seen as responsible for the onset of insanity and its more violent course.[128]

[123]Figures compiled from I. Pub. D., 25.8.1852, 56; I. Pub. D., 28.12.1855, 8; I. Pub. D., 2.7.1856, 9.

[124]Medical Board to Lieutenant Governor, 10.10.1854; NWP Pub. Proc., 12.12.1854, 87, 11.

[125]Ibid. The following figures were stated:
ratio deaths to treated: 15.08 (Bengal), 7.08 (England and Scotland)
ratio cures to admitted: 52.60 (Bengal), 37.04 (in 11 asylums in England).

[126]Ibid.

[127]Ibid.

[128]Ibid.

Directly related to the different causes of insanity in Europeans and Indians were the *causes of death*. In the case of Indian lunatics death was not seen as being occasioned by 'direct affection of the nervous centres, that is by the exhaustion of acute mania, by convulsions or phrenitis'.[129] Rather, death was in most cases regarded to be due to either ordinary physical diseases like fevers, dysentery, and diarrhoea, or cholera epidemics and/or low-scale diet. Death of the Indian insane was consequently taken as a result of the confinement in public institutions itself, rather than the natural concomitant to insanity. It was, however, pointed out at the same time, without further explanation, that Indians were hardly ever admitted in the acute stage.[130]

Towards the European practitioner's exclusive and superior expertise in matters of healing

The overall picture that had emerged in Bengal and the North Western Provinces according to the Medical Board's general review in 1854 was one seen to give evidence of great improvements. Cleanliness especially was mentioned as having changed for the better, and last but not least it was stressed that more medical officers had become interested in their duty.[131] The most distinct feature of the 1854 investigation was in fact that the surgeon's medical competence, his acquaintance with the treatment of the insane and, most importantly, his personal commitment to and interest in his duty was emphasised as being a major determinant of proper asylum management and effective treatment.

In 1818, in contrast, the surgeons had been characterised as being beyond any criticism – however bad the state and management of the institutions had been. In the middle of the century the Medical Boards even concluded:[132]

> to bring things up to the standard of modern European Asylums the same agency must be employed here as at home, and a medical officer must be the actual head of each institution, not merely its nominal superintendent.

The Board's recommendations consequently aimed at promoting specialised training for medical practitioners, as 'this disease', it was argued, 'requires most especial study'.[133] It was seen as being necessary to provide incentives for the medical

[129] Ibid., 12.
[130] Ibid.
[131] Ibid., 13.
[132] Ibid.
[133] Ibid., 14.

officers in order to encourage them to study insanity in more detail. The least that could be done was to make compulsory a few weeks' practical course at the Calcutta Lunatic Asylum for every medical officer who was to be sent out for duty in the presidencies. The most desirable measure, however, was in the Board's opinion to send one of the more knowledgeable surgeons to Europe so that he could make himself familiar with the most recent modes of treatment there.[134]

Whilst the shift in emphasis from institutional and environmental factors in asylum management to questions of medical knowledge, expertise and individuals' motivation for their duty as specialised doctors for the insane was very distinct, there was no mention made whatsoever of the Indian assistant's duties. And in fact it seems most likely that he and the head keeper as well as the staff of the asylum in general must have had a considerable impact on the inmates. As the European surgeon did not spend much time within the asylum compound and resorted to medical treatment in a few instances only, it must be inferred that insane patients were most of the time in contact with the Indian staff. *Their* interaction, however, was not to deserve a word in the white man's accounts of his achievements in the East; especially at a period when one objective of English presence in India was expressed to be to raise up an Indian middle class which could act as mediator between the English and the mass of Indian peoples – 'a class of persons Indian in blood and colour, but English in tastes, in opinions, in morals and in intellect'.[135]

[134]Ibid.

[135]Macaulay, Minute on Education, 2.2.1835. H. Sharp, *Selections from educational records* (Calcutta: Superintendent Government Printing, 1920), 116.

Part III

Modern observations

Chapter 11

Centella asiatica (L.) Urban in perspective: an evaluative account

R. P. Labadie and K. T. D. De Silva

AMONG THE MANY INDIAN MEDICINAL PLANTS *Centella asiatica* is a species of repute. Its plant material is used for many curative purposes, and as a food ingredient as well. Its traditional uses and reputation as such are not restricted to India and Sri Lanka though. In China, Malaysia, Indochina, Indonesia and Madagascar the medicinal and nutritive value of this plant is traditionally esteemed as well.[1]

The popular use of Centella in ancient and modern times in the Old World, in a way, seems to have been extended nowadays to the New World. Centella asiatica is marketed today on a large scale in the United States under names such as 'Gota Cola' or 'Gotu Cola', and 'Fo-ti-tieng'.[2] The product is used to serve as a body-strengthener and revitalizer that can promote longevity. In such a context the latest edition (1981) of a leading American textbook on pharmacognosy treats Centella asiatica under the name 'Gotu Kola'.[3] Especially the latter name of the product used in the actuality of today's New World brings us back to the traditionally used

[1]Lily M. Perry, *Medicinal Plants of East and Southeast Asia: attributed properties and uses* (MIT Press: Cambridge, Mass. and London, 1980), 413, 382; K. Heyne, *De nuttige planten van Indonesië,* third edition, (Wageningen: Netherlands, 1950), part i, 1211; W. A. Emboden, 'Centella asiatica: Elixir of Life?', *Pacific Horticulture,* xli (1980), 16–19; P. Boiteau, A. Buzas, E. Lederer and J. Polonsky, 'Derivatives of Centella asiatica used against leprosy', *Nature,* clxiii (1949), 258.

[2]Emboden, ibid.

[3]Varro E. Tyler, Lynn R. Brady and James E. Robbers, *Pharmacognosy*, eighth edition, (Philadelphia: Lea & Febiger, 1981).

vernacular name of Centella asiatica in the Old World. *Gotukola* or more specifically *Hin-gotukola* (also spelled *Heen-gotukola*) is the Sinhalese name for Centella asiatica.[4]

The prefix '*heen*' or '*hin*' means small, indicating C. asiatica to be the smaller variety of two related gotukolas, the other being *Hydrocotyle javanica Thunb.*, called Maha-gotukola.[5]

However, as will be dealt with later, Centella asiatica itself appears to occur in different subvarieties, phenotypes or at least as chemical varieties. The aspect to be given attention first is that of vernacular synonyms connected to this plant. As far as the geographical areas where *āyurveda* or *siddha* has been a longstanding practice are concerned, this medicinal plant has been associated with many names.[6] So in Sri Lanka besides the Sinhalese name Hin-gotukola, the following Tamil names have been reported:[7]

- Babassa[8]
- Ōrilaittāmarai
- Vallarai or Vallarī

In Hindi the name Vallarī seems to be in use.[9]

Sanskrit names associated with this species are the following:[10]

- Bhekaparṇī, Bhekī
- Brahmamaṇḍūkī, Māṇḍūkī, Maṇḍūkaparṇī, Maṇḍūkaparṇikā,
- Darduracchadā
- Divyā
- Mahauṣadhī
- Supriyā
- Tvāṣṭī

---

[4]D. M. A. Jayaweera, *Medicinal Plants used in Ceylon*, (Colombo: A publication of The National Science Council of Sri Lanka, 1982), part v, 135; R. N. de Fonseka and S. Vinasithamby, *A provisional index to the local names of the flowering plants of Ceylon* (Peradeniya: University of Ceylon, Department of Botany, 1971).

[5]de Fonseka and S. Vinasithamby, *A provisional index*, ibid.

[6]T. Dutta and U. P. Basu, 'Triterpenoids: Part I – Thankuniside & Thankunic acid – A new triterpene glycoside & acid from Centella asiatica Linn. (Urb.)', *Journal of Scientific Industrial Research*, xxi/B (1962), (Short Communications), 239; P. S. Rao and T. R. Seshadri, 'Variation in the chemical composition of Indian samples of Centella asiatica', *Current Science*, xxxviii(4) (1969), 77–79; C. L. Malhotra, P. K. Das, M. S. Sastry and N. S. Dhalla, 'Chemical and pharmacological studies on Hydrocotyle asiatica Linn.', *Indian Journal of Pharmacy*, xxiii(4) (1961), 106–107; A. K. Nadkarni, *Indian materia Medica*, third edition, (Bombay: Popular Book Depot, 1954), i, 662.

[7]Jayaweera, *Medicinal Plants*, ibid.

[8]According to a personal communication from G. J. Meulenbeld, this name cannot be Tamil.

[9]Ibid.

[10]Ibid.

In Bengal the plant is known as Thankuni or Tholkuri.[11]

Other literary sources mention that C. asiatica is also generally known by the name Brāhmī.[12]

A thorough philological and linguistic investigation is required to decide on the authenticity of some of the Sanskrit, Hindi and Tamil names. This is especially the case for those names which are also associated with other plant species than Centella asiatica. In fact the names Brāhmī, Maṇḍūkī, Vallarī, Divyā and Mahauṣadhī are also used for the plant *Herpestis monnieria H. B. K.* [= Bacopa monnieria (L.) Wettst].[13] Possibly a philological analysis of the classical texts might throw light on discriminative botanical descriptions and on the implications connected with biological actions and medical uses of Brāhmī preparations. Scientifically, there is no problem whatsoever in distinguishing Centella asiatica from Herpestis monnieria. Prasad gave an accurate description of both drugs,[14] but one should be aware of interchanges in the practice of *āyurveda* and other indigenous medicinal systems. Being two distinctly separated species of quite different plant families, Umbelliferae (Centella asiatica) and Scrophulariaceae (Herpestis monnieria), the general spectrum of their characteristic secondary metabolites can be expected to be distinctively different. The picture we have at the moment of the chemistry of both species confirms this principle rule. This, however, does not mean that preparations from material of each of these species might not show similar pharmacological actions, and hence be applied for similar medical purposes. In this respect the case of C. asiatica and H. monnieria in separate Brāhmī preparations would not be an isolated example. A literary survey of data in sources secondary to classical *āyurvedic* texts show some coherence in bioactivity claims and therapeutical applications.[15] *In general both Brāhmī drugs are considered to be active as tonics.* This is in accordance with data collected by Labadie and De Silva during a field inquiry in Sri Lanka.[16]

---

[11]Dutta and Basu, 'Triterpenoids', ibid.

[12]Dutta and Basu, 'Triterpenoids', ibid.; Rao and Seshadri, 'Variation', ibid.; Malhotra, Das, Sastry and Dhalla, 'Chemical and pharmacological studies', ibid.; S. Prasad, 'Pharmacognostical study of Brahmi. Stem and leaf characteristics of Herpestis monnieria H. B. et K and Hydrocotyle asiatica. L.', *Journal of the American Pharmaceutical Association*, xxxvi (1947), 393–401.

[13]Interestingly enough, according to Jayaweera, *Medicinal plants* – in this respect a secondary literature source – this plant species is also associated with the name *somā*. See also Malhotra, Das, Sastry and Dhalla, 'Chemical and pharmacological studies', ibid., and R. Hegnauer, *Chemotaxonomie der Pflanzen* (Birkhauser Verlag: Basel and Stuttgart, 1973), vi, 354, 366, 597, 746.

[14]Prasad, 'Pharmacognostical study of Brahmi', ibid.

[15]Perry, *Medicinal Plants*, ibid.; Jayaweera, *Medicinal Plants*, ibid.; Malhotra, Das, Sastry and Dhalla, 'Chemical and pharmacological studies', ibid.; Hegnauer, *Chemotaxonomie*, ibid.; Prasad, 'Pharmacognostical study of Brahmi', ibid.; Nadkarni, *Indian materia Medica*, ibid.

[16]R. P. Labadie and K. T. D. De Silva, 'Data from an ethnopharmacognostic field inquiry, in which twenty leading Āyurveda practitioners in Sri Lanka were consulted' (publication in preparation).

More specifically, Herpestis monnieria is said to be used as a '*nervine and a cardiotonic*' mostly, and Centella asiatica as an *alterative tonic, a rejuvenative and 'bloodpurifier'*. Both species have been examined for effects on the nervous system and the cardiovascular system.[17] *Malhotra et al.'s animal experiments showed good cardiotonic and sedative activities of extracts from Herpestis monnieria.*[18] The active principle hersaponin, earlier isolated by Sastry et al.,[19] was found to have neuropharmacological actions similar to reserpine and chlorpromazine.[20] Similar animal experiments were carried out with various extracts and fractions of Centella asiatica. The alcoholic extract was found to be most effective and the glycosidal fraction separated appeared to contain the active principle. The results obtained, however, showed that *the active compounds from Centella asiatica have cardiodepressant and hypotensive actions and a weak sedative effect.*[21]

It is of interest to note that the type of saponins (resp. sapogenins) which have been found in Herpestis monnieria[22] show interestingly corresponding structure features compared to those known from Centella asiatica.

The saponins described to have been found in Herpestis monnieria are: hersaponin, monnierin, bacosid A, bacosid B.

In addition, betulinic acid and a phytosterin mixture have been described as being present. On acidic hydrolysis, the bacosids yield a series of related sapogenins called bacogenin –A1, –A2, –A3, and –A4. Kulshrestha and Rastogi[23] showed

---

[17] Malhotra, Das, Sastry and Dhalla, 'Chemical and pharmacological studies', ibid.; C. L. Malhotra and P. K. Das, 'Pharmacological studies of Herpestis monnieria, Linn., (Brahmi)', *Indian Journal of Medical Research* xlvii (1959), 294–305; C. L. Malhotra, P. K. Das and N. S. Dhalla, 'Some neuropharmacological actions of hersaponin – an active principle from Herpestis monnieria Linn.', *Arch. int. Pharmacodyn.*, cxxix(3–4) (1960), 290–302.

[18] Malhotra and Das, (1959), ibid.

[19] M. S. Sastry, N. S. Dhalla and C. L. Malhotra, 'Chemical investigation of Herpestis monnieria Linn. (Brahmi)', *Indian Journal of Pharmacology*, xxi (1959), 303f.

[20] Cf. Malhotra, Das and Dhalla, (1960), ibid.

[21] Cf. Malhotra, Das, Sastry and Dhalla, 'Chemical and pharmacological studies', ibid.

[22] Sastry, Dhalla and Malhotra, (1959), ibid.; T. Dutta and U. P. Basu., 'Terpenoids: part II – Isolation of a new triterpene saponin, Monnierin, from Bacopa monnieria Wettst.', *Indian Journal of Chemistry*, i (1963), 408f.; ibid., 'Terpenoids: part IV – Stricture of tetrasaccharide of Monnierin', *Indian Journal of Chemistry*, vi (1968), 471f.; U. P. Basu and T. Dutta, 'The structure of monnierin', *Tetrahedron Letters*, xliii (1967), 191f.; N. Chatterji R. P. Rastogi and M. L. Dhar, 'Chemical examination of Bacopa monniera Wettst.: part I – Isolation of chemical constituents', *Indian Journal of Chemistry*, i (1963), 212–215; ibid., 'Chemical examination of Bacopa monniera Wettst.: part II – The constitution of Bacoside A', *Indian Journal of Chemistry*, iii (1965), 24–29; D. K. Kulshrestha and R. P. Rastogi, 'Bacogenin-A1: a novel dammarane and triterpene sapogenin from Bacopa monnieria', *Phytochemistry*, xii (1973), 887.

[23] Kulshrestha and Rastogi, ibid.; idem, 'Absolute structures of the novel genins, Bacogenins A1 & A2 from Bacosides isolated from Bacopa monnieria', *Indian Journal of Chemistry*, xiii (1975), 309–313.

bacogenin –A1 and –A2 to be stereo isomers and artifacts of the 'true bacogenin A' (see Figs. 1–3).[24]

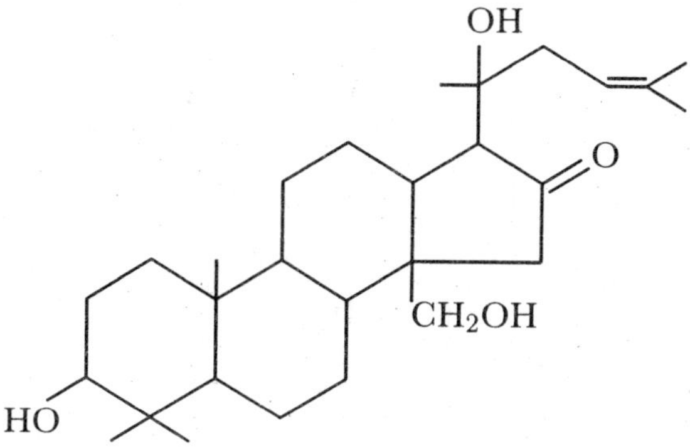

Figure 1: *Bacogenin A*
Bacosid A* = Bacogenin A1 + glucose + arabinose
Bacosid B = Bacogenin A1 + glucose + arabinose
Monnierin = Bacogenin A + 1 glucose + 3 arabinose.

N. B.: Related Scrophulariaceae species (Scrophularia smithii Hornem and Scrophularia calliantha Webb et Berth) accumulate a triterpenoid glycoside which after hydrolysis yields an aglycone called triterpene A, which is even more structurally related to those known from Centella (see Figs. 4 and 5).[25]

From Malhotra et al.'s findings[26] it can be deduced that any stimulant activity if executed by Centella asiatica (-preparations), is *not* effectuated through the nervous or the cardiovascular system, and *not* associated with the triterpene-glycosidal derivatives in the first place.

Recently, however, Deshpande et al. very briefly reported psychotropic effects of what they indicated as 'alkaloid' from Centella asiatica.[27]

- According to these authors this 'alkaloid' preparation from Centella asiatica increases narcosis of albino rats induced by pentobarbitone by 68.15%.

---

[24] D. K. Kulshrestha and R. P. Rastogi, 'Identification of ebelin lactone from bacoside A and the nature of its genuine sapogenin' *Phytochemistry*, xii (1973), 2074–2076.

[25] Hegnauer, *Chemotaxonomie,* ibid.

[26] Malhotra, Das, Sastry and Dhalla, 'Chemical and pharmacological studies', ibid.

[27] S. Deshpande, S. S. Gupta, S. Shinde, V. L. Iyengar and S. Shastry, 'Psychotropic effects of Centella asiatica', *Indian Journal of Pharmacology*, xii (1980), 64.

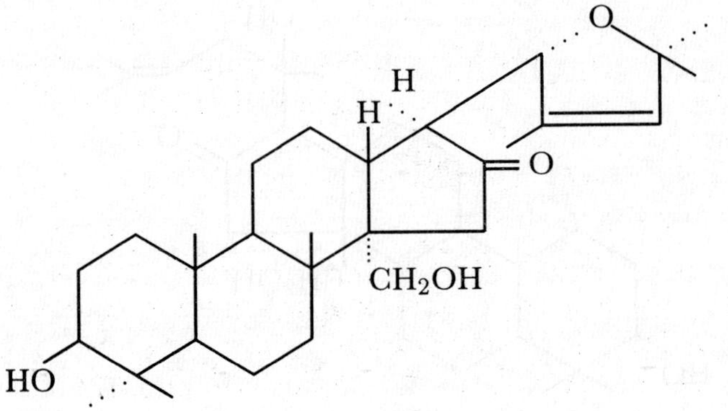

Figure 2: *Bacogenin A1*
(3β, 30-dehydroxy-20(S)-25-epoxy-22-methyl-24-nor-dammer-22-en-16-one).

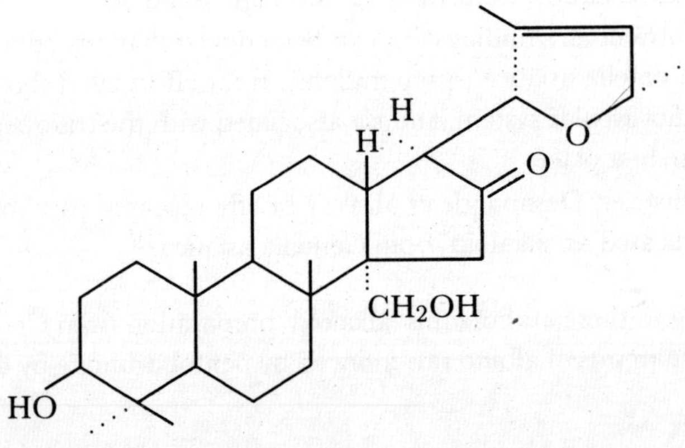

Figure 3: *Bacogenin A2*(the 20(R)-epimer of bacogenin–A1).

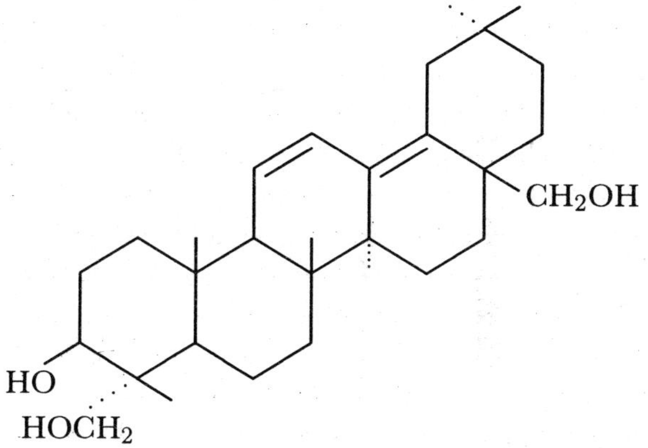

Figure 4: *Triterpene A* ($C_{30}H_{48}O_3$) ('Smithiandienol').

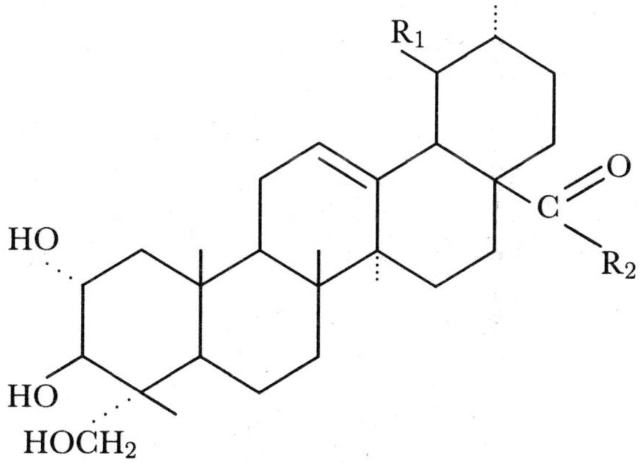

Figure 5: *Triterpene acids and glycosides from Centella asiatica.*

	R1	R2
Asiatic acid	H	OH
Madecassic acid	OH	OH
Asiaticosid (Polonsky et al. 1959)	H	-Glu-Glu-Rhamn.
Madecassosid (Pinhas et al. 1967)	OH	-Glu-Glu-Rhamn.

- On treatment with the Centella preparation trained rats manifested 'conditioned avoidance' in dos/effect relation. The effects were comparable with those of chlorpromazine in doses of 4 mg/kg.
- Again, in doses of 50 mg/kg and 75 mg/kg the Centella preparation effectuated a neurological deficit in rats by the 'rota rod test', suggesting impairment of muscular co-ordination and a tranquillizing effect.
- The increased activity caused by amphetamine as tested in photoactmeter was markedly reduced after treatment with the Centella preparation in doses of 50 mg/kg. The effects were comparable with those produced by meprobamate.

As it stands one should be careful with these results. Deshpande et al.'s report is not a full publication.

The exact origin of the plant material used is not given and the correct identity can not be checked yet. Phytochemical details have not been given as to the so called 'alkaloid' preparation from Centella asiatica. Until now only one report on an alkaloid, called *hydrocotylin*, [$C_{22}H_{33}NO_8$, mpt. 210 – 212°] has been published by Basu and Lamsal.[28] According to these authors the hydrocotylin is present in the herb at a concentration of 0.002%. This low content suggests that this compound is not likely to play any significant role in current *āyurvedic* preparations. Despande et al. might have had a special preparation which represents an alkaloid-enriched extract, or used a Centella asiatica variety with a high content of alkaloid, or might have used plant material of a species interchanged for Centella asiatica.[29]

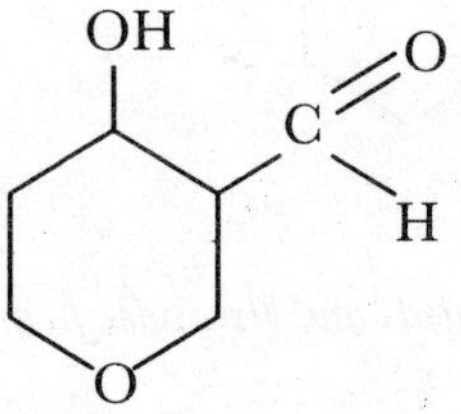

Figure 6: *3-Formyl-4-hydroxy-α-pyran.*

Herpestis monnieria (= Bacopa monnieria) is known to contain varying contents of alkaloid. As early as 1947 Basu and Pabrai isolated the main alkaloid

[28] N. K. Basu and P. P. Lamsal, 'Hydrocotyle asiatica Linn.', *Quarterly Journal of Pharmacy and Pharmacology*, xx (1947), 135f.

[29] Deshpande, Gupta, Shinde, Iyengar and Shastry, (1980), ibid.

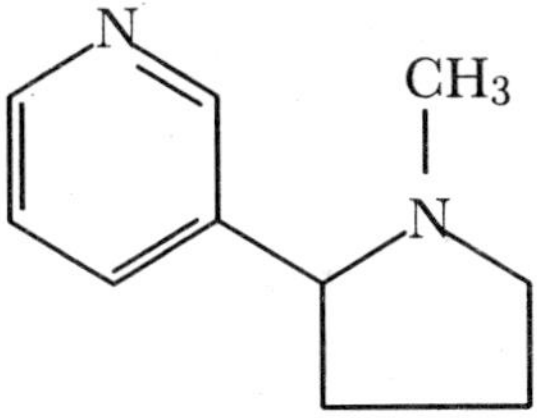

Figure 7: *Nicotine.*

herpestin [$C_{34}H_{46}N_2O_6$], the structure of which is not known.[30] Later Das et al. showed the presence of *three* alkaloids, one of which was identified as *nicotine.*[31] Schulte et al. found the content of basic compounds in this species to be *0.02%.*[32] Fifteen compounds were shown to display a positive reaction with the Dragendorff-reagent. Of these *nicotine* and *3-formyl-4-hydroxy-α-pyran* were isolated in pure form (see Figs. 6 and 7). This proves that not all Dragendorff-positive substances are to be considered alkaloids.

As far as effects of the nervous system and the cardiovascular system are concerned, it appears that there are still some vital questions to be solved. This also counts for activity claims like: *improvement of memory* and *the diuretic effect* which is mentioned for both medicinal plants.[33] Concerning the latter action, Sastry et al. connected this with a high content of *mannitol* and *potassium salts* in Herpestis monnieria (see Fig. 8).[34] The presence of sugar alcohols in the form of meso-inositol has also been reported by Singh and Rastogi in Centella asiatica (see Fig. 9).[35]

However, the most striking therapeutical and bio-activity claims in the traditional use of Centella are in cases of infections and skin diseases. Mention is made of its usefulness for chronic and obstinate eczema, secondary and tertiary syphilis with ulceration, chronic rheumatism, abcesses and in particular leprosy. Both internal and external applications are described by Jayaweera, but he does not mention these medical applications for Herpestis monnieria.[36] The question is whether

[30] N. K. Basu and P. R. Pabrai, 'Monnieria cuneifolia', *Quarterly Journal of Pharmacy and Pharmacology,* xx (1947), 137–139.

[31] P. K. Das, C. L. Malhotra and N. S. Dhalla, 'Studies on alkaloids of Herpestis monniera Linn.', *Indian Journal of Physiology and Pharmacology,* v (1961), 136–143.

[32] K. E. Schulte, G. Rücker and S. El-Kersch, 'Nicotin und 3-Formyl-4-hydroxy-2H-pyran aus Herpestis monnieria', *Phytochemistry,* xi (1972), 2649–2651.

[33] Jayaweera, *Medicinal Plants,* ibid.

[34] Sastry, Dhalla and Malhotra, (1959), ibid.

[35] B. Singh and R. P. Rastogi, 'A reinvestigation of the triterpenes of Centella asiatica', *Phytochemistry,* viii (1969) 917–921.

[36] *Medicinal Plants,* ibid.

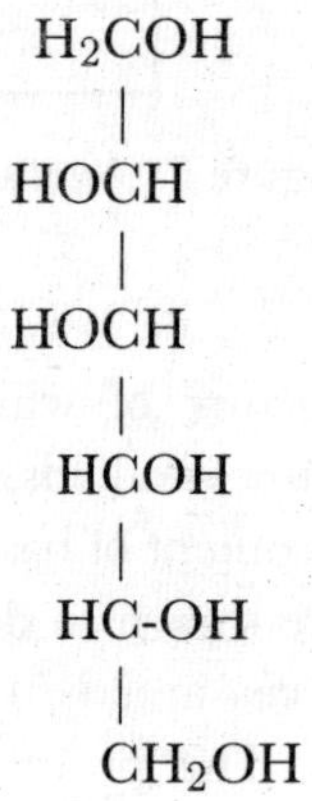

Figure 8: *Mannitol* (An osmotic diuretic, which is used to test kidney function, in dose: i.v. 25 g (25% solution)).

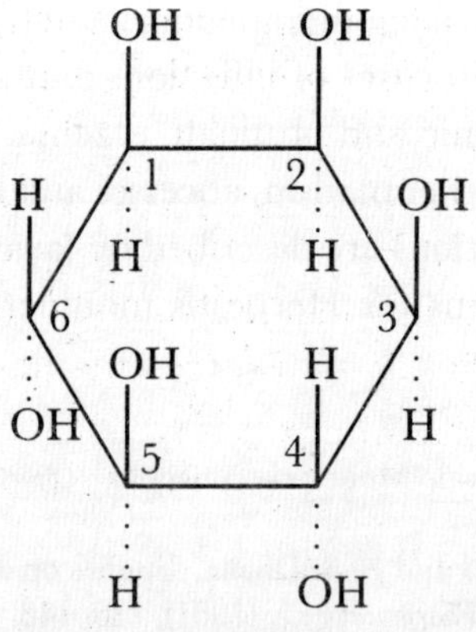

Figure 9: *meso-Inositol* (Nine possible (= cyclohexitol) isomers) (Has also been used as a lipotropic agent).

there are classical *āyurvedic* texts which describe these medical indications for Centella under names which are not used at the same time for Herpestis monnieria. Anyhow, in secondary sources only Centella asiatica, and not Herpestis monnieria, has a traditional reputation for curing skin diseases, ulcers, etc.

It is this reputation of Centella in India and Madagascar which has triggered the interest of western scientists. A long list of communications on the efficacy of Centella in all sorts of skin affections (including eczema, lupus, psoriasis, scrofulosis, lepra, etc.), made between 1850 and 1936, preceded a major breakthrough in the years around 1940.[37]

This breakthrough was, however, first achieved with plant material of Centella asiatica from Madagascar (and not from India). The clinical experiments of Boiteau with a compound preparation from Centella asiatica (then called: Hydrocotyle asiatica), containing a glycoside, had shown 'remarkable results in the treatment of advanced lepromatous cases of leprosy'.[38] However, this was achieved in doses of the drug approaching toxic levels. Bontems, a 'pharmacien lieutant de Troupes coloniales' working in Tananarive at the time, isolated a compound from Centella which he named *'asiaticoside'*.[39] He characterized the compound to be a glycoside, which was insoluble in water, slightly soluble in alcohol and very well soluble in pyridine. For further research Boiteau prepared a pharmaceutical solution which was suitable for injections to be used in clinical tests on leprous patients. Boiteau and Grimes, considering their observations, believed that their preparation from Centella 'acts as a solvent of the waxy coating of the bacillus of leprosy, which then becomes fragile and may easily be destroyed by the tissues or by an adjuvant drug.' The observations of these authors included 'softening and breaking down of nodules, followed by cicatrization.' It was even claimed that this remedy cured incipient eye lesions rapidly if treated before the posterior chamber is involved.

In following years the molecular structure of asiaticoside was studied and shown to be an esterglycoside of asiatic acid, the latter being a trihydroxylated-mono-carboxylated-dihydrogenated-α-amyrin. The glucidic portion, per molecule asiaticoside, consists of one rhamnose and two glucose units. One of the glucose units is linked with an ester bound to asiatic acid, and rhamnose constitutes the terminal sugar unit in the glucidic chain.[40]

---

[37] Reports: a) 'Asiaticoside in treatment of leprosy', *British Medical Journal,* (March 10, 1945), 338–339; b) 'Treatment of Leprosy', *Nature,* mmmcmxlii (May 19, 1945), 601. See also J. E. Bontems, *Bulletin of Science and Pharmacology,* xlix (1941), 186–191; J. Polonsky, E. Sach and E. Lederer, *Mémoires présentés à la Société chimique,* clxv (1959), 880–886; J. Polonsky, *Ciência e Cultura,* xx(1) (1968), 19.

[38] See reports a) and b) in footnote 37 above.

[39] Bontems, (1941), ibid.

[40] Polonsky, Sach and Lederer, (1959), ibid.; Polonsky, *Ciência e Cultura,* ibid.

After the encouraging initial observations by Boiteau and Grimes in Madagascar, the biological activity and therapeutical efficacy was linked with asiaticoside. In efforts to establish its therapeutical value further clinical testing was performed on patients suffering from lasting serious ulcerations, open wounds with phlebitic lesions and superficial gangrenic conditions.[41] Asiaticoside was sometimes administered locally as a powder but mostly by intramuscular injections. It was found that asiaticoside promotes the process of cicatrization slowly. Under its influence the formation of granulated tissue is initiated. Thiers et al. stated as their opinion, on the basis of their clinical observations, that asiaticoside would execute its action on mesodermic processes, i.e., within the connective tissue.[42] As a result of their observations, the same authors described how, in contrast to asiaticoside (the esterglycoside), the triterpene acid asiatic acid is toxic and does not show a positive activity on cicatrization processes.[43]

In a later clinical study, by Chakrabarty and Deshmukh, the efficacy of different pharmaceutical preparations containing plant material of the whole plant or a 10 : 1 mixture of asiticoside and potassium chloride, in capsules given orally, was compared to that of DDS (= diaminodiphenyl sulfone = dapsone).[44] These authors described how clinical improvements obtained with the Centella capsules and the asiaticoside capsules were comparable to those with DDS. In continuation and partly in support of the described effects of Centella preparations on ulcerations a number of clinical studies have been reported using titrated extracts of Centella asiatica (TECA). Pereira[45] and Tenailleau[46] described significant positive therapeutic effects of TECA on cases of cellulitis, an inflammatory affection of the connective tissue of the skin.

Darnis et al.[47] Barletta et al.[48] and Allegra et al.[49] reported positive healing

---

[41] H. Thiers, J. Fayolle, P. Boiteau and A. R. Ratsimamanga, 'L'asiaticoside principe actif de Centella asiatica, agent initiateur du processes de bourgeonnement, première ètape de la cicatrisation des ulcères cutanés', *Lyon Médical*, xvii (1957), 389–395.

[42] Ibid.

[43] Ibid.

[44] T. Chakrabarty and S. Deshmukh, 'Centella asiatica in the treatment of Leprosy', *Science and Culture*, xlii(11) (1976), 573.

[45] I. C. Pereira, 'Tratamento de celutite pela Centella asiatica', *Folha Medica (Brazil)*, lxxix(5) (1979), 401–404.

[46] A. Tenailleau, 'A propos de 80 cas de cellulite traités par l'extrait titré de Centella asiatica', *Quest. medical*, xxxi(13) (1978), 919–924.

[47] F. Darnis, L. Orcel, P. P. de Saint-maur and P. Mamou, 'Note sur l'utilisation de l'extrait titré de Centella asiatica au cours des hépatopathies chroniques', *Sem. Hop. Paris*, lv(37–38) (1979), 1749f.

[48] A. Barletta, A. Borgioli, C. Corsi, M. Pollastri and C. U. Tesi, 'Impiego della Centella asiatica nella I. V. C.', *Gazetta Media Italiana*, cxl (1981), 33–35.

[49] C. Allegra, G. Pollari, A. Crisuolo, M. Bonifacio and D. Tabassi, 'L'estratto di Centella asiatico

effects of TECA on respectively chronic hepatic disorders and chronic venous insufficiency. According to the observations of Legray and Greco the application of TECA in plastic surgery proved to be restorative and effective.[50] TECA also showed gratifying results in treating active bilharzial lesions of the bladder, bilharzial ulcers, early bilharzial infiltrations.[51]

In most of these clinical studies it was reported that TECA was tolerated well.[52]

The absorption of TECA through the skin was also studied using a preparation in which the triterpene acids, asiatic acid and madecassic acid, associated with asiatiocoside were labelled with tritium. Applied in a lano-paraffin gauze dressing or in an ointment on the skin of the rat and the mouse, the subcutaneaous tissue and the abdominal muscle in particular are reached rapidly and intensively.[53]

In the course of the following ten years several other compounds structurally closely related to asiaticoside and asiatic acid have been isolated from Centella asiatica and studied chemically. The picture, which has been revealed on the occurrence of these related triterpene esterglycosides and triterpene acids in Centella asiatica, shows that there are at least four different chemical varieties of Centella asiatica:

1. C. asiatica from *Madagascar* contains:

   asiaticoside and madecassoside
   ↓ associated triterpene acid ↓
   asiatic acid madecassic acid

2. C. asiatica from *Ceylon* contains:

   Centelloside
   ↓ associated triterpene acid
   Centellic acid other acids:
   Centic acid
   Centoic acid

nelle flebopatie degli arti inferiori, Ricerca clinico-strumentale comparativa con un placebo', *Cl. Terap.*, ic (1981) 507–513.

[50] P. Legray and J. Greco, 'Utilisation d'un tulle gras à l'extrait titré de Centella asiatica en chirugie plastique et reconstructive', *Quest. Medical*, xxxii(15–16) (1979), 1015–1019.

[51] Aziz Fam, 'Use of titrated extract of Centella asiatica (TECA) in bilharzial bladder lesions', *International Surgery*, lviii(7) (1973), 451–455.

[52] See footnotes 45, 46, and 48–50.

[53] A. Viala, J. P. Cano, A. Durand, R. Paulin, F. Roux, M. Placidi, H. Pinhas and C. Lefournier, 'Etude chez l'animal du passage transcutané des principes actifs de l'extrait titré de Centella asiatica L. marqués au tritium après application sous forme de "tulle gras" et "d'onguent" ', *Thérapie*, xxxii (1977), 573–583.

3. C. asiatica from *India* contains:
   a. asiaticoside and madecassoside, or
   b. asiaticoside and brahmoside and brahminoside or,
   ↓ associated triterpene acid ↓
   brahmic acid brahmic acid
   from *Calcutta*:
   c. asiaticoside and thankuniside and iso-thankuniside
   ↓ associated triterpene acid ↓
   thankunic acid iso-thankunic acid

Several molecular structure problems still have to be solved concerning these compounds, but it would not be unlikely to expect that we are dealing with at least four different chemical varieties of Centella asiatica.[54]

New directions

So far, however, the reports on bio-activity and clinical trials specifically concern asiaticoside and its derivatives.

A differently oriented pharmacological study showed that two of the constituents from a crude extract of Centella asiatica, namely isothankuniside and a so-called BK compound [= methyl-5-hydroxy-3, 6-diketo-23(or 24 nor-urs-12-ene-28-oate], cause consistent reduction of fertility in female mice.[55]

However, the actions of Centella preparations and constituents on lepra, bilharzial and other chronic ulcerative lesions are by far the most interesting.

In search of a correlative rationale of the action(s) of Centella on a molecular and cellular level we evaluated the available ethnopharmacognostic data. From this information it appears that an immunemodulative activity might be at the basis of the active constituents of Centella. Therefore, we carried out in vitro tests on human complement and the Migration Inhibition Factor produced by human lymphocytes. In the preliminary screening it was found that the strongest activity is executed by polar constituents. Further activity-directed fractionation showed that non-dialysable constituents of carbohydrate nature are promising as for their activity on complement. Whether glycosidic compounds like asiaticoside contributes

[54]Rao and Sheshadri, 'Variations in the chemical composition of Indian samples of Centella asiatica', *Indian Journal of Experimental Biology*, vi (1968).

[55]T. Dutta and U. P. Basu, 'Crude extract of Centella asiatica and products derived from its glucosides as oral antifertility agents', *Indian Journal of Experimental Biology*, vi (1968), 181f.

to the immunemodulating activity remains to be established and is under investigation. The finding of these immunemodulative polysaccharides is likely to contribute to the explanation of differential actions of Centella. The details of this study will be published elswhere.

Notes from Lilly M. Perry, *Medicinal plants from East and Southeast Asia* (Cambridge, Massachusetts: MIT Press, 1980), 413, *sub* Centella asiatica (L.) Urban:[56]

> ... the plant represents a whole apothecary shop.[57]
>
> The juice or an infusion is given as depurative [bloodpurifier] and cooling. If a small quantity is eaten, it stimulates the appetite, aids digestion, and is a remedy for bowel trouble of children.[58]
>
> ... the unfiltered juice has been found to be particularly efficacious against ulcers, syphilis and scrofula.[59]
>
> The plant has gentle diuretic action.[60]
>
> In Madagascar, a crystallized substance, asiaticoside, was found, thought at first to be a glucoside, but Boiteau *et al.* ... have shown that it is an ester. They prepared injections which broke down the leprosy nodules, perforating ulcers and lesions on fingers and early eye lesions. It has been suggested that this medicine probably dissolves the waxy covering of the leprosy bacillus so that it becomes fragile and can be easily destroyed either by the body or some drug.[61]
>
> The Indian and Ceylonese plants have similar constituents. The Ceylonese plant has three triterpenic acids and centelloside ... again similar to but different from the acid and ester of the Madagascar plant ... though both appear to be the same species.[62]

---

[56] References reformatted by the editor.

[57] From K. Heyne, *De nuttige planten van Indonesië*, third ed. (reprint of second ed.: *De nuttige planten van Nederlands-Indië* (Djakarta, 1927)), (Wageningen, 1950).

[58] From T. S. Liu, 'Medicinal plants', section 5 in *List of economic plants in Taiwan*, translated by T. S. Wei, (Tapei, Taiwan, 1952), 52, and I. H. Burkhill, *Dictionary of the economic products of the Malay Peninsula* (London, 1935), 1211.

[59] From J. Lepine, 'De l'Hydrocotyle asiatica Linné', *Journal Pharm. Chim.*, iii(28) (1855), 47–59.

[60] From L. A. van der Woerd, 'Over diurese-onderzoek II', *Chron. Nat.*, ciii (1947), 57.

[61] From *Wealth of India*, ii, 117.

[62] From B. Lythgoe and S. Trippett, 'Derivatives of Centella asiatica used against leprosy. Centelloside', *Nature*, clxiii (1949), 259, 260, and S. C. Bhattacharyya 'Constituents of *Centella asiatica*. Part I. Examination of the Ceylonese variety', *Journal of the Indian Chem. Soc.*, xxxiii (1956), 579. S. C. Bhattacharyya and B. Lythgoe, 'Derivatives of Centella asiatica used against leprosy. Triterpene acids', *Nature*, clxiii (1949), 259.

Chapter 12

The results of an analysis based on a video of consultations in five āyurvedic medical practices

D. von Schmädel and B. Hochkirchen

The doctor–patient relationship

EVEN THOUGH IN TODAY'S INDIA there is little difference in doctor–patient relationship between allopathic and *āyurvedic* medicine, especially in urban areas, we have to consider the fact that in *āyurvedic* medicine there is a concept of doctor–patient relationship which is still valid. This concept is closely related to the common religious background of *vaidya* ('traditional doctor') and patient. Thus, the treatment, for instance, has an effect on the *karma* of the patient, therefore it is the duty of the *vaidya*, not only 'to treat a patient's illness and to promote health, but in order for his treatment to be effective, it was necessary for patients to perform good deeds to mitigate negative karma'.[1] In contrast to the secular nature of the relationship of doctor and patient in the Western system, this relationship in *āyurvedic* medicine has a religious and moral aspect, especially in traditionally orientated village communities. The *vaidya* is not only seen as healer, but is also regarded as a wise, sometimes even holy man. Therefore he is expected to lead

[1] M. Nichter, 'Paying for what ails you: sociocultural issues influencing the ways and means of therapy payment in South India', *Social Science and Medicine*, xvii (1983), no. 14, 9.

a righteous life in the sense of Hindu tradition. On the other hand, the *vaidya* can not only demand trust and respect from the patient, but because of his unquestioned moral integrity he can also give advice regarding physical, social and religious aspects of the patient's life. This almost blind trust in the abilities of the *vaidya* that is demanded by him and also conceded to him by the patient brings the *vaidya* into a position of omniscience.[2] As our visual material shows, the consultation often seems to start with the motto: 'Don't tell me what's the matter with you, I shall feel your pulse, and I'll know.'

The manner of paying the doctor also brings differences in *āyurvedic* and allopathic medicine to light. Traditionally the *vaidya* was not paid directly for his services.[3] He might have been paid with gifts or would have had a second job and not have charged for his services at all. Even today, the *vaidya* receives payment rather indirectly through the sale of prescribed drugs. This is the case in our video recordings, where payment is not made separately for the doctor's services and his medicine.

The doctor–patient relationship in the *āyurvedic* system is, as we will see, far more marked by the domineering authority of the doctor than in the Western system. The idea of doctor and patient as partners, as put forward in western Europe, would hardly be understood by the *āyurvedic* system. It would not fit into its ideology. The concept of *āyurveda* tells the patient not only to pay for his drugs, and thereby pay the doctor, but also to be obedient and grateful. In today's reality, however, the *āyurvedic* practitioner has to allow and endure criticism and doubt from others about his therapy, especially in urban centres. This is caused by mainly two reasons: first, the *vaidya* has to face stiff competition from not only allopathic, but also homoeopathic and *yūnānī* physicians, especially in urban areas. The patient, especially the middle and upper class patient, is able to use this competition to his own advantage. Secondly, the payment by the patient to the doctor reduces medical care more and more to a secular matter. We see that the doctor–patient relationship in the *āyurvedic* medical system is in a phase of change.

In communication with his patient the *āyurvedic* doctor has to face a dilemma. On the one hand, he cannot put open non-directive questions to

---

[2]M. McKim, 'Western medicine in a village of northern India', in *Health Culture and Community: case studies of public reactions to health programs*, edited by Benjamin David Paul with the collaboration of Walter B. Miller, (New York: Russel Sage Foundation, 1955).

[3]Ibid.

his patient since he is supposed to demonstrate his knowledge. On the other hand, it is above all the *āyurvedic* physician, with his socio-psycho-somatic approach, who needs all the obtainable information about the patient, not only about his illness but also about his way of life, including its familial and social aspects. The *vaidya* resolves this dilemma partly by demonstrating his independence through using particular rituals on one side; these are taking the pulse and eye analysis which take place before the interview. On the other hand, he gathers a lot of information by asking very many leading questions especially within the context of out-patient treatment. Through the use of these directive and suggestive, but not open-ended, questions the *vaidya* signals that he has a very detailed picture of the patient's illness. Just like the Western doctor, the *āyurvedic* physician too is very interested in a good, firm and stable relationship with his patient. This study looks at the way the *āyurvedic* doctor secures and enhances the compliance of his patient.

We were expecting the *āyurvedic* doctor to interact with his patient through spoken language and also through body language. We thought that the setting in which the interaction takes place would also be important. We therefore chose the video-analysis of consultations as an appropriate method to record the interaction of doctor and patient.

Methodology

By analysing the video-tapes, we expected to get answers to the following question: 'What can we say about the doctor–patient relationship in *āyurvedic* medicine from analysing the consultations?'

The answer to this question requires methods of analysing and evaluating the interaction between doctor and patients, methods which take into account the entire consulting-room communication. This concept leads us to the next question: 'Do we have sufficient measures to evaluate these consultations?'

We intended to go about analysing the communication in different ways – this meant trying to get evaluation methods that were derived from different ways of looking at communication. For this purpose we video-taped consultations in *āyurvedic* hospitals and private practices. In detail, these practices were:

- two private practices in Poona
- one private practice in Bombay
- outpatient clinic of an *āyurvedic* hospital in Bombay.
- outpatient clinic of the *āyurvedic* hospital in Boradi.

The material that we analysed consisted of video-tapes that were taken from these five practices.

The doctors' and patients' shares of the consultation

To start with, we tried to make visible the shares that each partner had in the communication. After getting the video-tapes translated we measured the length of the statements each person made by counting the words. The general result was that the doctors' share of the communication was far bigger.

But there are interesting details. The patients' share of the communication tended to be bigger in private practices, e.g., in the practice of the *āyurvedic* doctor Lad, than in the outpatient clinics of hospitals. However, there was not even a single consultation in which the patients' share reached the amount of words the doctor said.

There was also a considerable amount of communication between the doctor and his assistants or fellow doctors. This intervening communication tended to increase under stress.

Concerning the content of the doctor–patient communication, we may say that the one who talked more was also the one who determined the topic. There were a few exceptions to this: in almost every consultation there were sequences in which the doctor determined the rules of answering, but the patient was free to choose the level to which he was willing to open up.

The patients' statements tended to get longer during a consultation. As their share increased they took the initiative in changing the subject more often. Coming closer to the end of a consultation, it was the doctor again who led.

These results suggest that a consultation may be seen as composed of phases in which the shares of communication vary to a great degree.

The phases of the consultation

One model for viewing a consultation as composed of different phases has been presented by Speierer.[4] In accordance with his approach to a person-centred medicine, he puts a great deal of emphasis on the psycho-social dimensions of a consultation. The four phases that he demands of a good consultation are:

[4] Gert-Walter Speierer, *Das patientenorientierte Gespräch: Baustein einer personenzentrierten Medizin* (München: Causa Verlag, 1985).

i the *psycho-social* phase
ii the *diagnostic* phase
iii the *information* phase
iv the *counsel* phase

If we apply this concept to the *āyurvedic* consultations, we see that great emphasis is put on parts iii and iv. Part i takes considerable time in private practice consultations; part ii is stressed in outpatient clinics of hospitals. Whereas Speierer stresses the importance of open questions, *āyurvedic* doctors tend to pursue a rather directive style. These facts, apart from other differences from Speierer's model, indicate that *āyurvedic* doctors intend to influence their patients strongly from the beginning of the consultation.

If we analyse every statement of the doctor separately, and try to put it into one of the four categories shown above, we can see that nearly all consultations follow a strict structure. In detail, that means that having reached the next phase, the *āyurvedic* doctor does not usually go back, only doing so if it is definitely necessary for readjusting the diagnosis.

The order of the phases is the same in nearly all consultations we analysed. But the amount of time that is spent in each phase depends on the setting and also varies from *vaidya* to *vaidya*. The structure, order and distribution of time in a *vaidya*'s consultations in any particular setting are quite stable and do not depend much on the patient.

The phases in detail

In a hospital setting, consultations tended to be shorter. The *psycho-social* phase was shortened to two or three statements that were absolutely necessary to establish a trusting relationship. This finding can partly be explained by the fact that the patients in the clinics we investigated were usually admitted by paramedical staff. So patients had often had close contact with hospital personnel before they saw the *vaidya*. Information concerning their illness and condition was put on a sheet of paper and handed over to the doctor. So the patient received attention before he actually saw the *vaidya* and, moreover, the importance of the consultation was even more emphasised.

The analysis of the *diagnostic* phase reveals some differences, too. In the outpatient clinics of hospitals the *vaidyas* stressed the importance of an elaborated scientific way of establishing the diagnosis (which is carefully documented, by the way). As it is recorded on tape, we can say that they sometimes joked about *vaidyas* in private practice.

Regarding the *information* phase, when passing on information to the patient, the *vaidya* used the same language, the same code as his patient. He made use of the belief system and sometimes reflected on the Hindu religion. The *vaidya* normally shared religion and belief system with the patient. The explanation of why the patient had become ill was mostly accepted by the patient at once, sometimes he asked the *vaidya* to repeat his explanation.

In the *counsel* phase, the patients expected advice regarding lifestyle and diet and received it with respect. As a healthy lifestyle is already demanded by Hindu principles, the *vaidya* may put his advice into this framework. The authority of the *vaidya* partly derives from his own lifestyle, as the authority of doctors does in traditional societies as well as in Christian mission hospitals in Third World countries. Advice based on good example is quite well accepted, as can be shown from the video-tapes. The situation in Western societies is different, not so much as far as the ideal of a doctor is concerned, but in reality, as a recent study by Hochkirchen and Speierer shows: 80% of first year medical students attending the University of Regensburg, Germany, expect a doctor to lead a healthy life and serve as a model for his patients. Their lifestyle in reality, however, does very often not fit into this model, according to their own statements.[5]

Further analyses

The doctor–patient interaction can also be analysed using the three scales that Speierer has developed recently.[6] The scales allow for the evaluation of three dimensions: freedom, confidence, and guidance in consultations. Summing up the results of the analysis we might say that *vaidyas* tend to be rather directive than non-directive, compared to recent concepts in European medicine.

We also applied Pendleton's consultation rating scale to the *āyurvedic* consultations. This scale has been developed to have comprehensive, practical criteria whereby the effectiveness of any consultation may be judged. The guidelines that

[5]Bernward Hochkirchen and Gert-Walter Speierer, 'Wie vorbildlich ist das Gesundheitsverhalten angehender Ärzte?', *Die Medizinische Welt–medwelt*, xxxvii (1986), 492–494.

[6]Speierer, *Das patientenorientierte Gespräch.*

Pendleton provides especially focus the viewer's attention on the fact whether a shared understanding of illness and therapy is achieved by doctor and patient or not. On Pendleton's scale, the *āyurvedic* consultations reach high standards.[7] This can be demonstrated by showing the video-tapes.

According to the criteria Hartmann uses to assess doctor–patient relationships, these can be interpreted as relationships on a subject to subject level, rather than on a subject-object level as often occurs in Western medicine. Hartmann is specifically interested in the patient being looked at as a person who is able to communicate and not as an object of study and management.[8]

Pfeiffer and Relleke can contribute to the evaluation of *āyurvedic* consultations too.[9] They see consultations, apart from other aspects, as bargaining procedures. Pfeiffer and Relleke provide a method of evaluation especially for those phases in the consultation where the positions of doctor and patient are markedly different. They aim at analysing the communication that follows such a contrast in opinions. We did not observe differences in attitudes so often in the consultations we analysed, but those that we found can quite well be viewed as procedures of bargaining.

Conclusion

Evaluation methods designed for the assessment of doctor–patient relationships in European medicine are also applicable for consultations in *āyurvedic* medicine. The results, as shown above, require further discussion.

[7] *Doctor–patient Communication*, edited by David Pendleton and John Hasler, (London: Academic Press, 1983).

[8] Fritz Hartmann, *Patient, Arzt und Medizin–Beiträge zur ärztlichen Anthropologie* (Göttingen: Verlag für Medizinische Psychologie im Verlag Vandenhoek und Ruprecht, 1984).

[9] Wolfgang Pfeiffer und Eva Relleke, *Methoden der Auswertung der Arzt–Patient-Kommunikation*, paper presented to the workshop of the Arbeitsgemeinschaft gesprächspsychotherapeutisch tätiger Ärzte in Regensburg, 1984.

Chapter 13

Contrasting treatment of witches in three communities in Mewar

G. M. Carstairs

FROM JANUARY, 1950 UNTIL THE END OF FEBRUARY, 1952 I lived for different periods in three rural communities in India. These villages differed from each other in a number of ways, including their attitudes towards witches. In the early weeks of my living in each of these villages in turn I was aware of the fact that the villagers were well aware of the presence of dangerous witches in their own and neighbouring villages. It was important that we should not talk directly about still living witches – although we could talk freely about witches who were no longer alive.

I propose to contrast the different ways in which three villagers dealt with their dreaded witches.

Sujarupa

This was a very small hamlet (population 98, in June 1950). They are all farmers, although several of them have spent some years in the army, or in a factory in order to earn more money. They were descendents of Mers (hill dwellers) whose predecessors frequently raided villages in the adjacent plains. For more than a century, however, this community has claimed to be Rajputs – descendents of the twelfth century warrior Chauhan Singh Rajput.

Among these newly asserted Rajput warriors it was my good fortune to treat one, Amar Singh, who had succumbed to acute gastroenteritis but made a rapid recovery. I knew Amar Singh to be a talented exorcist, especially of witches. At my request he placed his forefinger across the pulse and the movements of my tendons (but on this occasion found no malevolent agency at work). We were afterwards quite often both invited in the hope that our gifts would work together. On such an occasion we were called by one Lom Singh to treat his six months old child who was already in a serious condition. I treated him with the best medicine at my command (in 1950) while Amar Singh supervised a midnight offering. This consisted of offering a black goat, whose head and entrails were carried in a chipped earthenware pot and left beyond the village at a place where three paths meet. No word was spoken about the much feared witch. Later on, however, a number of women and children conveyed to me by gestures that my closest neighbour, Dhapu, was the witch of this village. I found it impossible to see her as in a villainous role, and expressed my regard for this elderly widow. There had been two violent quarrels between Dhapu and Umibai who became blind as a result of her suffering from smallpox. Dhapu was finally so severely beaten by a young woman suffering from fever, and by her relatives, that she died during the night.

Her son Hira Singh decided that his mother had not been fairly treated, so he reported to the police with the result that five of his kinsmen were committed to varying terms in jail – from three months to twelve months. By the time of this event I was working some ninety miles from Sujarupa, but on hearing the news I travelled next day to try to intervene between the angry factions. This was resolved only at the end of the year, when Hira Singh admitted that he should not have brought the police into it, while Dhapu's attackers admitted that they should not have struck her so hard.

While visiting the jail in Bhim I learned from the local magistrate that deaths of witches still happen at least once a year in the magistrate's domain. The episode reminds us that in the region of Bhim there is a recurrent fear that someone is at work, threatening to 'devour the liver' of anyone who is sick or feverish. In short, therefore, witches seem to be secretly working to destroy the health of young people who would otherwise remain whole. Parents feel obliged to make offerings, to placate the destructive witch (or witches). These women strongly deny that they are actual witches.

Delwara

This is a towering multistoried palace, ringed all round by defensive walls which screen stables for horses and elephants. The village and bazaar ensure a constant coming and going between the Maharana, the bazaar and the main road to Udaipur. My task was to talk at length with male representatives of the Brahmin, Kshatriya and Banniya castes. It is noticeable that the men informants almost never talk about witches: on the other hand young women will quite often believe that they have become victims of threatening charms which must be counteracted if the victims are to survive.

A great deal of magical transactions go on both in the temples of the lower castes and in the negotiations with people who know powerful magic – at a price.

It seems that the upper castes are comparatively safe from witches' threats, once the male children have passed through their infancy: but it is a very different thing for the married young Banniya girls who discover from time to time that their consciousness is taken over by a witch, who usually demands gifts to be awarded to her.

It is man's role to confront and, if necessary, to castigate a *dakan*, or witch. This is especially done under the guardianship of Vijayshan-Mata, the protector of her followers. One evening I saw a group of Banniya women gather in front of the Mataji in order that four young women could be relieved of the way in which some *dakans* have at times usurped the women's own preferences. As the priest of the shrine makes ready, two other men clasp the girls' pigtails. Unless this is held securely, the *dakan* can invade a different person. Once the priest is ready there is a period of a *dakan's* abuse and refusal which brings out the Mataji's rage, so now the invaded girl is beaten resoundingly with a bundle of peacock's feathers. At last the *dakan* surrenders and promises that she will no longer torment her young victim.

Each of these confrontations of Mataji and *dakan* work up to an apex of surrender. When I talk with the four women I ask whether the beating was painful, but they assure me that the beating hurt her very little while the *dakan* was glad when the torment came to an end.

Bhils

In each of the two punishments up to this point there have been elements of danger and pain: but there is a different element in the Bhils' sadistic threat. If a woman persists in denying that she is a witch, then she had her ankles bound with rope and she is then hoisted over a high branch and set swinging back and forward. Many women who are only suspected of being a witch may surrender at this point, and promise to give up behaving like a witch. Some others continue to insist defiantly that they have nothing to do with the practice. This provokes the men to swing the suspected women again, but now with powdered chile paste put in their eyes and in their vagina. This gives rise to acute pain, so much so that the victim soon calls out in surrender and promises to give up any witch-like practice.

This cruel form of torture is now rarely practised even in the remote hill villages, but one belief is still held by the tribal Bhils: this is their conviction that every woman in their tribe becomes a witch, sooner or later. This warning becomes active in middle life. Young Bhils not infrequently fall in love and elope with a young Bhil woman. This is a dangerous game. The runaway finds himself the target of a deadly feud because the young woman's spouse is doing his best to kill him – and this does sometimes happen. Meanwhile the head men in the two villages concerned begin a process of reaching the sum of goats and cattle which must be given to the aggrieved fighter before he will accept a satisfactory award. Only when the village headmen are agreed, and the deprived husband is willing to accept his demand of cattle and goats – only then will the two husbands eat a pinch of opium together as a token of settlement.

There is, I suggest, an underlying distrust in each of the three village communities. This mistrust is usually evidence in the unhappiness which clouds the frequent scolding of a young wife. (The local saying goes: 'A young girl is happy at home, but not among strangers'.)

A girl slowly comes to feel at home, especially once she has given birth to one or more male children. With luck, her husband may come to treat her with consideration; but in many junior families the young wife leads a harsh life. Among the young Bhils there is often a spell of several years following either a mutual choice of partner, or an elopement and the feud which invariably follows.

After several years together the Bhils reluctantly believe that their womenfolk have accepted the role of being witches: but both men and women rely upon the awe-inspiring gods (Sikotri or Kamria-path) whose worship with dancing, drums and flutes often extends far into the night.

It is not known since how long the belief in women's witchcraft has prevailed, full of apprehension, among the parents of young children. I know only that one Colonel Dixon was astonished, in 1837, at the unquestioned prevalence of fear of witches.[1] He even challenged any witch in the village of Taragarh to display her power – but nothing came of it; yet still today country folk are fearful of the witches whom they believe to exist among them.

[1]Cf. Charles George Dixon, *Sketch of Mairwara* (London, 1850), and other works.

Chapter 14

Dialogue in research on traditional Indian medicine

Johannes Laping

RESEARCH ON TRADITIONAL SYSTEMS OF MEDICINE in India (and in other parts of the world) until now has been mostly of two kinds:

- philological and comparative study of the textual evidence wherever there was a scholastic tradition, as in the case of *āyurveda, yūnānī*, Chinese medicine, etc.,
- social-anthropological study of medical or healing practices and health behaviour in given contexts.

A third kind of research has arisen in recent years which is concerned with

- clinical studies and biochemical analysis of the phytotherapies and pharamacopoeias of those systems.

A dialogue between the various research approaches is developing very slowly, and often it is difficult.

One of the main reasons for this difficulty may be the predominance of the modern (Western) model of medical care all over the world, with its scientific achievements, with its successful therapies, but also with its professional and business interests behind it. All this leaves little scope and least of all funds for research in traditional systems of medicine, unless such research is likely to produce results that are of direct use to the above interests. The tussel for the remaining funds, however, is unlikely to promote dialogue between the disciplines.

This situation has improved a little since it was realised by international health professionals a few years ago[1] that a health care system that goes beyond the alleviation of acute suffering, and that would cover the health care needs of all sections of the population, especially in less developed countries, in a comprehensive manner, is impossible to achieve by the Western or allopathic model of medical care alone. In this way, traditional systems of medicine have been admitted into the picture again.

India is a particular case in this respect, because we have there an ancient scientific system of medicine, i.e., *āyurveda*, along with a few other elaborated systems, and also numerous minor or folk traditions of medicine and health care. The platform for 'traditional Indian medicine', however, is widely occupied by *āyurveda*. The predominance of *āyurveda* over the other traditions is strengthened further by the fact that various issues of relevance to the concept of comprehensive health care are more or less explicitly mentioned in the ancient texts such as: positive health, nutrition and hygiene, as well as specific treatments for diseases that are prevalent in the subcontinent. To what extent these things are useful and practicable under the present economic, social and political conditions, is a matter for future research.

From this brief analysis the demand for the combined effort of various research disciplines becomes obvious. Beyond a dialogue and exchange between the research approaches outlined above, there is also a need for a research design that would address the complexity of the subject: *āyurveda* is a textual tradition, and as such it has become partly calcified. *Āyurveda* is also a living tradition of medical practice which at times differs considerably from its own textual norms. *Āyurveda* is also a 'way of living' or a 'philosophy of life'. *Āyurveda* is also the 'national heritage' of India and it is said to have served the ailing masses from time immemorial, and it continues to do so even today. *Āyurveda* also has to its credit a number of effective treatments for diseases where western medicines fail. There are one hundred *āyurvedic* colleges in the country, even an *āyurvedic* University. There is an enormous output of *āyurvedic* doctors every year. *Āyurveda* is also becoming a big business. One could go on. And yet people continue to suffer and die ...

At present, there are more questions than answers about traditional Indian medicine in general, and about *āyurveda* in particular. And when we start looking into it, more questions will arise. Traditional research of the philological, anthropological and clinical type has generated a considerable body of knowledge so far. But these results remain to be interrelated and explored further in dialogue.

---

[1] Cf. *First report of the International Conference on Primary Health Care* held at Alma Ata, USSR, 6–12 September, 1978.

There is also a need for another kind of dialogue, that is with the people themselves and from whom our knowledge is generated. Traditionally, we have extracted our knowledge about *āyurveda* and other systems of traditional medicine from the written sources and from the protagonists of the system living today. But little of that has been communicated back into the country and the culture and to the people. Likewise, the findings of anthropological research remain of little value and meaning to those population groups whose living and health conditions they try to analyse, unless these findings are reflected back to and for the people.

In view of the global WHO aim of achieving 'Health for all by 2000 A.D.' and of the Primary Health Care concept, thought to be an appropriate strategy towards that aim, and with the new focus on traditional systems of medicine as a part of that strategy, new research designs become necessary: research designs that should do justice to the complexities of the subject and to the task before us, which is basically a humanitarian one, and in which all the established research disciplines have their place.

'Health for all' will remain a utopia unless the whole campaign is also one of progressive democratisation of knowledge and of medical knowledge in particular. For future research this means the adoption of new democratic or participatory methods through which knowledge is generated by and with those people in whose interest this campaign is launched, and thus making them subjects in the actions in which they are involved.

The contributors

- Gerrit Jan Meulenbeld was born on May 28th, 1928, in Borne (Netherlands). After studying medicine and Sanskrit at the State University of Utrecht (1946–1954) he specialized in psychiatry (1956–1961) and psychotherapy. He was a member of the psychiatric staff of the Deltaziekenhuis (Poortugaal) during the years 1961–1978. On November 1st, 1978 he joined the psychiatric staff of the Dr S. van Mesdag-kliniek (Groningen); at the same time he began teaching Sanskrit and *āyurveda* at the Institute of Indian Studies of the State University of Groningen. He abandoned his position at the University on April 1st, 1986 but continues functioning on the staff of the Dr S. van Mesdag-kliniek. He is the author of a doctoral thesis on the *Mādhavanidāna*, published in 1974, and of several articles on various aspects of Sanskrit medical literature.

- Rahul Peter Das was born in 1954 in Haan, Germany. His schooling and pre-Medical examination (1973) were in Calcutta, where he was National Merit scholar and Jagadish Bose National Science Talent Search scholar. He studied Indology, Islamic studies and Tamil studies at Cologne, Bonn, Hamburg and Kiel. His M.A. thesis (1981) was entitled *pāpá und pāpman im Śatapathabrāhmaṇa*, and his D.Phil. thesis (Hamburg 1985), entitled *Das 'wissen von der Lebensspanne' der Bäume: Surapālas Vṛkṣāyurveda*, will be published in 1987. He is the author of about seventy articles and reviews on various topics in German, English and Bengali. He was the editor of the *Kleine Schriften* of Walter Neisser (published in 1980) and Alfred Hillebrandt (published in 1987), as well as co-editing with R. E. Emmerick *Problems relating to Āyurvedic textual tradition and study*. Since 1981 he has been preparing line and verse indexes of the *Aṣṭāṅgahṛdaya*, the *Aṣṭāṅgasaṃgraha*, and the *Saṃhitās* of Suśruta and Caraka. He has been a part-time teacher of Bengali at Hamburg university since 1981, and is preparing a *Lehrbuch der modernen bengalischen Hochsprachen*.

- Antonella Comba was born in Torino, Italy. She graduated in philosophy with a thesis in Indology, with first class honours. From 1978 she has contributed the Indological articles to the *Grande Dizionario Enciclopedico UTET*. From 1980–1984 she was Secretary of the Associazione Italiana di Studi Sanscriti, affiliated to the International Association of Sanskrit Studies. In 1981 she studied in the Department of Basic principles of Banaras Hindu University, and translated selected passages of the *Suśrutasaṃhitā*, under the guidance of Dr Jyotir Mitra. From 1983 she has contributed Chinese and Indian articles to the *Enciclopedia Bompiani. Filosofia e Scienze Umane.* She has contributed papers on a range of medical Indological topics to several conferences. Her interests include Indian embryology, thanatology, deontology and philosophy.

- Ronald Eric Emmerick was Research Fellow of St John's College, Cambridge (1964–1967) and lecturer in Iranian Studies at the School of Oriental and African Studies (1964–1971), and Visiting Associate Professor of Old and Middle Iranian at the Oriental Institute, University of Chicago (1967–1968). Since 1971 he has been Professor of Iranian Philology at the University of Hamburg. His publications include *Tibetan texts concerning Khotan* (1967), *Saka grammatical studies* (1968), *The Book of Zambasta: a Khotanese poem on Buddhism* (1968), *The Sūtra of Golden Light* (1970), *The Khotanese Śūraṅgamasamādhisūtra* (1970), *A guide to the literature of Khotan* (1979), and *The Siddhasāra of Ravigupta*, volumes 1 and 2, (1980, 1982). He has also published numerous articles on Middle Iranian, Tibetan and Sanskrit grammar and vocabulary.

- Marianne Winder took her first degree at London University, and her Masters degree at Nottingham University. On retiring from her post as Curator of Oriental Collections at the Wellcome Institute for the History of Medicine she has taken up a position as a Consultant on Tibetan Medicine at the Institute. Among her recent publications are 'Tibetan medicine compared with ancient and mediaeval Western medicine', *Bulletin of Tibetology*, N.S. 1 (1981), 5–22, 'The Buddhist antecedents of Tibetan medicine', *Tibet News Review*, 2(1/2) (1981), 29–34, and 'Der Buddhismus und die tibetische Medizin', *Tibet Forum*, 4 Jahrgang no. 2, (1985), 7–10.

- Arion Roşu took his B.A. and M.A. in classical philology at Bucharest, his D.Phil. at Paris University, and took the Certificate course in Indian Medicine at Banaras Hindu University. He is a Senior Research Fellow at the Centre national de la recherche scientifique in Paris. His fields of special interest are Sanskrit philology (Āyurveda, Rasaśāstra), and the cultural history of India.

His doctoral thesis *Les conceptions psychologiques dans les textes médicaux indiens* was published in 1978, and more than forty of his papers, on Indian medicine and alchemy, as well as other Indological topics, have appeared in journals.

- Johannes Laping is a Sanskritist who has worked for some time under the auspices of the Institut für Tropenhygiene, in the South Asia Institute, Heidelberg University, Germany. He is interested in preventive medicine and community health, and has worked extensively in the field with traditional practitioners of *āyurveda.*

- T. J. S. Patterson was in hospital practice as a surgeon for more than thirty years; his publications included work on the history of Plastic Surgery. Later his interest turned to the history of Indian surgery, and then to medicine in India in general. Since 1978 he has been working in the Wellcome Unit for the History of Medicine, Oxford University, mainly on the medical practice of the English East India Company from 1600–1850. He is also collaborating with a group at the Banaras Hindu University on a new translation of the *Suśrutasaṃhitā.*

- Dominik Wujastyk was born in London in 1954. He has degrees in Physics from Imperial College, London University (1974), and Sanskrit with Pāli from Brasenose College, Oxford (1977). His doctorate, also at Brasenose College (1982), concerned an early *paribhāṣā* text on Sanskrit grammar. Since 1982 he has been on the staff of the Wellcome Institute for the History of Medicine, with responsibility for cataloguing the Institute's large Sanskrit manuscript collection. He has published the first volume of a *Handlist* of this collection, as well as articles and reviews on Sanskrit linguistics, codicology, and computing.

- Waltraud Ernst was born in Rosenheim in 1955. From 1975 she studied international politics and psychology at Konstanz University, where she graduated in 1982. Her thesis concerned the psychological determinants of rural–urban migration in Kenya. She trained in psychotherapy (transactional analysis), and worked as a part-time lecturer in psychology, and as a research assistant in the Department of Sociology, Konstanz University. From 1984 to 1986 she carried out research for her doctorate in history at the School of Oriental and African Studies, London. Her thesis was entitled 'Psychiatry and colonialism. The treatment of the European insane in British India, 1800–1858.' Recently she has been working as a tutor in transactional analysis for the University of Surrey, and since January 1987 has been a research fellow of the Wellcome Institute for the History of Medicine, London.

She has carried out fieldwork in Sri Lanka, India and Kenya and has published articles on non-governmental organizations in third world countries, women's migration in Kenya, and sociological and social-historical aspects of mental illness in British India. At present she is working on a book concerning the history of European madness in India (1750–1947).

- R. P. Labadie was born in Parimaribo, Suriname. He got his primary and secondary education in Suriname and Curaçao. He studied pharmacy and specialized in pharmacognosy at the University of Leiden, The Netherlands. After getting his Ph.D. at the same university, he joined the Department of Pharmacognosy at the University of Utrecht, The Netherlands. He was appointed Professor of Pharmacognosy at the latter university in 1982. Within the general field of drug development from medicinal plants, he focuses his research efforts on those crude plant drugs and plant constituents which show immunemodulating activity.

- K. T. D. De Silva studied chemistry in Sri Lanka, University of Peradeniya. He continued studying pharmacy at the School of Pharmacy in London and chemistry at the University of Manchester. He is Professor of Chemistry and the present Dean of the Faculty of Applied Science at the University of Sri Jayewardenepura, Nugegoda, Sri Lanka.

- Dieter von Schmädel was born in Fürth/Bavaria, West Germany, in 1939. He obtained a doctor's degree in sociology, having also studied ethnology, political science and philosophy. In 1976 he was inaugurated in the field of medical sociology at the University of Ulm. In 1978 he became professor of the sociology of medicine at Regensburg. He has worked on the social norms of illness behaviour, non-compliance with medical advice, occupation and the illness to mortality rate. Since 1981 he has been interested in ethnomedicine, especially in the traditional Indian system of medicine, *āyurveda.*

- Berward Hochkirchen was born in Essen in 1956. He obtained a medical doctor's degree at the Westphalian Wilh. University, Münster, and has been licensed as a physician since 1980. In 1982/83 he compiled a field study on self-destructive behaviour among native Indians in Canada. He has also investigated the history and present state of medical services in remote areas, especially in British Columbia. Now working in the Department of Medical Psychology, Regensburg University, he focusses his research interests on medical care in different cultures, and change in attitudes of medical students. He is presently taking part in the improvement of methods of analysing doctor–patient relationships and communication in groups.

- The late George Morrison Carstairs was born in Mussoorie in 1916. During a long and distinguished carreer in medicine he was professor of Psychiatry at the University of Edinburgh from 1961–1973, President of the World Federation for Mental Health (1967–1971) and Vice-Chancellor of the University of York (1973–78). Among other posts, he was visiting Professor of Psychiatry at the Post Graduate Institute in Chandigarh (1979–1981), and Fellow of the Woodrow Wilson Center, Smithsonian Institution, Washington (1981–1982). He gave the B.B.C. Reith Lectures for 1962. His publications include *The twice born: a study of a community of highcaste Hindus* (1957), *The great universe of Kota: stress and mental disorder in an Indian village* (with R. L. Kapur, 1976), and *Death of a witch: a village in north India, 1950–1981* (1983).

Index

Iranian religion and mythology, 28n
Isidorus of Seville, 92
Islamic tradition, 103, 112; magic squares, 96, 101, 102–3
isothankuniside, 204
Italy; encyclopaedias, 131–2

Jabbalpur, 174
Jābir, corpus attributed to, 102, 103
Jacobi, H., 39–40
jails, 155, 173–4
Jainism, 47, 101, 116
Jambhalā (ogress), 100–1
Jammu State Library, 108
Jātaka, 90–1
jayā (plant), 33, 35–6, 37
jayantī (plant), 30, 33, 34, 35, 36, 37
Jenner, Edward, 121–2, 130, 138–9, 140, 144
Jiyālālā sāhab, 145
Jodhpur; Rajasthan Oriental Research Institute, 107
Jolly, Julius, 39
Jones, Sir William, 117
journals, medical, 118, 172

Kālidāsa; *Kumārasaṃbhava*, 87n
Kamria-path (deity), 218
Kaṇāda, 42–4
Kangra, 23
Kaṇvas, 28n
Karkaria, R.P., 150, 151
karma, patient's, 207
karman (actions), 5, 12, 46
kartṛtva (agency) of *ātman* (self), 45–6, 47–8
Kashmir, 23
Kauśikasūtra, 19
Kaviraj Binod Lal Sen; *Āyurvedavijñāna*, 146–7, 148, 151
Keith, A.B., 40
King, Walter Gaven, 141, 146–51
King Institute of Preventive Medicine, Madras, 146, 147, 148, 154
Kirke, K., 181–2
Kishore, P., 108
Kolaba Asylum, 156
Korapalla, Puri District, 106
krimiroga, 108
kriyāvattva, 45–6
kúṣṭha, 9, 18

La Loubère, Simon de, 101
Laghuratnaparīkṣā, 94
lapis lazuli, 85–6, 86–7, 93–4
Latin; loan-words from Indo-Aryan, 18
Law, John, 151
Leekie, J., 178, 179
legal system, 155
leprosy, 199, 201, 204, 205
licensing of practitioners, 113, 120, 172
lifestyle, advice on, 212
liu-li (Chinese, gem), 85, 93, 94
lupus, 201

Macaulay, Thomas Babington, 1st Baron Macaulay, 126, 188
Maclean, William Campbell, 145
Madagascar, *Centella asiatica* from, 191, 201, 203, 205
Madecassic acid, *197*, 203
madecassoside, 204
Mādhavakara; *Mādhavacikitsā*, 105–8
Mādhavanidāna, 136
Madras: asylum, 156; British Medical Service, 116; Committee on Indigenous Systems of

motions (*karman*), 5, 12, 46
mudga (drug), 10
Murshidabad Asylum, 156, 168, 183, 184; building, 159, 160n, 177
mushroom, *sóma* as, 22

Naccajātaka, 90
Nāgārjuna; *Rasavaiśeṣikasūtra*, 6n, 12, 15
Naick, Swamy (vaccinator), 141–2
nāma (plant), 30, 33
Narahari; *Rājanighaṇṭu*, 88, 89, 90, 94
Nārāyaṇa Paṇḍita; *Gaṇitakaumudī*, 99
nasal rinses for epilepsy, 61
Nasik, 101
nationalism, Indian, 120, 220
nervous system, 95, 194, 195, 199
Netherlands, 111, 113, 116
nicotine, 199, *199*
nighaṇṭus, 10
Nīlakaṇṭha; commentary on *Śivatāṇḍava*, 101
nimba (drug), 10
Nimi, 15
niṣṭhāpāka (digestive process), 7, 8, 9
Nobili, Roberto di; Ezour Vedam, 149
Norris, William, 157
Norton, Charles, 139
Nouveau Dictionnaire de médicine et de chirurgie pratiques (1864–86), 132
Nyāya philosophy, 39, 40–1, 42, 44–5, 51
Nyāya-Vaiśeṣika, 40, 42, 47

occult literature, magic squares in, 96
offerings to witches, placatory, 216, 217
order, public, 155, 156, 159
Orientalist-Educationalist controversy, 172
Ōrilaittāmarai (synonym for *Centella asiatica*), 192
Orissa State Museum, Bhubaneswar, 105–7
Orta, Garcia da, 112–13

Pāli Canon, *veḷuriya* in, 88–91
Pañcaśikha; *Mahābhārata*, 41
Pandey, H.S., 108
Paradise of Wisdom (*Firdaus al-ḥikma*), 102, 104
Parliamentary Select Committee on Madhouses in England (1815/16), 157
pāṭā (medicinal plant), 17–38; colour, 36–8; mythical and magical interpretations, 27–9; references in Vedic literature, 19–22, (*Atharvaveda-Saṃhitā*), 19–21, 22–4, 32–3, (*Paippalāda-Saṃhitā* of *Atharvaveda*), 21–2, 30–3; and *suparṇá*, 20–1, 24–7; as synonym or surrogate of *sóma*, 19, 22–4, 25, 26, 27, 29, 37–8; as truffle, 22–4; as tuber, 36–8
pāṭhā (plant), 19, 32
Patna Asylum, 156, 162, 183, 184, 185; building, 159, 177; cure and death rates, 159, 168; shortcomings, 170–1
Paton, G., 179–81
Pattana, 114
Pendleton, D., 212–13
Perry, C.B., 122
Perry, Lily M., 205
Persia, 94, 101; vaccination, 129–30,